MYSTERY

MYSTERY

An Anthology of the Mysterious

in Fact and Fiction

1952
LONDON: HULTON PRESS

First published in 1952
by Hulton Press Ltd

*The jacket design is an adaptation
of the original engraving done by
Joan Hassall for the cover of
The London Mystery Magazine*

PRINTED IN GREAT BRITAIN BY
FERNDALE BOOK COMPANY LIMITED
FERNDALE, GLAMORGAN

PREFACE

This book is a compilation of original material first published in The London Mystery Magazine. *In its first issue of June, 1949, the Editor set out his aims. He said he hoped to make his magazine the best in its class of mystery-crime-detection; the accent was to be heavily on mystery—the mysterious in life, literature, and art; it was his intention to present the best authors and the best artists in the best way, and to fit the L.M.M. for a permanent place on every reader's bookshelf. Entertainment and food for thought was to be provided for the connoisseur in this popular field; though a London-born enterprise, he said his hope was that it would reach kindred spirits throughout the world.*

The Editor was Michael Hall, and his aims and aspirations were fulfilled over the fifteen issues to a quite remarkable degree. The L.M.M. has reached readers all over the world and it made friends in most countries—even some behind the Iron Curtain. The standard of its material and its originality of presentation speak for themselves; its contribution to the art of modern illustration has been acknowledged in many significant places.

Michael Hall's pious hope, expressed in his first editorial preface which was dated from the sacred "address of the late Sherlock Holmes, Esq," that "we shall be tenants worthy of our great predecessor" has been amply fulfilled. By the courteous and most understanding co-operation of the Abbey National Building Society (whose Head Office building covers the site) the magazine was always published from 221b Baker Street, the address which has been said to be the best known private postal direction in the world.

To create and develop a new magazine which is neither a copy nor an adaptation of an existing one is a notable feat, all the more so in these days of exhaustive explorations for new media. To start it up from

PREFACE

scratch, single-handed, and "out of the air", i.e., without the backing of a representative organisation, is a tour de force. Michael Hall did both these things, with the aid of one devoted Fleet Street colleague, John Shand. The two of them together, plus one secretary, were The London Mystery Magazine—the Editorial, Literary, Art, Production, Advertising and much of the Sales Promotion all combined under just two hats. All contributions were original, and most of them were commissioned by Michael Hall to his carefully tailored plans.

In normal times the enterprise would have gained its economic reward and have been counted a considerable commercial success, as well as a journalistic one. That it should have been started just before the worst publishing blizzard in Fleet Street history was its bad luck. Presumably the fantastic rise in the price of paper, and the increase in printing and other costs, made an insoluble financial problem for a publication which was never intended to have a mass appeal.

Perhaps the day of small circulation and quality appeal publication has gone for ever—together with other ornaments of an age of individualism and personal achievement. Perhaps the L.M.M. will rise again, a sign that once more there is a place for the humanities at a light but adult level, and that even Welfare Man does not live by coupons alone.

The last word of this introduction must be one of congratulation to Michael Hall for what he accomplished in the name of journalism, and to John Shand for the way he helped him do it. For the rest—Resurgam?

A.L.C.C.

CONTENTS

CONTENTS

BEAT OF A LIFETIME

NEGLEY FARSON

Illustrations by Calvin Grey

CAN'T tell you the state this happened in, it might get me into trouble; and I've had enough trouble already in that state. I never want to see it again; but, knocking about down there—with Nick in the yawl—we used to say that it was the prettiest place on God's green earth. It was, too.

The night we ran into Deep Harbour was pretty and peaceful enough to set you dreaming. Low country, with miles on end of wavy green corn, red patches where they had the tomatoes in; and every now and then we'd run past a little whitewashed shack set back from the water, with an orchard and "truck" patch behind it—and an old hunting dog barking somewhere.

It is a thirteen-mile run in from the bay, around a neck in the reach, and we anchored about two hundred yards off the town just at sundown. A low bank of clouds under the sun looked like wind, so we put down the port bower and gave her plenty of cable, in case we had to ride out a blow. A little cabin-cruiser lay between us and the shore.

We had caught some horn-pouts up-bay the night before; and while Nick cooked, I furled the canvas and made every-

I

thing tidy. After putting up the riding-light I came down, and
Nick had the stuff already laid out on the centre-board table—
fish, sauté potatoes and black-jack. Skimpy; but we were living
that way about then, as we were just about broke. Eighty-five
cents stood between us and starvation; we'd counted it that
morning and decided to put into Deep Harbour to see if we
couldn't get a job on some farm.

We grumbled over it washing the dishes, but we figured that
a couple of weeks would get us enough cash to last until we
reached the salt-water. When we'd finished we pushed off for
shore.

"Work!"—the gang in front of the drug-store laughed at us.
"Why, we all doan' want no hands this time of the year. Come
'long 'bout hawvest."

"When's that?" asked Nick.

That tickled them; we didn't know when harvest-time was!
We didn't, either; farming wasn't our game. And as far as that
goes, I'll bet you that not one of them louts could have tied a
bowline, or done a sheepshead, if you'd done it for him right in
front of his eyes. But we didn't talk back to them. We had to
connect with that job.

After they had got done laughing Nick dug up the "makings"
and passed them out—just to show we were friendly.

"We can't live on the fresh air and scenery," he said to them;
"we simply got to find work. Don't you know of anything at
all?"

"How 'bout your boat, stranger?" one asked. "Want to sell
her?"

"How much?"

I knew Nick was just joshing.

The big fellow who had asked the question scratched his head,
tried to look like he knew what he was talking about, and said
he "figgered" the *Panther* was worth about two hundred bucks.

"Two hundred dollars!"

Nick was as sore as a crab.

"Why, —— it, she's worth more than your whole —— little
one-horse town!"

The big guy got up and shook his fist under Nick's nose.

"You dasn't talk thataways to me!"

"The —— you say!" Nick tells him.

"Go git 'm, Lucky!" the crowd pipes up; and the big guy draws back a fist about as big as a ham.

But Lucky didn't want to "git" anybody after the slashing punch in the mouth Nick handed him.

You know how these small-town crowds fight—like a pack of wolves. They were all over us. I was winded in no time. So was Nick. And there's no use trying to make out those boys couldn't fight; they were knocking us all over the road. It was a shell road; and when they'd grind your head into those oyster-cases it cut like blazes!

"I've broken my hand!" calls out Nick.

"Kick 'em!" I managed to gurgle. "Kick the living day-lights out of the ——"

We got to the boat, and —— pleased we were to get there; but even then we had to row out quite a piece, as that bunch of swine stood on the beach and pegged stones at us. We lay there and got back our wind.

"Nice little crowd," growls Nick miserably. "My flipper's just giving me ——. I tell you what we'll do: we unscrew those boom trees—and then you an' me'll go back—and just walk up the street of that town."

"We will not!" I told him flatly. "I've had all I want. I'm going to soak your hand in hot water."

"Oh, well——"

Nick tried to make out that I was depriving him of some-thing; but I knew he was just as glad as I was to get clear of that bunch of high-binders. Those oyster-shells kept sticking into me all over, too. It was a rough town.

"Well, anyway," said Nick, "I got a few of 'em. That town won't forget us in a hurry."

That was incident No. 1; and we hadn't been down in the *Panther's* galley fifteen minutes when No. 2 comes along. Some-body hailed us from alongside.

"Is anybody in there?"

"You bet," answered Nick with his head stuck out of the hatch. "Two of us. How many are you?"

"One," came a laugh out of the darkness. "Don't be alarmed; I'm friendly."

Nick told him to come aboard; and a strapping big chap in town clothes came over the rail. He stood there, peering down in the galley, and at first all I could see of his face was a whacking black beard, as thick and as shiny as the back of a cat. Looked like a foreigner of some sort, not at all what you'd expect to find in a place like Deep Harbour. He stood there grinning and wagging his head from side to side.

"Beautiful!" He spoke at last. "Never have I seen such a fight. It was ferocious. Splendid! By the way, I heard one of you shout that he had broken his hand; better let me look at it."

He stared from one to the other of us; and Nick held up the bad paw.

"Ah."

The big fellow's face lighted up; he leaned over and began feeling it.

"So," he smiled down at Nick, "grit your teeth. I shall hurt you a little"; and before Nick could do anything, he had poor old Nick's thumb locked in two crooked, hairy fingers.

He gave a jerk.

"Yow!" Nick howled and jumped all over the galley; and the big fellow stood there laughing at him.

"A dislocation of the ——"

Here he used some word that I couldn't quite catch.

"You must hit very hard," he told Nick. "It will be all right now."

It was funny to watch Nick, breathing on his thumb and not knowing whether to get mad or not; and the way that other fellow took no notice of it at all. He had already taken out his cigarette-case and was holding it out for Nick to take one. He held the match for our two, and then blew it out and lit another for his own.

"Three is unlucky," he told us. "They light the church tapers with one."

Nick had evidently decided to be friends.

"Carlson's my name," he said, reaching up to shake hands. "Much obliged. This man here is my pal, McNab by name. Come down and have a seat."

The big fellow slid through the hatch and soberly shook hands with me.

"Pugh," he said, "is my name."

I saw Nick, who was making some blackjack, start up at that. Sounded odd to me, too; "Pugh" didn't seem to mate with a face like that! The newcomer didn't seem the least bit embarrassed; leaned his back against the foot of the mast and gave the place the once-over. All the time he was chuckling and rubbing his hands over the knees of his trousers. Clean hands, too. Queer! Me sitting there, staring straight at him, and never twigging at all who he was! I'd seen his picture in the papers often enough!

"Nice little boat you have here," he said, looking up at the racks in the neat little galley. "Yours?"

"Yep," Nick told him; "mine. We're working her together."

"So?" said the other, beginning to smile. "I thought I heard you say before your—ah—combat that you were in search of that?"

"Work?" grunts Nick. "You bet we're looking for work; but this shore of the bay down here is dead. They don't even know the Civil War is over yet."

Here Nick went on to explain how things stood: enough alcohol to cook the next three days' meals—providing we could find them—twenty gallons of gas for the engine, and that eighty-five cents I mentioned before.

"How would twenty-five dollars a day suit you?" cut in the big chap.

Nick whisked round so quickly I thought he had slipped. I was never more surprised in my life; thought the big chap was joking, but he came through to back up his statement.

"I want your boat for a week," he said. "I want you to take me to some uninhabited island in the bay here, some place where I can be by myself, and call for me at the end of that week. I will pay you for the whole of that time."

"Is that all?"

Nick looked suspicious.

"It is," said the big fellow. "And one other thing: I want you to promise that you will say nothing about it—during that week—to another living soul. After that you can say what you like. Does it please you?" he said, turning to both of us.

I think he must have seen some of the doubt in our faces, for he continued:

"I give you my word of honour that there is nothing criminal about this. Everything is quite regular, I assure you."

Regular! Twenty-five dollars a day—a lonely island—and us to say nothing about it; it didn't seem very regular. Looked like there was a nigger somewheres in the wood-pile; but Nick jumped at the chance—he often bragged that he would do anything once—and reached over to shake hands on the deal.

"I'll take you," he said; "but I'd be a little more happy if I knew you were telling the truth, Mr.—Pugh."

Pugh smiled, just as if admitting that he knew his name wasn't Pugh, and said:

"Fine; that is a bargain."

"It is," said Nick; "and when do we start?"

"At once, if you can," said Pugh. "Just make for the first island that fits the description. If possible, I wish to be put ashore before daylight."

In a way which I would find it hard to explain he seemed to have taken command over things at that instant. He made us feel as though the *Panther* no longer belonged to us.

He was in the little cabin-cruiser we had noticed lying between us and the shore when we had come in at sunset. He told me, while I was rowing him back in the dinghy, that she had broken down. He was in the drug-store, just about to telephone across the bay to Oriole for another when we came along and kicked up our shindy. He said we had looked "likely"; so he had changed his mind and come over to offer us the job.

"There is another man with me," he said.

There was, too—a queer, baby-faced youth, with thumping thick eye-glasses that made his eyes look like a cat-fish. He was sitting down in the cabin among a litter of suitcases and one big pine-box, which I first took to be a coffin.

"Mr. Garrick," Pugh said to the other as soon as we saw him. "Mr. Garrick, this is Mr. McNab, our new *voyageur*. Mr. Garrick, will you please get your articles together; we are going aboard that little sailing-ship out there ahead of us."

Mr. Garrick had a shape like an elephant; but I guessed that it must have been all fat—or else the big box had something

mighty heavy in it—for, when he gave it a heave, it just stayed where it was, just as though it were stuck to the floor. Pugh stopped him.

"Mr. McNab," he said; "will you please put these things into your little boat?"

He pointed to the small stuff.

When I came back Pugh had managed to get the big box up the companionway all by himself; at least, it looked that way. Garrick was standing, blinking down below, with a couple of leather suitcases in his hands.

"Here, let me give you a hand with that," I offered to Pugh; but he waved me aside and got the thing over the rail, cussin' away at a great rate.

Garrick just hopped around and did what he was told.

The wind had picked up a little, hit me quite cold on the back of the neck, and it was a bit of a job to get their stuff over the rail of the *Panther*. The big case in particular made Pugh sweat not a little; and I could have sworn that during one of the heaves he made to get it aboard something like a groan came from inside it. Nick laughed when I told him about it.

"You're balmy," he said, making fun of my nerves, which had been knocked skew-whiff by the Heinies. "You'll be having another spell of the jim-jams if you don't take it easy. That was only the squeak of the wood."

Nick said he was going to put them ashore on Poplar Island, which was a low bit of land we had passed about four miles above the mouth of the reach coming in.

"You remember it?" said Nick. "'Member you said it looked just as though the trees were standing in water?"

I remembered it all right—just a strip of blue mud with a fringe of green, shiny poplars, and a flat, sedgy marsh lying behind them.

"He'll curse you for landing them there," I objected.

"I should worry!" said Nick. "Old Blackbeard said he wanted to be by himself. Well, if you know any more forsaken spot than Poplar, then go out and find it. Besides, there ain't another spot that would fit his description within a full day's sail of us. Why, I'll bet you there are twenty square miles of spladder-docks in back of that ribbon of mud."

It answered the bill; there was no mistake about that. It was the mournfullest place one could think of. No man in his right senses would ever set foot there; and I couldn't help puzzling over what Pugh had up his sleeve. I could hear him and Garrick gabbling away down in the cabin; they seemed awfully earnest about something. Too earnest somehow to please me; and the more I thought of it the more dissatisfied I was over the contract we had made with them.

It was a hunch—my common sense trying to warn me—but I put all my uneasiness down to the gloomy feeling of putting out of a snug port on a thick night—and that miserable moan of the wind in the shrouds, a sound which will make any bluenose unhappy.

Once we got the anchor aboard I began to feel better, as motion, no matter what, takes a mind off the strain. We went out under jib and jigger, and even with these two light sails the old *Panther* just stepped it along. That's the nice part of a yawl; she's handy when she's got no more on than a pocket handkerchief. And sitting up there on the sprit—watching, in case some fool had forgot to put a riding-light up on his craft—I was just about as well pleased that we were rather bare. The *Panther* was taking a bone like a big drift of snow under the bow.

Coming aft, I stooped to peek into the cabin; but Pugh and Garrick had pulled the curtains over the ports. It struck me that it was either a very useless thing to do, or else it was something very much the opposite. In which case they were doing something down there they didn't want us to see.

I told this to Nick, and said I thought I'd butt in on them; but he said to leave them alone; we'd have them ashore in a few hours, anyway; and Pugh had already forked out over one hundred dollars just to show he meant business. We agreed that that seemed as if he was square; but even Nick admitted that he wouldn't be sorry to see the last of them.

We sat there by the wheel, arguing about what we'd do with the money. The *Panther* needed attention; once she had been white, but the greasy waters of the oil-works in the bay had left a dirty scum all over her.

"Black's the colour," Nick was saying; "black, and then the dirt won't show——"

A most unearthly yell came from the cabin. A —— awful yell!

Nick was across, wrenching at the companionway doors. They were locked!

"What the —— are you drivin' at," he roared, banging on the wood with his fists, "lockin' me outa my cabin? Open these doors, —— you!"

He was mad as a hatter.

There was a rumble of voices, and then Pugh stuck his head out. He was very apologetic.

"My friend has cut himself," he explained. "He dropped a box on his hand. See!"

There was Garrick with a bloody handkerchief wrapped round his hand, and a sickly, scared grin on his face.

"Gee!"

Nick forgot all about being mad.

"You sure let out a yell. Must have hurt you like sixty. Want anything?"

"It is nothing."

Pugh waved a hand.

"I fix him in a few minutes."

And with that he slammed the doors in our faces. He certainly let us know he'd rented the use of the boat all right.

"There's a cool one for you," growled Nick. "Nothing bashful about him. Now what do you make of a cove like that?"

I wasn't thinking much about Pugh just at that moment; I had a whiff of something in my nostrils, something which I had got to know pretty well over in France, but which I couldn't place at all. Also, Garrick's yell was worrying me too; it was too much like Pugh's name to suit me. Didn't fit. It was a sort of deep-chested roar; and from Garrick's shape one would have expected him to yell like a tenor—high and squeaky.

I told Nick about this, but he was one of those hard-headed persons who take an earthquake to make them see anything.

"Aw," he growled at me, "you're a regular old woman; you and your squeaks and yells an' smells—you'll be seeing things next."

Well, bless my soul, I did! I saw Pugh's face come out of the hatchway. It stayed there some time—looking at us; and

I watched it. I watched it with all the hair crawling up the back of my neck, but I said nothing about it to Nick. I wish I had now; I wish I had jumped along for'ard and flapped him out of that galley and on to the deck. If ever a man kept his mouth shut when he ought to have been raising a row, it was me then, I can tell you. It would have saved the lot of us.

And as it turned out it was just this seeing things of mine which was to save Nick and me in the end.

But that night I had a feeling that if I voiced any more fears Nick would think I was yellow, so I just kept all I was afraid of bottled up inside me. I did—without Nick knowing it—try the companionway doors, only to find them locked tight as a drum. And I did, telling him that I was going up to make black-jack, slide quietly in the galley and try the little door which led into the cabin. Locked; I knew it would be.

Nick and I might as well have been sailing a raft for all the use we had of that cabin. I sat there in the dark and laughed. Here were Nick and I, who, to draw it mild, could hardly be classed as good members of the parish, being bossed around on our own craft like a couple of deck-swabs.

While I was down I felt the roll of the sea get under the *Panther*. Big sea, too; I had to hold the kettle on to the burner. We had a hundred miles of open water to windward; and quartering, as we were, once we left the lee of the reach, the *Panther* just smashed into the seas. Coming aft I had to hang on; and there, sitting alongside Nick in the cockpit, was Pugh— sick as a cat. I gave him half a cup of scalding-hot black-jack, and he was all over me with thanks.

"You are a gentleman," he shouted at me. "You have all the fine feelings. Ah, my friends"—he jerked round his head to be sick—"my friends, pain is the only real thing in life. Pleasure—all else—is illusion; but this"—he was violently sick again, and by George, he finished up laughing—"this is real, isn't it? Ha! Ha! Ha!"

Some more of the same line of gibberish followed; he talked as if life wasn't worth living, and then laughed as if he enjoyed it. I kicked Nick's foot, and we sat there and listened. I guess Joe and I had never heard a man talk that way before in our lives. He seemed out of his nut. What with the sea, and that hairy-faced man shouting to make himself heard above it, I began to feel nervous as ——!

He seemed in great fettle in spite of his stomach.

"You take it well," Nick told him.

"Ah, no." He laughed delightedly, and slapped Nick on the knee. "I give it up well; that's what you mean. Ha! Ha! Oh——"

He was sick again and gave up quite a lot.

Whatever he was, good, bad or indifferent, that fellow was game!

There's no use telling you how we put them ashore. It was just the usual dirty job of a night landing. Old Blackbeard insisted on being landed at once, though it was as black as the ace of spades. We could see that Garrick wasn't at all keen to take a chance on capsizing; but Pugh wasn't letting a little thing like that interfere with him. Nick's hand wasn't much use for handling an oar, so I put him ashore with a lantern and some of the small stuff on the first trip.

Next I took Garrick and their dinghy, which we had brought along with us. Then I went back and got the old man and his box. He wouldn't let us help them pull their stuff along to the poplars; just kept insisting on saying "Good-bye; see you next Tuesday"; so we pushed off and left them. We let them keep the lantern and, as we rowed back, we could see them already unpacking their stuff, Pugh leaning over the box.

As soon as we got back in the *Panther's* cabin we unscrewed all the ports. I knew what that smell was now—ether. The cabin reeked with it. Smelt like a hospital!

"Now," I said to Nick, "do you believe me that you and I have seen some rough stuff? Or do you still think we've been transporting a picnic?"

He had chucked himself down in his bunk for a smoke; but he sat up at this. He was commencing to show some signs of being worried at last.

"You're sure it's ether?" he asked me.

"Just as sure as I ever was of anything in my life."

"Well, what do you think?" he said, passing the buck to me. I told him.

"Either we've helped to Shanghai a man—or else murder him."

"Aw," he said, trying to laugh, "you're crazy as a fish! You just pick out the worst thing you can think of and then say that was it. Be sensible. Of course we've sat in at something that ain't on the level. I've known that all the time; but you and I are too broke to pass up a chance like this. A hundred and seventy-five iron men will do a lot of good to us and the *Panther*."

"Yeah!" I pointed out. "And a fat lot of good the *Panther* will do you in jail!"

He got sore at that.

"Jail! Why, look here. If they were bumping a guy off, do you think they'd stick around this island for a week—waiting for us to call back for them? What's eating you?"

"Nothing; but something's made a meal off your brains all right!" I shot back at him. "Who said they would stick around here for a week? You forgot all about their dinghy, didn't you? How do you know that week stuff isn't a blind, anyway? How do you know they have not killed him already and aren't rowing ashore right this minute? And listen."

I grabbed hold of his arm, as he was already scrambling up on deck to look for them.

"How do you know they haven't taken any amount of stuff from this boat—and left it alongside him?"

We took an inventory of the *Panther* right then and there; but we couldn't find anything missing except Nick's old mate's cap. He had been wearing that earlier on in the evening, and he couldn't remember now what he'd done with it—whether he'd laid it down some place where it might have gone overboard, or left it on the beach, or what he'd done with it. It had his name and the yawl's inside the hatband. I'd printed it there myself!

"There you are," I said to him. "Plain as day; we're planted."

And planted we were; but not in the way we had it doped out. It was just as if they suspected we might come ashore after them; when we came on deck with that idea in our minds, there wasn't a sign of the lantern. In fact, until our eyes got

used to the dark, we couldn't even find the bulk of the island.
It took us some time to stumble on the fact that the wind had
shifted while we had been arguing down below; and instead of
being bow on, the island was almost astern of us.

We gave up the idea of going ashore, and took the *Panther*
up the other shore of the island to wait there for daylight. From
the first crack of smoky-grey dawn until the sun was high in the
sky we kept a sharp watch in case they should attempt to cross
over to the mainland. And, finally, Nick couldn't stick it out
any longer; about noon he shoved off in the dinghy; and
through the glasses I saw him land at the foot of the island and
strike into the swamp. About an hour later he came over the
rail, pleased as Punch with himself.

"A fat prophet you are!" he told me disgustedly. "Here I go
and crawl through half a mile of black mud, expecting to see
something shady—and what do I see? I see Pugh an' Garrick
and a big buck nigger playing tag on the beach. Murder! You
make me sick!"

"Where did the nigger come from?"

"How the —— do I know? Beachcomber, I suppose. Looked
that way, anyway—half-naked. Nigger name o' Fairfax."

"How do you know that?"

" 'Cause I heard them calling him that."

"Oh, you didn't go over?"

"No; catch me butting in on their party and losing the rest
of our money that's coming to us. I lay there in the bushes and
watched. Garrick was sitting on a rock, writing; and Pugh and
this nigger were galloping about on the beach. Every now and
then Pugh would yell out something about no reaction, and
Garrick would jot it down on his pad. The silliest game I ever
saw. Fairfax was a bit deaf, too, as Pugh had to holler his
name. —— fool way to spend a hot day, I'll tell the world."

While Nick was talking he was peeling off his clothes—all
covered with mud—and getting ready to sluice himself down.

"You know," he spluttered with his head half in a bucket, "I
think it's a booze party. The nigger was drunk at any rate—
staggering all over the place!"

Sitting up on deck there in the hot sun and watching Nick,
just as I'd seen him on many and many a morning, everything

seemed so peaceful and usual that I began to feel almost ashamed of what I had been sure of the previous evening. A booze party might have answered the bill; niggers were all over the bay, running crab trot-lines, and there was no reason on earth why one couldn't have been on the island; but—twenty-five dollars a day! That was the poser; and in spite of all that Nick said, I knew that that smell couldn't have been synthetic gin.

We cracked on every stick of canvas; and as we shot past the foot of the island I could just make out two figures at play on the beach. It was the last look we ever had of those people. Five days later we walked into the ship-chandler's at Oriole to get some seam-cement we'd ordered the previous day, and were arrested for the murder of Professor Volotov!

"Is this the man wot was wit' you in Deep Harbour?" one of the plain-clothes men asked Nick; and at the same time he took a firm grab on my arm.

"Why—ye-yes," stammered Nick, hardly able to speak.

"Right!" said the Irishman. "Come along quietly."

Have you ever run foul of the law? Been in jail and faced the prospect of soon being hung for a crime that you'd never committed? No, I guess you haven't; when the courts get their hooks on to you you're in for it.

Between innocence and crime is sometimes a very small difference; but in this case it was as big as a mile—and the court couldn't see it. Guilty? Why, it was as plain as the nose on your face! —— murderers! That's what we were. People sat in the courtroom and glared at us.

I am not going to take much time telling you what happened to us in that court; and the court didn't waste any either. There was nothing human about justice in that court. It was just a bunch of fixed rules; and as soon as they could finish the rigmarole we were going to be hung.

The judge sat there, scratching his nose, already composing the speech he would give with the sentence! How—how could anyone explain to a crowd like that something which he couldn't explain to himself?

From our fight in Deep Harbour—and the whole town came over to swear what hard characters we were—to the finding of

Nick's cap on the beach at Poplar, we had left a string of clues like a paper-chase.

And, knowing this yarn as you do, look what we had to put up against it! Hunting a job—broke—in Deep Harbour; and then three days later turning up in Oriole—and living like kings. Why, even the bum lawyer the state gave us believed we were guilty; he simply got furious when we told him about the hundred dollars.

"Now look here," he yapped, "don't try to kid me! I'm your lawyer! How the —— do you think I'm going to clear you if you don't come across with the truth?"

I told him to go to ——!

"Come now," he said, beginning all over again. "Why did you start changing the colour of your boat? Wasn't it to——"

People were just the same when I told the story in court. Laughed out loud when I tried to tell about the box. The judge had to rap for order when I came to where Nick told about Pugh and the nigger playing tag on the beach. And, mind you, this in a state where they still run the Jim-crow cars!

It just shows you how satisfied everyone was that we were guilty. I got the feeling of a man trying to swim against a five-mile tide; he knows that no matter how hard he tries, he's bound to be carried away. People had their minds already made up for them by the papers. Photographs! Volotov, and his assistant George English, which was Garrick.

Long interviews with the man who had rented them the boat, explaining how they had set off on a fishing-trip.

The keeper of the light on Sharp Island tells how he sees Pugh's—Volotov's—body come floating past underneath in the sea. And then a gory description of Pugh's face, which has been mashed to a pulp. Great arguments as to what had we done with Garrick's corpse. (They had found the boat high up on the beach; but a high tide had washed the sands clear of all footprints.)

But worst of all were the talks given out by James K. Harvard. He was the millionaire who had endowed the Yardley Institute of Research. He came down to Oriole himself to see that his money got its revenge. Here we'd gone and killed their best surgeon! A couple of other philanthropists came down to take a look at the villains who had done in their pet. They talked! And the newspapers printed it all.

Propaganda! A fat chance we had against a combination like that. Why, I'm willing to bet that there wasn't a man within fifty miles who hadn't his mind already made up to hang us. A nice lot to furnish a jury!

The case was hurried on; and then one day, when they had me on the rack, I reached the end of my patience. All the time that empty-headed lawyer of ours had been trying to put a story into my mouth, asking questions and then saying—

"Now I'm going to suggest——"

And all the time I had been watching Harvard's fat face leering away, like a spider would watch something walking into its net; and somehow I just got the feeling that if I didn't force a showdown Nick and I might just as well plead guilty and be done with it all. Anyway, I couldn't make things any worse than they were.

Our lawyer was drawling:

"Now, I put it to you——"

"Your honour," I cried out to the judge, "this man is a fool; he's mixing up everything."

And before they could stop me I shouted out all about the rows we had had; how our man had refused to believe us. There was a —— of a row. I was removed.

Back in my cell I had a fit of nerves—trembling all over; and just as I was settling down, in walked Spinx. I'd seen him a day or so before when he had come in for my story—a clever little pale-faced man, reporting the case for a big New York paper.

"Well," he said when the warden had left us, "I think you're innocent. Now just tell me this story from beginning to end—and don't forget anything!"

"Do you mean it?" I gasped.

"Sure," he said, lighting up a little black cigar. "I think you are telling the truth; but don't get perked up over that. That won't stop these hicks from hanging you. We've got to slap 'em in the face with some cold-blooded facts. Otherwise you're outa luck. Shoot!"

He was a good listener; but that was the hardest job I ever had in my life.

"Make it live!" he kept saying. "Just try to act as if it was all happening again."

When I told him how Pugh set back Nick's thumb, he made me try it on him. He made me try it; and he made me repeat all the gibberish Pugh had spouted while sick in the cockpit. And, what was astonishing, he corrected me in several places and said—

"Now, didn't he put it this way?"

And he would go on and repeat almost the very words Nick had said.

"Sure!" I exclaimed. "Now, how in ——'s name did you know that?"

"Why, my simple-minded friend, you're the most innocent man I ever met in my life. You're as naïve as a schoolgirl!"

I frowned at that; and he stood there, chuckling at me. Then his face grew serious, and he came over and sat down beside me.

"You have satisfied me," he said. "It's a safe bet that you've never read Schopenhauer; and yet you have been reeling off bits of him—straight from the matrix. Now, if Volotov was easy enough in his mind to philosophize with you, it's a cinch that you weren't carrying him off by the scruff of his neck. That lends colour to your story.

"Also, that superstition about the church tapers and 'three'; there is not one chance in a thousand that anyone but a Russian like Volotov would mention a thing like that. You wouldn't be able to think of it, anyway. So that last tends to prove that part of your story is true, at any rate.

"But what makes me believe the whole tale, aside from my opinion that you two could never concoct such a one, was your scene in the court just now. You are not clever enough to work off anything subtle like that. That was genuine."

"Thank God!" I almost sobbed, and reached out and took hold of his hand.

He snatched it away and lit another cigar.

"Yes," he said, puffing away like an engine; "I'm satisfied. It fits in with my theory. And a —— weird theory it is, too;

too wild for these single-track minds down here to believe in—
unless we furnish the goods."

He stopped here and paced up and down, thinking over
something.

"You're sure," he said, "that the name of this negro was
Fairfax?"

"Certain; I made a note of it in my mind when Nick told
me. Ask him."

"I have," said Spinx; "several times already."

And then he drove his fist into his palm.

"By ——!" he said half to himself. "They used to pull this
stuff off over in England and France; but to think that
Volotov tried to get away with it here!"

"What?" I asked, feeling more bewildered than ever.

He paced up and down, talking excitedly to himself, and I
got bits of it like—

"Yardley Institute—millions—buys judges—buys lawyers—
yes, by Jove! Why couldn't they do that, too?"

"What?" I asked.

"Shut up!" he snapped, and then he said:

"Look here, my friend, how long will it take me to get over
to Poplar Island?"

I told him that with a fast motor-boat he ought to get there
before nightfall.

"Right!" he said; "I'm going."

He called out for the warden to let him out of my cell, and
just before going he said to me:

"I'm either the biggest idiot alive, or else I've got a story
that will make the whole world sit up. This tale will be a
knock-out!"

"What?" I begged him to tell me.

He saw the warden coming down the corridor, and said to
me hurriedly:

"Keep these two facts in your head, and in case anything
should turn up to delay me, use 'em in court: Professor Volotov
left New York on the Florida Limited for Oriole on the night
of June the thirteenth. Ask what he was doing on the fifteenth
of June at daybreak! Make them tell you—and don't forget
the name of that negro Fairfax. I——"

Here the warden jangled his keys.

"Come out of it. You've been gassing long enough."

"Just a minute," Spinx asked him.

But the warden said he had to go off some place and made Spinx leave me.

The fifteenth of June! That was six weeks ago. I couldn't see what that had to do with the case. For the next three days I racked my brains as to how that would help me. I guess if Spinx hadn't turned up I never would have succeeded in making our lawyer put those questions. But three days later I sat in the court, listening to the judge summing up the case for the jury, when Spinx came in and did it himself.

It was a pretty exciting scene. Here we were just about on the edge of the grace; everything nicely set for the state; and along comes a little man who insists on asking some questions. The prosecuting attorney fought against them; said there was nothing new to be said on our behalf. The case must go on its way to the jury.

While his honour had been talking, Spinx had scribbled something on a sheet of paper, which he then passed over to our lawyer.

He called upon Nick.

"You say that Professor Volotov called this negro you mentioned Fairfax?"

"Yes," said Nick; "I heard them calling him that."

"You saw him clearly?"

"Why, yes, I've told you already I could have reached out and touched him."

"Did he have a scar, a big scar, running diagonally across his forehead, sloping down from the left?"

Nick thought for a moment and then said:

"I don't know. He had something white tied round his head, something flat like a—like a bandage."

Our lawyer then handed Nick something which Spinx had just passed up to him.

"Now here are five photographs. Do you see him among them?"

Nick looked them over carefully and then shook his head. Our lawyer looked pleased at that, and then handed him two more.

"Is he one of those?"

"Sure," said Nick, holding one up. "'That's him."

There was quite a little stir at that; and everyone in the room watched our lawyer as he marked that one with his pencil. I chanced to look at James K. Harvard, and if ever I saw a man looking puzzled, it was he.

"Your honour," said our lawyer, "was there not a negro hanged in this county for murder on the fifteenth of June? A negro named Fairfax?"

"There was," said the judge.

"Is it not the custom in this state to have, aside from the man who pulls the drop, two witnesses to any execution—the sheriff and doctor? Is that not so?"

The judge nodded his head.

"Very well," said our man. "Might I have the names of the two witnesses to the hanging of Frederick Fairfax?"

In the stillness that followed that request, everyone in the court heard the gruff whisper of James K. Harvard to the prosecuting attorney:

"Object!"

The judge looked over his glasses at Harvard in a pained sort of manner, as if to say that this was going too far, and overruled the objection as soon as it was made. As soon as the prosecutor sat down Harvard began talking furiously to him.

There was a low hum of talk all over the room; and when the record clerk read out the two names of the men who had seen Fairfax destroyed by the state, it broke into a babble of excitement.

The doctor had been Professor Volotov.

Our lawyer stood there, smiling; and as soon as order had been restored he turned to the judge.

"Your honour, I will ask you to look at this photograph; it is the Bertillon of Frederick Fairfax."

He passed up the photo that Nick had dentified, and the judge glanced at it obediently.

"Thank you," said our lawyer; and then he handed the judge another photograph—an enlargement—about a foot and a half square.

"Can you see a resemblance, your honour?"

I wish I could make you see what we all saw come over the face of the judge. First he just looked sort of officially bored, then curious, and then mad—just as though someone was trying to play a trick on him. Then he took the two photos, held them side by side, and a look of absolute horror came into his eyes. We watched, just like one would look at a movie.

When he spoke it was in a sort of a daze.

"Who took this picture?"

With that question the whole procedure of the case seemed to change; there was a hush just like one feels in a crowd that's watching some bad accident. A sort of awful curiosity. Spinx stood up and answered the judge:

"It was taken last night, your honour, in the swamp on Poplar Island by a wild animal photographer. We set a flash powder on a trap-wire—just the way George Shiras takes his deer pictures—and you see what we caught on the plate! It shows where Professor Volotov took one liberty too many with the devolution of man. From simian to man is all right; but not from man to——"

At this juncture Harvard literally hurled himself across to the judge and began talking as if it was his own life he was trying to save; and I guess the people of that state are still talking about that sudden adjournment.

And that was the end of the case; it never appeared again in the papers. Not a word. It was just as if James K. Harvard—and his money—had said to the Press of the world:

"Here, forget it! It was all a bad dream——"

"It's no use," said Spinx, who came down to see us off on the *Panther*. "I've lost the beat of a lifetime. The world's greatest story is climbing the trees of that island——"

"Oh, I say, not in the Sherry!"

SCREAMING
SKULLS

CHRISTINA HOLE

A T Bettiscombe Manor, in Dorset, the upper part of a
human skull was kept for many years in a small box
placed in a niche on the staircase. It could still be seen
there at the beginning of the present century, and was freely
shown to anyone who asked to see it. But it was never moved
from its resting-place on the stairway, and no one was allowed
to take it out of the house on any pretext whatever. Local
tradition said that the most shocking disturbances invariably
followed any attempt to remove it; and though in late Victorian
and Edwardian times the tenants affected to disbelieve the old
story, no one was bold enough to put the matter to the proof.
At all events, the skull was left undisturbed for two or three
generations, and some years ago the niche that contained it
was filled in for greater security. Thus the gruesome object that
once haunted the house with terrifying noises is now walled into
its fabric, and there in all probability it will remain for so long
as the building itself stands.

The story of this curious haunting has its roots in the late
seventeenth century. During the Commonwealth, Bettiscombe
Manor was the home of John Pinney, the Puritan minister of
Broadwindsor. After the Restoration he was ejected from the
living and went to Ireland for a time, but eventually he returned
to Bettiscombe and died there in 1705. The last twenty years
of his life were saddened by the misfortunes of his two sons, John
and Azariah, who both fought for the Duke of Monmouth in
1685 and were subsequently condemned to death by Judge
Jeffreys. John was executed, but Azariah, more fortunate than
his brother, was reprieved and transported to the West Indies,

2

where he lived to regain his freedom and become a highly respected and prosperous merchant in the Isle of Nevis.

When he finally returned from exile, he brought with him a negro servant. This man's name is now forgotten, but the local people were later to have good reason for remembering that he once dwelt among them. His life in Dorset can hardly have been very happy, what with home-sickness and cold, and the suspicion with which untravelled peasants doubtless regarded his black face and alien ways. But, perhaps fortunately for himself, it did not last very long, for he died of consumption within a few years. On his deathbed he declared that his spirit would never rest unless he was buried in his own country, and begged that his body might be shipped back to Nevis. Probably this was outside the bounds of possibility in those days of slow transport, or the request may not have been taken seriously. Certainly, no attempt seems to have been made by anyone to grant it, and, like other deceased members of the household, he was buried in Bettiscombe churchyard.

His skull, however, was kept in the house for some reason that is not now remembered. It is a little difficult at this distance of time to understand why this should have been done. There are other instances of skulls being retained in houses while the rest of the remains were laid in consecrated ground, but in almost every case this was done at the express wish of the dying person. The negro's sole desire was to be buried in Nevis, so it is scarcely likely that he would have made such a request, and surely only the most morbid individual would keep so strange a relic in his home without good cause. But whatever the reason may have been, the skull was separated from the trunk and brought to the Manor, and there it remained for some years without any untoward result.

The trouble started in the mid-eighteenth century, when some tenant, less fond of gruesome curiosities than his predecessors, ejected it. Appalling and continuous screaming thereupon broke out, filling the house with uproar for days on end, and rendering life almost unendurable for all who heard it. Disease appeared amongst the cattle on the farm, the crops withered, and everyone connected with the household met with some misfortune. At first no one connected the disturbances with the

skull, but eventually it was suggested to the harassed farmer that this might be the cause. By this time all the inhabitants of the Manor were driven nearly mad by the noises, and were willing to try anything that might stop them. The skull was therefore retrieved from the pond into which it had been thrown and brought back to the house, whereupon the screams immediately ceased, and life resumed its normal quiet way. In later years two or three further attempts were made to dispose of the relic by burial in the garden or in the churchyard. On every occasion the same thing happened, until finally even the most sceptical tenant realized that it was dangerous to tamper with it. Thenceforward it was placed in the staircase niche and left untouched until in the end all further peril was averted by walling it in.

Such is the legend of the famous Screaming Skull of Bettiscombe. It is not the only tale of its kind, but it is one of the most interesting, if only because the reason for the haunting seems so obscure. In most other stories there is some record of deep love for his home shown by the skull's owner in life or sometimes a desire for revenge upon the resident family. Here there is neither. The negro had no cause to love Bettiscombe or to wish to remain in it, and it was not the Pinneys who suffered from the disturbances, but later tenants who were quite unconnected with the exile's history.

In all these legends of screaming or haunting skulls, it will be noted that there is nothing ghostly about the thing itself. It is a purely material object that can be touched and handled like anything else. So long as it is quiet, it is not even very frightening, except in so far as all proofs of our mortality may be said to be so. When Higher Chilton Farm was being altered in 1826, the workmen are said to have used the skull kept there as a drinking-cup for their beer, and this rather unpleasant piece of bravado had, as far as we know, no startling consequences of any kind. In some tales, like that of Burton Agnes, the ghost of the skull's former owner is seen also, but more often there are no such spiritual manifestations. The thing itself appears to have a curious life of its own, to be able to think coherently, and certainly to pursue its own ends with relentless determination. It is in some way so closely associated with the building that it will not leave it, and consequently the unfortunate householders are unable to dispose of it even by Christian burial. Being itself material, it cannot be exorcised like an ordinary ghost, and all that can be done is to put it in some safe place from which it is certain it will never be moved.

It is true that there is one legend in which exorcism was successful, but here the supernatural element is more than usually evident throughout. At Calgarth, in Westmorland, Kraster and Dorothy Cook were cheated out of their home in a peculiarly evil manner during the eighteenth century. A local magistrate, Myles Phillipson, wished to buy the place, but they would not sell. So, taking a leaf from the story of Joseph and his brethren, he invited them to his house, hid a silver cup in their luggage, and then accused them of stealing it. As theft was then a capital offence, the Cooks were both hanged, and Phillipson duly acquired the farm. But before she died, Dorothy Cook cursed him and all his family, saying they would come to ruin and lose all their lands, and that she herself, with her husband, would haunt Calgarth for so long as the Phillipsons remained there.

Twelve months later someone in the house found two fleshless skulls lying at the head of the staircase. They were removed and buried some way off, but a few days afterwards they were found in the house again. Once more they were taken out and once more they returned. Unlike the negro of Bettiscombe, they did not scream or make any disturbance, but their mere presence was enough to strike horror into the hearts of all who saw them. They appeared to be material objects, but that they were not really of this world was shown by the fact that they could not be destroyed. On one occasion they were thrown into the lake, on another they were burned to ashes. Many times they were buried as far as possible from the house. Driven almost desperate by the silent and relentless persecution, Myles Phillipson caused them to be pounded to atoms and their dust scattered to the winds. But whatever was done, they were always found in the house a little later, lying side by side and watching with their sightless eyes the struggles of the wretched family to free themselves. Eventually Dr. Watson, Bishop of Llandaff, exorcised them, and after that they were never seen again. But the rest of the curse was not lifted, and the family

gradually sank into poverty, losing all their possessions, including the farm which they had committed murder to obtain.

The details of this melodramatic story are not well authenticated, and probably most of it is an imaginative local effort to
account for the rise and fall of a perhaps unpopular family.
Nevertheless, there must have been something very wrong at
Calgarth to induce the Bishop to undertake the rare rite of
exorcism. Probably there were in fact skulls in the house, and
these may actually have been the centre of the haunting. The
bones of the dead have always been regarded as powerful agents
of psychic force, and if the remains of some unjustly treated
individuals were preserved at Calgarth, they may well have
been the channels through which an ancient curse or some
malevolent entity could work.

Another noisy skull with a decided mind of its own was kept,
and probably still is, at Tunstead Farm, near Chapel-en-le-
Frith. It was apparently that of a woman, but it was locally
known as Dickie. A vague tradition of murder at some un-
specified date was supposed to account for it, but no one was
ever quite certain whether the victim was Ned Dixon, a former
owner, or an unnamed girl said to have been killed in the room
where it was kept.

Like all the rest, Dickie refused to be moved, and once when
it was stolen and taken some miles away to Disley, an unendurable uproar broke out both at Tunstead and at Disley. So
horrifying were the noises that the thieves were only too glad to
return it. On another occasion some pious person thought it
ought to be buried in consecrated ground, but this clearly did
not suit it. Bangings, crashes, thuds and clatterings raged
through the house continuously by day and by night, and
eventually the skull had to be dug up again and brought home
in a basket.

But Dickie's chief interest is that it was something more than
a supernatural nuisance. From the beginning it seems to have
acted as a sort of guardian to the family. By gentle taps or loud
thuds it predicted deaths in the house, and gave warning of the
approach of strangers. When Alfred Fryer visited the farm in
the 'eighties of last century, the farmer told him that during the
lambing season, or when any of the stock were ill, he was often

roused by soft taps on the window. He never disregarded these signals, but always rose at once to see what was wrong, and on no occasion had he ever been misled. The presence of outsiders was always made known by loud noises. This had its advantages on a lonely upland farm, but it was not without its inconveniences also, for Dickie did not always distinguish between strangers who had a right to be there and those who had not. When Irish labourers were lodged in the outbuildings during the haymaking reason, it sometimes drove them away by a continual clattering noise, as of forks and hay-rakes violently moved about, and the sound of whetting of scythes. Of late years it seems to have refrained from some of its more turbulent manifestations, but as recently as 1938 it was locally said that the family were still warned by the skull when anything went wrong on the farm.

Dickie's protecting qualities perhaps shed some light upon the origin of these curious legends, all of them so persistent and so very much alike. It may well be that when the dying person asked that his head should be preserved at home, he had some clearly or dimly formulated idea of guarding that home after death. Theophilus Brome, for instance, may have thought along these lines in 1670 when on his death-bed he arranged for his skull to be kept in Higher Chilton Farm, though his body was buried in Chilton Cantelo Church. In the eighteenth century his grave was opened and the skeleton found to be headless, so there seems little doubt that the skull in the hall was actually his. And if so, he saw to it that it was not removed, for Collinson tells us in his *History of Somerset* that later tenants who tried to shift it "have as often been deterred by horrid noises portentive of sad displeasure".

The same atavistic notion may have actuated Anne Griffith, the youngest of the three sisters who built Burton Agnes Hall. When the house was finished in 1628, Anne conceived a passionate love for the beautiful place. She did not, however, live to enjoy it long, for soon after its completion she was attacked by robbers on a lonely road, and so badly injured that she died within five days. In her last moments she made her sisters promise they would keep her head at home, and threatened to haunt them if they did not. But when she was dead they disregarded her request, which they probably ascribed to delirium, and laid head and body together in the family vault.

Two or three days after the funeral they were violently reminded of their broken promise. Thundering crashes, bangs and rolling noises, slamming doors and the most horrifying groans were heard throughout the house, continuing without cessation and without visible cause for several days together. Anne's threat was then remembered, and on the advice of the Vicar, the two women had the grave opened and the head abstracted. Local tradition says that the body was found still uncorrupted, but the skull was already fleshless and had somehow become detached from the trunk.

Henceforward it was preserved at home, and the strictest orders were given that it must never be moved. When the Boyntons inherited the estate, they buried it in the garden, but the ensuing disturbances were so dreadful that they were obliged to bring it back, and the same thing happened whenever any other attempts were made to dispose of it. Now, like the Bettiscombe skull, it is bricked up in the walls. But Anne Griffith was not content to trust her beloved home to her material remains alone. Her spirit also haunts it, sometimes in the form of a small woman in a fawn dress, and sometimes invisibly, with only the faint rustling of silk skirts and the sound of tapping footsteps to betray her presence.

In this house we see two separate forms of haunting, which in their turn spring from two differing philosophies of life after death. The skull, clearly, represents the older of the two. Some primitive races believed that the dead lived on in the tomb in a sort of half-life that was shared by the body as well as the soul. In the Scandinavian sagas there are several stories of physical violence offered to grave-robbers or other intruders by the dead, who were obviously capable of using their hands and teeth for the purpose. In the horrible tale of Asmund and Asvid, for instance, Saxo Grammaticus relates that the dead man came to life every night, and ravenously devoured first his horses and then his dog; and when these were gone, he attacked his living brother. The flesh might wither and the blood dry up, but life lingered in the bones, and nowhere more strongly than in the skull. Bran the Blessed directed that his head should be taken to London and buried where the Tower now stands. So long as it remained on guard there no hostile army could invade the shores of Britain. In one of the Icelandic sagas we are told how a farmer commanded his children to bury his head on a high hill, so that he might overlook the labourers at their work. And the same sort of idea, less clearly defined, seems to have inspired Theophilus Brome and Anne Griffith, and perhaps also to explain the retention of Father Ambrose's skull at Wardley Hall, near Manchester.

It may seem strange that traces of this ancient notion should persist so long after the belief from which it sprang had vanished from our conscious thought. Yet we can hardly doubt that it is so. The early creeds of the human race are only shallowly buried in our subconscious minds, and sometimes they rise to the surface and are seen again of men. In these curious tales, none of them more than two or three hundred years old, we see an example of that queer duality of thought which enables many people to believe two opposite things at once—in this case, that the soul alone lives after death and the body is a mere discarded garment, and at the same time that the bones, or at least the skull, have a distinct life of their own. Indeed, we need not look to our skull-stories alone for proof that we have not yet entirely shaken off the notions that inspired them. It is sufficient to consider for a moment the odd reluctance shown by many good Christians—perhaps even by the reader of this article—to pass after dark through a peaceful and consecrated church-yard whence, as their faith teaches them, the souls of the dead have departed, and only lifeless and inanimate bones remain.

THE ZOMBIE OF ALTO PARANA

W. STANLEY MOSS

Illustrations by John Buckland Wright

Mr. W. Stanley Moss is still a young man—he was born in 1921 in Yokohama—but has already had enough adventure to content half a dozen ordinary men. He has been twice round the world. In the last war, becoming a major when he was 22, he fought in Africa, the Balkans and the Far East, and ended as a successful secret agent in Greece, Crete and Siam. While in Crete he arranged his most dramatic adventure—the capture of a German general in the midst of his own troops, the story of which he has modestly recounted in "Ill Met by Moonlight".

FROM his deck-chair on the veranda, Emil could see the paddle-boat nosing around the bend in the river. Like a water-beetle it came, squat and ungainly, insinuating its crustacean frame with a fanfare of hooting and splashing into the placid exhalations of the landscape.

Once a month the boat from Buenos Aires came up the Alto Parana to the Jesuit country of Misiones, and always it stopped alongside the tongue of land where Emil's bungalow squatted

33

at the water's edge. When, as now, the river was low, a fringe
of beach would separate the water from the curtain of *tacuara*
which rose to the height of the jungle behind; but later, when
the rains began, the beach would vanish overnight, and Emil
would awaken to find the water lapping at the wooden stays
which supported the veranda on which he slept.

The boat never stayed at the station for more than an hour,
but remained just so long as the business of unloading, the
checking of inventories and the signing of receipts took to be
concluded. And now Emil watched the ungainly craft looming
larger before him, its paddles churning up a trail of muddy
water which receded like some monstrous reptile in its wake.
He saw Silvestro, the foreman, and a couple of Indians making
their way along the wooden jetty so as to be ready to start unloading. These things he viewed with detachment, as though
he were the spectator of a film which he had seen many times
before. The sight bored him.

A sallow-faced, compact figure, with a straggling red beard
and down-slanting eyes and little hair on the top of his head, he
looked like one of those portraits which present an altogether
different picture when you turn them upside down. If you had
inverted his face, you would have seen an unshaven Chinaman
wearing a large red fur hat.

Presently he got up and sauntered down to the water's edge.

Sitting in the captain's cabin, papers before him on the desk
and a glass of warm whisky in his hand, he looked up and said:
"That's the lot signed. Is there anything else?"

The captain was an elderly man. Hair grew in abundance
from his nostrils and ears. His clothes were shabby, and the
glossy peak of his cap was cracked in half. "There's one more
thing," he replied. "I've got a passenger on board who wants
to get off here."

"Get off here? What on earth for?"

"He wanted to go as far as the boat would take him."

"Why?"

"Don't get me wrong. I didn't ask him to come. He paid his
fare and I brought him, that's all."

"What does he want?"

"He's going to make his fortune," the captain said. "It's the same old story. But he seems quite a nice young fellow. Couldn't you put him up for a while?"

"You know very well that I refuse to have anybody staying with me."

The captain had eyes of pale, tired blue—blue that grows thinner and more delicate with the years—and he glanced at Emil, eyebrows raised. "Are you still adamant?" he asked, and then, when he saw that the other did not intend to answer him, "What about the hut?" he added. "The hut on the point? It's been empty since Schlesinger died, hasn't it?"

"Yes," said Emil, as though caught off guard, "yes, it's empty. I suppose he could stay there if he wanted to."

He turned his back on the captain and poured himself another glass of whisky from the decanter on the filing cabinet. He was thinking of Schlesinger, the last mad night, and having to carry the still-warm body two hundred yards through the rain and dumping it in the river. "But I'm against it. I know what happens when two people get stuck in a place like this."

"Like you and Schlesinger?" the captain suggested.

"Yes. Like me and Schlesinger."

The captain spread out his hands on the desk. "Don't be cruel to this boy," he said, now raising his right hand as if in absolution. "He's not like Schlesinger."

Emil wheeled around, the whisky splashing out of his glass, his hand trembling. "Stop acting, you old quack!" he snapped. "Don't you start preaching at me." He came close to the desk and gripped its edges, and leaned across it so that his beard fell almost in the captain's face. In his down-slanting eyes there gleamed a veneer of power, the knowledge that his shaft had struck on tender skin. "You know as well as I do that everybody turns into a Schlesinger here, no matter how they start."

And then the door opened, and they looked up and saw the young man standing in the entrance. He was wearing an open-necked shirt and shorts, and on his bare knees the skin had gone lobster-red with sunburn. His blond hair, his peeling nose and wide-open expression gave him the appearance of a schoolboy who has just had a wash and comes to present himself at the tea-table. When he saw Emil he stopped, his hand still on the door-knob, and hesitantly he said: "I—I'm most awfully sorry. Am I interrupting something?"

The captain's sigh of relief was audible. "No," he quickly replied, his blue eyes creasing in tune with the smile that crept upon his lips. "Not at all. We've finished our business." Then he rose from his chair and said: "I'd like you to meet one another. Emil, this is Mr. Clift whom I've brought along from B.A."

"That's right," said the young man, his countenance brightening. "We've had a splendid trip, absolutely thrilling. I'm almost sorry it's come to an end, really. But the skipper's told me lots about you and I know that it'll be grand here. I'm terribly glad to meet you." He spoke very quickly, erratically, as though he had a lot to say and all too little time in which to say it. Now he forsook his place in the doorway and came forward, blushing slightly beneath the lobster over-coating of his skin, and made as if to shake Emil by the hand.

For a moment Emil watched his approach, making no move to accept the proffered hand, then turned abruptly to the captain. "Is there anything else?" he asked, his lips curling in a sneer. "Anything else, Father?"

"I hope you'll show Mr. Clift the ropes a bit. And perhaps you could let him have a bed in your bungalow until Schlesinger's hut is ready. . . ."

Emil made no reply. Behind him, he heard Clift saying: "That really would be terribly decent of you."

They left the jetty and started to walk towards the bungalow. Emil noticed the expression on the young man's face, the rather incredulous look in his eyes as he saw the building for the first time. There was no concealment of his thoughts, and Emil understood them. He remembered how he himself had experienced that same feeling when first he had set eyes upon this pile of wood and corrugated iron. "So this is my home," he had thought, a ripple of disgust trembling down his spine.

"So this is your home," Clift said.

"That's right. Don't you find it charming?"

As if in reply there came a hoot from the boat's siren, and

turning they saw the paddles beginning to churn in reverse as the craft put off from the jetty and swung away into the centre of the river.

"Look," said Clift. "The skipper's waving to us." He started waving his arms in return and shouted a good-bye which was inaudible above the noise of the engines. Then he turned to Emil. "Isn't he a delightful old man—the skipper, I mean? Such an unusual type for this part of the world. I always imagined that the captains of river-boats were hard-drinking, cursing, tobacco-spitting tyrants; but not a bit of it. Just the reverse, in fact. He's so gentle and quiet—more like a priest, really."

Emil grunted. "He *was* a priest—once upon a time—the old fool."

"You mean——?"

"No, he wasn't defrocked. He just gave it up because he hadn't got the guts to go on with it. But that was years ago, before you were born."

And then, before the other had time to reply, Emil waved to the foreman on the jetty. "Silvestro!" he called. "Come here!" The foreman came running up the stretch of sand to where they stood. He was an elderly man, tight-skinned, with a small head which looked like an Aztec skull that had been arrested in its shrinkage.

"Silvestro, I want you to have Mr. Clift's things taken to my bungalow for to-night. He'll stay in the spare room until you've got Schlesinger's hut ready." To Clift, Emil said: "This is Silvestro, my *capataz*. He'll be able to help you if you need anything."

"Thank you," said Clift. "Thank you very much." He did not face Emil as he spoke. He was looking away along the river, watching the boat as it straightened out in midstream and started with a hustle of paddles to churn its way out of sight. He heard Emil saying, "Come on, I'll show you your room," but he found himself unwilling to take his eyes from the boat. Again he was the schoolboy, reluctant to leave the carriage window while he could still see his parents waving good-bye to him from the platform; but then he slowly turned and found himself looking once more towards the bungalow—the school, first night away from home, nostalgia and a pillow wet with tears.

Still Emil was talking. "Good chap, Silvestro. He's a sort of magician at producing things. He'll be able to fix you up with a *compañera* if you want one." He glanced at the young man. "I suppose you *do* want one?"

"A *compañera*? I don't know what that means."

Emil chuckled into his beard. "Child," he said. "It's a sort of wife which can cook."

"You mean an Indian girl?"

"What did you expect, a white one?"

"No, but——"

"They are quite cheap, and you can change them if you don't find them satisfactory."

"I—I don't think I really need one."

Emil laughed out loud; then suddenly he stopped and said: "Now I'll take you to your room."

Clift was glad. "Grand," he said, with eagerness pursuing the change of subject. "There must be a splendid view of the river from the bungalow."

They did not meet again until dusk.

Emil was lying on his bed when he heard a knock on the door and Clift's voice asking: "May I come in?"

"What do you want?"

"I wondered if you could lend me a mirror?"

"Come in, come in. There's no need to shout."

Clift entered, a hand stuffed shyly in his pocket, and stood just inside the doorway. "I've just been unpacking," he explained, "and I found my mirror smashed to smithereens." He laughed nervously. "Seven years' bad luck, I suppose." Then, after a pause, added: "Do you think you could lend me yours?"

"Mine?" Emil grunted and sat up so that his legs dangled over the edge of the bed. "What makes you think I've got a mirror?"

"Well—after all—one likes to look fairly presentable. . . ."

"For whose benefit? Mine?" Emil burst out laughing, the wind whistling through his teeth and his red beard twitching. "Presentable!" he echoed. "**That's wonder**ful!"

Clift stood with his back against the door, his fingers jingling a bunch of keys in his pocket. Abashed, "I don't see what's so funny about it," he said.

"You'll see what's funny all right," Emil told him. "You'll find out in time. Shall I tell you something? I broke my mirror too. I can't remember now how long ago that was . . . perhaps it was seven years ago, perhaps it was yesterday. But do you know how I broke it? Can you guess? No? Well, I'll tell you. I put my fist through it, bang in the middle, because I couldn't stand the sight of it any longer."

They had supper on the veranda, and afterwards, with cigars and drinks, settled themselves in deck-chairs overlooking the river. From here they could see the red eyes of the alligators, like coupled tail-lamps straying across the water, while to their ears there came the first notes, the tuning-up, of the frog orchestra.

"Do you hear the noise of frogs? It sounds crazy, doesn't it? But it isn't creepy, not eerie like the *uru-tau*. You wait until you hear the *uru-tau*. It's unearthly. Sends the shivers down your back."

Clift asked: "What is it? An animal or something?"

"It's a night-bird. The Indians say it contains the souls of haunted men. I'm inclined to believe them. It laughs like a madman, like a raving lunatic. You'll understand when you hear it."

Emil stretched a hand for the bottle of *caña* beneath his chair and refilled his glass, then: "It was one of the things that really got Schlesinger," he continued. "That, and the red eyes of the alligators. He got so he used to see alligators everywhere." He held out the *caña* bottle towards Clift. "Help yourself to another drink."

The other shook his head, and with a flavour of apology he replied: "Thanks very much, but I don't think I will. I haven't got much taste for that stuff."

Emil replaced the bottle on the floor. "You'll soon get used to it," he said.

Clift made no reply. Instead, "Who was Schlesinger?" he asked.

"He was the chap who died in the hut which you're going to stay in."

"He *died* there? What a horrible thought."

"It was as well that he died."

"Why? What was wrong with him?"

"There was almost nothing right with him. He lost his reason, he was diseased, he wouldn't eat. But, to tell you the truth, it was rather fascinating to watch his progress. One felt as though one were actually witnessing a metamorphosis. I was quite young then, you know, and I found it strangely amusing. Can you understand that?"

"I—I don't know. I don't think I can. Perhaps you could have done something to help him. . . ."

"There was nothing to be done. He was always drunk, crazy drunk."

"And what happened to him in the end? What did he die of?"

"The Indians got him, just like that."

For a while Clift said nothing; then he gave a nervous little laugh and said: "Well, that won't happen to me, thank goodness. I'm not staying here long enough—just a matter of days while I find a good guide and collect the necessary kit."

"And where do you think you're going?"

"Into the jungle. I heard there was silver to be found in the hills."

"Who told you so?"

"There've already been one or two expeditions, haven't there?"

"Certainly. But who's to know if they ever found anything? They never came back." Emil paused for a moment to sip his drink. "Do you realize that you have to cut your way through every yard of this jungle? It could take you a week to travel a quarter of a mile."

"I've been told that it's going to be very difficult, but I'm determined to have a try. I've got to make money, lots of it." He clasped his hands across his knees and, as if in a nutshell to explain the reason for his expedition, added: "You see, I've got a debt to pay."

"A debt? Do you mean to say that you're proposing to go and get buried in there"—Emil waved a hand airily towards

the jungle that lay behind the bungalow—"buried alive just
because of a debt? Well, I'm damned! That's the sort of crazy
thing one would expect from an Englishman." Then, as if the
thought had not until that moment struck him, he asked: "I
suppose you *are* English, aren't you?"

"Of course. Didn't you know?"

"You never told me."

"By my accent, I mean." Clift turned towards his companion. "I'm sorry," he said. "It never struck me that you
might not have guessed I was English—any more than I could
have doubted that you were a German."

"Did you say German?"

Emil spoke the words very slowly, as though to chew each one
before spitting it out. "What makes you think I'm a German?"

"I—I really don't know. Just instinct, I suppose. You look
like a German, and you talk like one."

Emil said: "If ever you repeat those words in front of the
Indians, I'll wring your neck." And then he burst into a great
roar of laughter, drowning Clift's attempted apology, and
slapped his thigh with barrack-room gusto. "Go on," he urged,
the mirth still bubbling within him. "What debt do you owe?
Tell me all about it."

The Englishman, reluctant to reply, drew into himself like
some pricked mollusc.

Emil patted him on the knee. "Don't be silly," he said. "I've
got to be humoured. I've been here for a long time, you know,
and I'm not much accustomed to company."

Clift's rosy face looked sulky. "It's a debt of honour. I can't
go back to England until I'm in a position to clear it." He
clasped his hands together, as if to crush some invisible nut
between his palms. "It's as simple as that."

"Simple, my foot! It's mad, crazy. My dear fellow, if it's
only money that you want——"

"*Only* money?" Clift interrupted, eyebrows up, hands raised.
"For what else could one want to come to a place like this?
Surely you don't stay here for pleasure?"

"There are other things," said Emil. "If it was only money
that I wanted I could have retired years ago. Why, you could
make a fortune here even by selling *caña* to the Indians,"

"But that's illegal, isn't it?"

"Everything's illegal. But who's to stop you up here?"

"Things like that get known."

"You think so? Why don't you try it and see?"

"I've got my plans. I believe that everything will turn out all right—my way." The Englishman yawned loudly, exaggeratedly. "I feel dog tired. Would you think it rude if I were to turn in now?"

"Am I so forbidding a companion?"

Again the nervous little laugh. "Of course not. It's just that I'm tired. Didn't get any sleep last night."

Clift got up from his chair and rested his hands on the balustrade and stood for a moment looking out across the river; then slowly he turned and started to walk towards the door of his bedroom. Emil watched him closely. He knew what the Englishman was feeling. It had been the same that first night with Schlesinger.

From his bedroom door, Clift said, "Good night, Emil. . . ."

Emil said nothing, but poured himself another glass of *caña*. Without turning, he knew that the Englishman had not yet gone into his room, but was still hovering at the door.

"You—you don't mind my calling you by your Christian name, do you? It's more friendly, somehow, especially as we're the only two white men here. . . ."

Emil said: "For God's sake stop talking like a dying schoolgirl. Good night."

For a moment there was silence, then he heard the door creak shut behind him; and then, as if in applause, there sounded the full-blooded roar of the frogs' chorus, while from somewhere, not far off in the jungle, there came the mad, chilling laugh of an *uru-tau*.

High above the *tacuara* there rode a round moon, and in the water, flashing, its image dodged like an uncatchable ball among the red eyes of the alligators.

On the eve of Clift's departure into the jungle Emil walked across from his bungalow to Schlesinger's hut and found the Englishman giving his stores a last-minute check-over on the veranda.

"Hullo," said Clift brightly, looking up from a rucksack's contents which he had emptied out on the veranda floor. He appeared to be in high spirits, as though packing his tuck-box on the last day of term. The ruddiness of his skin had toned down during the past two weeks, but apart from this his appearance was as spruce and as boyish as it had been on the day of his arrival. "All set, as you can see," he announced.

The Englishman was smiling. "I've collected three Guarani porters, and Silvestro has produced a guide for me who says he knows of a good track through the jungle. So everything's shipshape at last. I can scarcely wait to leave."

"There is no such thing as a track through the jungle. No such thing exists." Emil glanced at the Englishman's face: the blue eyes, the wavy blond hair, and the chin which was shaved perhaps every third day. There was nothing new in this sight. He had seen it all before—how many years ago? It was as though he were looking at his own ghost; and the realization sent a chill wind through his bones. For a moment he hesitated, staring before him; then, muttering something beneath his breath, he suddenly turned and started to walk away from the hut.

"What was that you said?" called Clift; but he received no reply.

Clift had gone, and once more life for Emil resumed its normal course. It was not that the Englishman's presence had in any way altered his routine; but the mere existence of another European in the vicinity had created an undercurrent of interest and curiosity; and now that the young man had departed, Emil was conscious of a new emptiness in his life.

It was on a Sunday that Clift had gone, and it was on a Sunday, exactly five weeks later, that he returned.

The sun was low in the sky when Silvestro, the foreman, came running to Emil's bungalow, and Emil, who did not like being disturbed at this time of day, asked gruffly: "What's the matter?"

"The Englisher," panted the foreman. "He come back, señor."

Emil was surprised. Curtly he dismissed his *compañera* and came out on to the veranda.

"There," said Silvestro, "there, señor."

Emil followed the foreman's pointing arm until his eyes rested upon a small, lurching figure coming along the narrow fringe of sand between the *tacuara* and the water's edge.

"Shall I go help, señor?" Silvestro asked, already making as if to go; but Emil laid a hand on his arm.

"No, no," he said. "He'll be here in about ten minutes. There's nothing you can do to help."

When Clift arrived he did not go straight to the bungalow, but went instead to Schlesinger's hut, and it was not until supper-time that he came to see Emil. His skin was the colour of walnut stain, and over his chin and upper lip there straggled a film of hairs as though his flesh had gone mouldy. Thus he stood in front of Emil's deck-chair, a look of mingled reticence and embarrassment in his eyes, and said: "Well, here I am. May I invite myself to supper?"

Emil motioned him to sit down.

"Sorry I couldn't make myself a little more beautiful. I've lost all my kit. Haven't even got any soap, but perhaps——"

"What happened?"

Clift sat down in the empty chair beside Emil, and helped himself to a drink from the bottle of *caña* which stood on the floor. He took a long gulp at the drink, drew the back of his hand across his lips, then said: "The Indians ran away one night and pinched all the stores. Fortunately, I had a knife and compass in my belt. I realized that it would be hopeless to try to continue alone, so I struck a course for the river. It took me seventeen days to reach it, and another two to make my way back here."

Emil grunted. "I could have told you all that before you set off, you pig-headed ass."

Clift said: "It's better to find out these things for oneself, otherwise one would never learn anything."

"Damned silly way of going about it."

"I don't think so. I know now, for instance, that a human

being can live for nineteen days on nothing but slugs and not
feel too bad about it. And I've learned another thing. I know
that I'll never go on another expedition like that as long as I
live."

Emil looked up, smiling.

The Englishman leaned towards him. "I know what you're
thinking," he challenged. "You're thinking that this is the best
joke you've heard in ages, aren't you?"

Emil did not reply.

"Well, I'll tell you something. *I* think it's the best joke I've
ever heard in all my life."

During supper Clift talked a great deal and ate very little.
"Funny," he said, explaining himself, "I imagined that I'd be
able to eat a horse when I got back, but now that all this food
is here in front of me I find it somehow nauseating."

Emil listened to him, fascinated.

The Englishman was sitting with a bottle of *caña* in front of
him, and from time to time, without prompting from his companion, he picked it up and refilled his glass. "Strange thing
about the jungle," he continued, "is that you don't get frightened by it. You can get into a panic, yes, and perhaps lose your
head, but not in the way that you read about in books. You are
scared at the very beginning—that's true—but it only lasts so
long as you don't find out the secret. I wonder if *you* know the
secret of the jungle?"

Emil said nothing.

"Aha! You don't know. So I'll tell you. The secret is that
everything, every living being in the whole of the jungle, is
scared stiff. Fear travels through the trees like electricity, and
there's so much of it on every side of you that—Bingo!—it just
cancels itself out. Two minuses make a plus. Just like that.
When everybody is somebody, then nobody is anybody. Who
was it made that remark? Can't remember now. But whoever
he was he knew what he was talking about. He knew all about
the jungle. Take off my hat to him. . . ."

He picked up the bottle from the table, and to draw attention
to the fact that it was empty, he turned it upside down and

shook it. Then he looked across at Emil. "I say, you haven't
got another bottle tucked away somewhere, have you? What
about a night-cap?"

Presently they went out on to the veranda and sat down in
the deck-chairs overlooking the river.

"I bet you can't guess what I was thinking about most of the
time on my way back here? I'll tell you—I was thinking of that
idea of yours—the one about selling *caña* to the Indians—and I
decided that it wasn't at all a bad proposition. I've got some
gold left—had it hidden in my belt—better invest it before it
all goes." He leaned forward with a conspiratorial air. "Is it
really as easy as you said? What are the snags? Will you tell
me more about it?"

"There are no snags," Emil replied. "The only people you've
got to be careful of are the Indians themselves."

"Of the Indians? Why on earth?"

"Because alcohol makes them behave in a very odd way. You
will sell them a bottle of *caña*—a bottle which you have bought
for thirty centavos on the other side of the river—and you will
ask two pesos for it. That's nearly six hundred per cent profit.
O.K. In an hour or two perhaps they will come back and ask
you to sell them another bottle. All right, you sell them the
second bottle for five pesos. That's nearly sixteen hundred per
cent profit. . . ."

"And so on? But it sounds too easy for words."

"That's where you are wrong. It's just the damned-fool sort
of way a person like you would go and land himself in trouble."

"Perhaps you'd explain. . . ."

"Rather than sell a third bottle to an Indian you'd do better
to jump off a precipice. Listen, the man is already drunk. He
probably hasn't got the money and knows you are swindling
him. Perhaps he can even see the third bottle hidden under
your bed, and the only thing that's stopping him from having
it is you yourself. For him it's simple arithmetic. You must
be subtracted—that's all."

"Oh, well, so long as one remembers when to stop it's all
right. Still make a roaring profit. . . ."

Near at hand there sounded the wild laugh of an *uru-tau,*

high-pitched at first, then hilariously descending until finally it
died away.

"How I hate that noise. The bloody bird's always laughing
at you, never *with* you. Gets on my nerves. . . ."

One morning during the following week Emil met the
Englishman walking along the fringe of sand by the *tacuara*.

"Good morning," said Clift jauntily. He was unshaven, but
the dirtiness of his face was offset by the lively, almost gay blue
of his eyes. "How's life?"

"All right," Emil told him.

"What about coming to my place for a drink? You haven't
seen the hut since I tidied it up. It's looking quite attractive
now."

Emil hesitated. He had once told himself that never again
would he set foot in Schlesinger's hut, never, never; but now
his resolution gave way to curiosity. "Why not?" he said,
shrugging his shoulders and joining step with the Englishman.

The hut was a two-roomed affair, low on the ground and
almost without windows, surrounded on all sides by a corridor-
like veranda. "Not very beautiful from the outside," said Clift,
"but there's nothing to be done about that." He led the way
up the steps on to the veranda and threw wide one of the doors
that led off it. "Need a few chintzes, I suppose, and some
geraniums. Good old cottagey atmosphere. For geraniums read
orchids throughout—exotic note."

Emil stood in the open doorway looking around the bedroom.
He saw a large, brand-new mirror hanging over the wash-basin
in the corner, while partly concealed beneath the bed he noticed
a cluster of long-necked bottles. Clift followed the direction of
his eyes. "Business is booming," he said, his voice undergoing
an inflexion of cheerfulness. "Sold a couple of dozen yesterday.
Managed to swap one for that mirror, too. Jolly nice mirror,
isn't it?" He walked across to the washstand and regarded his
reflection in the glass. "Got to be able to keep an eye on my
beard, you know. It's coming on, don't you think? Not as good
as yours yet, but just wait and see." He stroked his chin, fond-
ling the flimsy growth which straggled across his skin. Over his
shoulder he asked: "Like a drink?"

"Not now."

"Mind if I have one?" He moved away from the mirror and pulled one of the bottles from under his bed. As he uncorked it he said : "Had a spot of bother last night. One chap wanted to buy a third bottle—just like you said—and we had a bit of a row. It was nothing very serious, but I beat him up just to show him who's wearing the trousers around here. Don't suppose there'll be any more trouble now." He swallowed a mouthful of *caña* straight from the bottle and wiped his hand across his lips. "Incidentally, do you remember asking me if I needed a *compañera*? You know, a sort of cook extraordinary? Well, I've been thinking that perhaps it wouldn't be a bad idea after all."

Once the rains started the visits of the paddle-boat became less regular, and the captain, so as not to risk injury to his craft, was in the habit of travelling only by daylight and mooring for the night at any station where dusk had found him. So it was that one evening the boat drew up alongside the jetty, and from his veranda Emil could hear the captain shouting orders that the boat should be made fast to its moorings for the night. The rain was coming down hard, and already it was too late to start unloading, so Emil sent Silvestro with a message to the captain asking him if he would care to come and have some dinner on shore.

At seven o'clock the captain arrived. He was extremely grateful, he said, for the invitation. He hadn't seen Emil in such good spirits or in so kindly a frame of mind since—well, since the old days when Schlesinger had been alive.

"You know, Emil," he said, as they sat taking a drink before supper, "it never did you any good to live here absolutely alone. You are a person who needs company. It's natural for a fellow to become morose and depressed if he doesn't see another civilized being for months on end. Why, you're a changed man now that you've got a companion again." The older man was nodding, the wrinkles around his eyes creasing into a smile of satisfaction. "How is he, by the way?"

Emil said : "I think he's all right. But I don't see a great deal of him, you know."

"And what does he do with himself?"

"A bit of trading."

"Successful? He was so keen to make a lot of money when he came out. Something about a debt in England. He told me all about it on the way here."

Emil laughed. "I don't think his intentions are quite so honourable now."

The captain was surprised. "Really?" he queried. "He seemed so earnest, so determined at the time. Isn't it extraordinary how quickly people can change out here? Why, it isn't even a year since he came to this place, is it?"

"Eight or nine months, that's all. But it feels like a long time."

The captain said: "I'd quite like to see him. He seemed such a nice young fellow. I suppose he's coming over for supper?"

"For supper? No, I don't think he'll come. As a matter of fact, I didn't think of asking him. We never eat together."

"You *never* eat together? But how extraordinary! I simply don't understand. . . ."

"You wouldn't," said Emil.

"But—but is there something wrong? Anything the matter with him?"

"Voluntary liquidation, that's all. He's got a *compañera* now, and lots of *caña*. I think he's quite happy—after a fashion. We leave each other alone."

"I see," muttered the old captain, touching together the tips of his fingers in one of his more priestly attitudes. "But I can scarcely believe it. What's wrong with him? D.T.s?"

"Worse than Schlesinger," said Emil.

Not until supper was over did the captain return once more to the subject of Clift. He broached it tentatively, uncertain what would be his companion's reaction to its repetition. "You know, Emil," he said, "it's about this fellow Clift. I can't get over what you told me about him. It seems all wrong somehow. Please don't think I'm trying to interfere or anything, but——"

"There's nothing to be done."

The captain's voice verged on timidity. "Are you sure about that?" he asked. "After all, eight months isn't a very long time. . . ."

"It's long enough."

"I know you'll laugh at me. But I was wondering if you wouldn't take me to see him. . . ."

Emil said: "By all means go, if you want to. But I think you'll find it's a waste of time."

With a flash-lamp to guide them, they walked through the rain along the higher path which followed the fringe of *tacuara* towards Schlesinger's hut. When first they came to the clearing at the end of the path they were unable to discern the outline of the hut, for there was no light burning in any window; and it was only because they could hear the resonant drumming of rain upon the corrugated-iron roof that they knew they had reached it.

"Wonder where he is?" muttered the captain.

Then, like a fist, a loud voice checked them.

"Who's there?"

Emil stopped. He did not flash the torch in the direction of the voice, but instead lowered the beam and quietly said: "It's me—Emil."

"What the hell do you want?"

"We just walked over to see you. The skipper's here. He thought it would be nice if——"

"It's out of visiting hours."

Now their eyes had grown accustomed to the darkness, and they were able to see him, stark naked, sitting in a wicker chair on the veranda, his legs propped up on top of the balustrade.

"Visiting hours," he went on, "Mondays and Thursdays, three o'clock." Then he lowered his legs and leaned forward so that his face came close to the railings. "Why do you come creeping up like this in the middle of the night? What's the idea of spying on me?"

The captain said: "You remember me, don't you? We weren't spying. I merely thought that it would be pleasant to call on you and have a chat."

"Chat about what?"

"About anything you like. I thought maybe you'd want to hear the latest news from Buenos Aires; and besides, I wanted to see how you're getting on out here."

"Why can't you mind your own business? I suppose you

want me to sell you a bottle of plonk. Is that why you came? Well, you can have one. Five pesos. Cash down."

"May we come in out of the rain?" asked the captain.

"No. You might be shocked. Wouldn't do to shock an old gentleman." They heard the tinkle of a bottle-neck against the rim of a glass. "Anyhow, I don't want any haggling. Five pesos—no more, no less."

"I don't want to buy a bottle," said the captain.

"Well, what the hell do you want then?"

Emil took the captain by the sleeve. "Come on," he said impatiently; but the elder man checked him and said to Clift: "Why are you sitting there in the dark like that?"

"Why?" came the turbid echo. For a moment there was silence, save for the rain on the tin roof and the croaking of frogs in the *tacuara*. Then Clift started to laugh, and once more put his face close to the bars of the balustrade. "Do you know what you look like from here? You look like a couple of monkeys in the zoo. Very wet and miserable. You'll start sprouting in a minute. If you stand long enough in the rain, you'll go green—just like everything else around here—the sky, the rain, the river, even the mud and the leather of your boots. Horrible colour—too clean, too glib. What wouldn't you give to see red again—lovely sticky bloody red? Red!" Suddenly he threw up his arms and jumped to his feet. "For God's sake go away!" he shouted. "Stop standing there and staring like a couple of apes. Go away! Go away and leave me alone!"

An empty bottle splashed into the mud at their feet.

Emil saw the wildly gesticulating body as it pranced across the veranda; and in his ear he heard the hollow voice of the captain saying: "It's you, Emil, damn you. It's you who have done this."

Emil was still asleep when the door of his bedroom opened and a stream of sunlight fell across his eyelids. From somewhere a long way off he heard a voice saying, "Good morning," and suddenly he found himself wide awake, sitting up in bed and seeing the figure of Clift in the open doorway.

"What the devil do you mean," he demanded, "busting into

here at this hour of the morning?" His throat was still thick with sleep, his voice clogged.

"I wanted to be certain of catching you," replied the Englishman. "Besides, it isn't as early as all that."

Emil said: "Go and wait on the veranda until I'm ready."

"There's no need for that. I only wanted to ask you one question."

Emil lit himself a cigarette. "Well, what is it?"

"I want to know when the boat's due in again."

"You know as well as I do that it calls once a month."

There was embarrassment, almost shyness in the Englishman's face—an expression he had not worn since the first days after his arrival—as he replied: "Yes, but when did it call last? I don't seem to remember having seen it for quite a long time. My memory's a bit hazy, you know. . . . I haven't been too well lately. . . ."

"Why do you want to know when the boat's coming?"

"Why? Because I want to catch it. I've decided to go back."

"And is that the reason why you've come and woken me up —just to tell me that?"

"This place is getting me down, Emil. I want to get away from it before—before it's too late."

"You're crazy."

"Perhaps—perhaps I am—but not completely. I've suddenly become disgusted by myself. I often used to think that it would be fun to go to pot—you know, chuck everything overboard— but now that I've tried it . . . It's funny, but I can scarcely remember a thing that has happened during the past year. But a man needs memory. Life is hell without it."

Emil said: "You think so? I'd give a great deal to be able to dispense with mine."

"You are an older man," Clift replied, then hesitated, uncertain as to how he should qualify his remark. Finally he said: "I have so little to forget. I often think of what you once told me about that chap Schlesinger; how he became obsessed with small things—the eyes of alligators, a night-bird, the noise o frogs. I can understand him now. All through the rains I found my mental horizon growing narrower and narrower, until finally I was scarcely aware of anything at all. Even the bottles of *caña* just came and went. I suppose I drank most of them, but I can't remember much about it. I might as well have been dead. . . ."

"Why are you telling me all this?" asked Emil.

"Merely to show you that I am independent of you."

"What do you mean? As far as I'm concerned you could as well not exist."

"That's not quite true, is it? You're a strange fellow, Emil. I wonder what satisfaction you get out of these—these experiments of yours? I could stay here for another year and you wouldn't care tuppence if you ever saw me or not; but the idea that I might one day decide to go away would be something quite hateful to you." Now he treated Emil to a smile, as if to wash over the words he had just spoken. "Well, anyhow, there are no hard feelings so far as I'm concerned. I shall often think of you after I've gone. You've taught me a lot. Perhaps I should even thank you."

"Oh, shut up," said Emil. "I've never heard such drivel in my life."

On the eve of Clift's departure Emil walked over to the hut and found the Englishman on the veranda, leaning on the balustrade and gazing out across the river.

"Hullo, Emil. I was just taking a look at this view for the last time. The sunset's never been lovelier."

Clift had shaved off his beard and combed his hair, and except for the colour of his skin, his appearance, at first glance, was as fresh and youthful as on the day of his arrival at the station. It was only upon closer scrutiny that his eyes appeared to lie deeper in their sockets, his lips to be slightly down-turned at the corners, his skin to be drawn more tightly across the framework of bone beneath it.

Emil said: "I thought we might have a farewell drink together, so I brought this along with me." From within his shirt he fished out a bottle of whisky. "Scotch," he announced, mounting the steps to the veranda and placing the bottle upon the bamboo table in the corner.

"That's terribly nice of you," said Clift. "I know how hard

it is to come by a bottle of that stuff. But I'm off it, you know. On the wagon. Haven't had a drop for a couple of weeks."

Emil smiled. "So Silvestro told me—but I didn't believe it." He shrugged his shoulders, and over his face, in place of the frozen smile, there crept a look of disappointment. "Ah, well," he said, "it was just an idea. I suppose I shall have to drink it by myself."

For a moment Clift hesitated, then, "I'm awfully sorry," he said. "I didn't mean to be unsociable. Of course, let's have a drink together—for old times' sake." And giggling, he added: "But just one—no more—because I know I'd get terribly tiddly. Funny how quickly one becomes light-headed once the stuff has gone out of one's system. . . ."

It was dark by the time they had finished the bottle, and already the night's voices, like a jazz band which has not yet warmed up, were producing their passionless overture.

Clift said: "I'm feeling pretty fine." He tapped the whisky bottle and listened to its empty ring. "Pity it's finished," he muttered, and got up and went through the door to his bedroom. A moment later he reappeared, a bottle under each arm and a broad grin across his face. "I was keeping these as a farewell present for Silvestro," he announced, placing the bottles on the table, "but I think we might as well drink them, don't you? I can give him something else instead."

"Of course, of course," agreed Emil. "Silly to stop drinking now—now that we both feel so good."

"Besides, we've really got something to celebrate this time, eh? Think of it, the last night in this damned hole. Can scarcely believe it. Are you jealous of me, Emil? Bet you are, whatever you say. . . ."

Emil was pouring out drinks from one of the fresh bottles. "Jealous?" he said. "I don't think so. I'm happy for your sake, but I'm not envious of you. Why should I be?"

Clift laughed. "Liar," he said, and leaned forward and patted Emil on the knee. "Poor old Emil, going to be left behind. You'll be so lonely, all by yourself. No one to practise on. No more blood-sucking by remote-control. Who'll be your

guinea-pig when I've gone? What'll you do with yourself in
the evenings?" He thought his last remark was very funny, and
again started to laugh. Then suddenly he stopped, and sat bolt
upright in his chair. "Listen," he half-whispered, raising a
finger.

From far off, riding on the night, there sounded the mad
laugh of an *uru-tau.*

The Englishman was peering out into the darkness as if his
eyes could pierce into the depths of the jungle. "My spiritual
mother," he said, his voice very low. "Did you hear her
calling?"

"You're mad," Emil exclaimed. "As mad as Schlesinger."

Clift chuckled. "That's what you'd like to think, isn't it?
What a kick it would give you! Can't you hear yourself telling
people: 'The bird got him—the bird and the alligators and
caña—just like they got poor old Schlesinger?' Isn't that exactly
what you'd say? 'I warned him,' you'd tell them, 'but he took
no notice. He wouldn't listen to my advice, the young fool. So
he went off his head.' Think of the satisfaction you'd get out
of being able to say that! The omniscient Emil knows all, sees
all, hears all. Sole survivor. Clever fellow."

Emil said nothing. He was aware of a strange numbness in
his brain, as though an old photograph were being projected
before his eyes and occupying the entire theatre of his mind.
This was Schlesinger sitting in the chair before him—a blond
Schlesinger with blue eyes and bare knees—speaking dead
words, making the ghosts of gestures. The Englishman was
talking to him, but he scarcely heard a word that was said. The
voice came to him blurred, through a screen of fog.

"Bloodsucker-in-chief. . . . Thought you'd get me drunk to-
night, didn't you, so that I'd start on another bout and miss the
boat to-morrow? That was why you brought along the bottle
of Scotch, wasn't it? Very cunning—I don't think! Did you
imagine I was such a fool as to be taken in by that sort of child's
trick?" Again he started chuckling, then leaned forward and
refilled his glass to the brim. "I'm going, Emil. I'm going to-
morrow, and you'd better get used to the idea, because nothing
that you can do will stop me. I'm drunk now, so I'll tell you
this straight: I despise you—you and your diseased brain. It's

you who's mad, not me. You're riddled through and through like a worm-eaten cheese—a dirty German cheese——"

Through clenched teeth Emil said: "I told you once before——"

"You've told me a lot of things. So what?"

Emil was staring at the unopened bottle on the table before him. It was only a few inches away from his finger-tips, big and heavy, bigger and heavier as he watched it. His hand crept forward; and then of a sudden he had gripped it around the neck so tightly that it seemed his knuckle-bones would burst right through the skin of his fingers.

"So this," he said, slowly rising to his feet, the bottle like lead in his hand.

Emil was checking over the pile of canvas bales on the jetty when he heard the captain's voice close behind him.

"Emil, I've got some receipts I'd like you to sign in my cabin. Can you spare a moment?"

Emil shrugged his shoulders. "All right," he said, and turned and followed the captain across the gang-plank.

In the cabin the captain said, "Just the usual lot of stuff. Nothing extra this month." He walked over to the desk and pushed a sheaf of papers on to the blotter.

Emil sat down and took a pen and started signing the receipts. Paraffin, tinned peaches, mosquito nets, atabrin tablets, oil, a case of rum, corned beef, salt, more salt. . . . He scribbled his name automatically at the bottom of each sheet, not troubling to check the items whose delivery he was acknowledging. He knew that the captain would never cheat him—would never cheat anyone, for that matter, through fear of eternal damnation. For a while the scratching of the pen was the only sound to break the silence in the cabin; but presently, in a voice that simulated casualness, the captain said: "I've just been having a chat with Silvestro. He told me about Clift. It's too bad."

"Yes, it's too bad," Emil agreed, still writing, not looking up. The nib made a noise like a rodent's teeth upon wood.

"Is it true?"

"I don't know what Silvestro told you."

"He said that Clift had intended to catch the boat to-day."

Emil went on writing. Speaking to the papers in front of him: "Yes," he replied. "Yes, I believe he did say something about leaving. But he didn't mention when or how. As you know, we didn't see much of each other."

"But weren't you with him last night, saying good-bye? Silvestro said he heard voices. . . ."

"Not mine. Never went near the hut. But you know how these Indians love gossip."

"You mean, you didn't see him at all last night?"

"Not after supper. He came over to my bungalow earlier in the evening and asked me to sell him a bottle of Scotch. I let him have one. He didn't say what he wanted it for."

"Didn't he mention that he was intending to leave?"

"Not then, no. Not a word. He told me he had some Indians waiting for him at the hut. I presumed he was going to sell them the bottle. Anyway, we scarcely spoke. He was pretty drunk."

"Drunk? Silvestro didn't think he was. . . ."

Slowly Emil laid down the pen and leaned forward, his elbows resting upon the papers which were strewn across the blotter. "What are you getting at?" he demanded. "Is this an inquisition?"

"I couldn't help my curiosity, Emil. The whole thing reminds me so much of Schlesinger. . . ."

"Except that Schlesinger was killed."

"But what of Clift?"

"He'll live. I'll look after him all right."

The captain seated himself upon the edge of the desk, his fingers spreading themselves across the warm mahogany border. "Emil," he said, almost implored, "why don't you let me bring the young fellow on board? I could take him down to Buenos Aires and have him put in a proper hospital."

Emil raised his hand. "Out of the question," he replied. "He's far too ill to travel. He'd never stand the journey."

"But what chance has he got here? You've no facilities, no proper medical kit. . . ."

"I've got my knowledge. That's enough. Besides, he's still unconscious. It would be madness to risk moving him."

"Silvestro says that his head's in a terrible mess. How do you think it happened?"

Emil grunted. "The same old story, I suppose. The young fool didn't take my advice. I told him never to sell a third bottle of liquor to the same Indian. He obviously did."

"But what of his *compañera*? Surely she could have prevented it?"

"He gave her the sack a fortnight ago. There was nobody with him."

The captain shook his head, helplessly. Then he asked: "Will you make me a promise, Emil?"

"That depends. What is it?"

"Promise me to do your best for him. Promise to keep him alive."

Emil looked indignant. "What the hell else do you think I'd do? Kill him off? Don't be so damned silly. I'll look after him as though he were my own son. I'm fond of him, you know, even though I don't see much of him, and I enjoy his company too. It'll be nice to have him around for a while longer. . . ."

THE MYSTERIOUS SENSE OF DIRECTION

PETER SCOTT

Headpiece by the Author

A PIGEON is put into a basket and sent away by train. A hundred miles from its home loft it is released, and three hours later it is home again. A swallow is caught at its nest and a tiny aluminium ring attached to its leg; in the autumn it flies southward to Africa and returns in the spring to the very same nest in the very same barn, and is recognized by the number on the ring. A Manx Shearwater taken from its nesting burrow on the Welsh island of Skokholm and released at Venice is back in the burrow in ten days. A dog or a cat taken by train to the seaside disappears, but is found again on the doorstep at home when the holiday is over.

How can these creatures find their way? How do they know in which direction to set off? How did Anabel return so surely to the lighthouse?

Anabel was a young wild Pink-footed goose who spent a winter, in those far-off days between the wars, staying voluntarily with some tame Pink-footed geese which lived in the enclosure round my lighthouse home on the Wash. It was in May that the migratory instinct finally overcame the instinct which directed her to stay with the little flock of tame pinioned ones, and she disappeared. Greenland, Spitzbergen, and Iceland are the breeding-grounds of the Pink-feet, and Anabel's summer must have been spent in one or other of these northern countries.

I shall never forget the thrill on that October morning four months and twenty-four days later when I heard her voice high in the sky, and watched her circle and settle and come up to my feet to be fed. I marvelled then, as I have marvelled many times since, at the strange power which brought Anabel back so unerringly to the home which she had found a year before.

In the history of scientific discovery certain mysteries and unexplained things have always made a special appeal to the imagination of mankind. In the field of Natural History, orientation is perhaps the most fascinating mystery still unsolved. So far, in spite of a recent and at first sight attractive theory, science has not been able to produce a satisfactory explanation of the phenomena. Scientists do not yet know *how it is done*.

Each year millions of creatures—birds, mammals, fishes— migrate hundreds, even thousands, of miles, many of them finding their way with considerable, if not perfect, accuracy. And apart from migration many animals seem to possess a well-developed sense of direction for independent and individual movements—such as those of the homing pigeon; of the Shearwater from Skokholm; of the dog reported to have crossed the North American continent from west to east in order to get home; of the hare which returned more than 600 miles to its home farm in Hungary, including a crossing of the Danube; of the salmon which find their way back into the rivers in which they were born. Even among human beings we speak of a good or bad sense of direction. This may only spring from good or bad powers of detailed observation, but alternatively it may prove to be a subconscious remnant of an unexplained capacity still more or less highly developed among all these animals.

Is it safe to assume that the mechanism which finds the

answer for them in their individual movements is, at least in principle, the same as the mechanism which takes the swallows on their migratory flight to Africa and back? I think that it is. I believe that the methods of orientation used by animals for homing will prove to be the same as those used for migration.

The most striking examples of this strange capacity are to be found in the bird world, and it is therefore among ornithologists that the most extensive work on the problem has been done, and although the mystery is not solved, its solution seems at the moment to be near.

How far have the scientists got and how do the different theories stand? The schools of thought can be fairly sharply divided into two—those who believe that the powers of orientation will be shown ultimately to be derived from the known senses and those who believe that some special sense or senses as yet unrecognized will provide the answer. Most of the recent theories have come from the second category, and those who back the known senses (and principal among them the sense of sight) have for the most part been cast in the rôle of "debunkers".

Their argument goes on these lines. A bird may be born with an instinct to fly towards the midday sun as the days get shorter in the autumn. This is no more remarkable than many of the accepted instincts which are known to be inherited, as, for example, that a young grebe should, within a quarter of an hour of hatching, go to its mother's tail, where it can then climb on to her back and be protected by the feathers of her wings, or that the newly-hatched cuckoo should undertake the extremely difficult and arduous task of ejecting the eggs or young of its foster-parents from the nest.

In the northern hemisphere the sun is in the southern half of the sky and therefore gives an indication of the direction in which to fly. The position of the moon, and even of certain groups of stars, might continue to give direction at night. An accurate sense of position might be obtained by a correct estimate of the height of the sun correlated with a sense of time, which birds are known to possess, and which is shown by the extraordinary regularity of their time of starting to sing in the morning. This time-sense is recognized in man and may explain the capacity, which many people claim, to wake at a given time without the assistance of an alarm clock. Bees and ants are now known to use the position of the sun and its relation to various landmarks as a means of finding their way back to the hive or nest.

Into this theory of a general migration line on a particular bearing and orientated by heavenly bodies can be fitted the experiments of the German ornithologist Rüppell, who found that young Hooded Crows, which migrate on a line N.E. and S.W. along the southern shore of the Baltic, continued to use a parallel line if captured and displaced several hundred miles north or south.

The phenomena of migration alone could perhaps be explained by such a comparatively simple theory connected with the sense of sight; but what of homing? The argument here begins with an area of familiar territory around the bird's home from any part of which it could quickly return to the nest (or loft, in the case of pigeons). If a number of birds were released at some distance away and radiated evenly in all directions from the point of release, a proportion would hit this area of familiar territory. The percentage would depend on the angle subtended by the familiar territory at the point of release. But if the birds, instead of radiating, were to perform an even spiral outwards from the point of release, they would all in due course hit the familiar territory. It is not suggested that either of these things happens in this regular manner, but it is pointed out that a modified form is possible in view of the fact that birds are not infallible and that not by any means 100 per cent of homing birds actually get home. In 1948 two Canadian scientists, Griffin and Hock, published an account of some experiments in which they released some Gannets which had been taken from an island in the Gulf of St. Lawrence to a point about 100 miles inland. The Gannets were then followed, at a respectful distance, by the ornithologists in a helicopter. About 60 per cent of the birds eventually got home to their island, but the initial directions which they took were apparently at random, and the tracks followed by the birds did not suggest any innate sense of direction.

Not only is the percentage of released birds which reach home very significant, but also the length of time which they take to do it. The Gannets averaged about 100 miles per day; and Griffin has shown that in this and a number of other homing experiments the percentage of recoveries and the average speeds on the journey are not inconsistent with what he calls "spiral exploration".

Many other suggestions have been put forward in order to support the theory that the sense of sight is the key to the power of orientation. Professor V. C. Wynne-Edwards of Aberdeen University has suggested that the accurate time-sense of birds might detect the differences between the times of sunrise and sunset, which change rapidly if you travel east or west. For every hundred miles in these latitudes the difference is about ten minutes. James Fisher has ingeniously suggested the comparison between a bird trying to find its way and a man in a maze. If, he says, you accept the principle of always turning in one direction, it will probably bring you to the middle or to the beginning of the maze, but if it brings you back to a place at which you have previously been, you should take a new turn and then continue as before. You can do this in a maze because mazes have walls. For a bird, so Fisher's suggestion goes, the principal objects of geography— coasts, rivers, mountain ranges—take the place of the walls of the maze. And anyway, as Fisher points out, a great many birds do in fact get lost.

But although these explanations may cover a large number of the recorded phenomena of homing, they do not, as their adherents would be the first to admit, explain everything. For instance, it is well known that birds immediately after release circle around gaining height, and that in a large proportion of cases they set off, after three or four circles, in the correct direction for home, irrespective of the topography of the neighbourhood and often without a sight of sun, moon, or stars. Furthermore, many of them can find their way in a fog and at night as well as they can by day, although this is not the case with pigeons, which are by no means the best homers among birds. On the other hand, pigeons are moderate homers which are easy to keep and to tame and which breed freely in artificial conditions. It is for this reason that they are used for carrying messages and for racing. Since they are descended from the Rock Pigeon, which is a non-migratory species, it is perhaps curious that their homing faculties are as good as they are.

If the stimuli of the known senses do not provide an adequate explanation of the homing performance of birds, what are the theories which postulate the possession of an extra sense or senses? Most of them are based upon a sensitivity to the earth's magnetic field, and in this different observers have obtained different results on two very important pieces of evidence about which further experiments should be performed. First of all, some scientists have stated that powerful wireless transmissions have upset the orientation of pigeons, while others have been unable to find any confirmation of this; and secondly, a number of experiments have been carried out in which birds have been released carrying magnets of sufficient strength to "drown" the effects of the earth's magnetic field. In some of these experiments results indicate that the magnets may have had some adverse effects on the homing capacities of the birds, but it appears that in all such cases the results were not really conclusive, as insufficient "control" experiments were carried out at the same time. Other observers have tried in vain to show any significant difference between the performance of a bird carrying a magnet and one carrying a small piece of non-magnetic metal of equal size and weight.

In any event, an appreciation of the earth's magnetic field —a built-in compass, as it were—would not be enough to fix a bird's position on the earth's surface, for a compass is no good to a man if he has not a map, a chronometer, and a sextant. He must know where he is before he can tell what course to steer to reach his objective.

It was at this point that Ising's theory of orientation by an appreciation of the Coriolis forces of relative momentum was put forward in 1945. Professor Ising's work was entirely theoretical, and it was taken a stage further by Professor H. L. Yeagley of the Department of Physics of Pennsylvania State College, who, in conjunction with the U.S. Army Signal Corps, put the theory to the test. Yeagley's hypothesis was a com-

bination of previous theories of magnetic reception with the
new suggestion that birds might detect the Coriolis force due
to the rotation of the earth. What is Coriolis force? If you
throw a cricket ball out of the window of a moving train and
at right angles to the line, it does not follow a path at right
angles to the line, but rather a diagonal path due to the
momentum imparted by the movement of the train. If, instead
of being in a train, you imagine yourself standing at the
Equator and facing northward, you will be travelling at the
speed of the rotation of the earth. Since the earth's circum-
ference is 25,000 miles and it makes one revolution in twenty-
four hours, the speed is a little more than 1,000 miles per hour.
North or south from the Equator your speed will be reduced
until, as you reach the poles, it is nothing at all. If, as you
stand at the Equator, you fire a rifle bullet, instead of throwing
a cricket ball, in a due northerly direction, it goes from a part
of the earth's surface travelling at 1,000 miles per hour to one
which is only travelling at, say, 999.99 miles per hour, and it
finishes up, as it were, a little farther ahead than the parallel
of longitude along which it was fired; the rifle bullet drifts
to the right. This is the effect of Coriolis force due to the earth's
rotation. High-speed aircraft find it necessary to make correc-
tions on the courses steered on northerly or southerly bearings,
in order to compensate for this effect.

Ising's theory was that the semi-circular canals of the inner
ear—the balancing mechanism of the bird—might be sufficiently sensitive to detect the Coriolis force.

Yeagley superimposed a magnetic sense upon the Coriolis
factor and pointed out that a kind of grid could be built up
based upon the two possible stimuli. Since the lines of latitude
and longitude are related to the earth's rotational axis, the lines
of latitude will also represent lines of equal intensity of the
Coriolis force. On the other hand, the lines of equal intensity of
magnetic field will be centred upon the magnetic rather than
the true North and South poles, and might be termed "magnetic
parallels" as opposed to parallels of latitude. If these magnetic
parallels are superimposed upon the parallels of latitude, the
result is a gridwork of two systems of concentric rings which
cross each other and which give an exact position on the earth's

surface. If the bird could detect these two stimuli together, it could fix its position precisely. But any particular magnetic parallel crosses a parallel of latitude twice, although the points may be many hundreds of miles apart. Such points are found on either side of the line of longitude on which the magnetic pole lies, and this passes more or less down the centre of the North American continent. On one side of this line the pattern of both magnetic and Coriolis intensity is, as it were, the mirror image of the intensities on the other side, and any point will have on the opposite side what Yeagley has called a "conjugate point" at which the magnetic and Coriolis intensities are identical with those at the original point. When Yeagley decided to put his theory to the test with homing pigeons, he found that the "conjugate point" to the Pennsylvania State College, where his pigeons lived, was 1,100 miles away at the town of Kearney in Nebraska. If the pigeons were trained to return to a special loft at Pennsylvania State College, and if the loft and pigeons were then transported to Nebraska and the pigeons released at normal distances from the loft (between twenty-five and seventy-five miles), they should, if the theory was correct, return to the loft at Kearney instead of attempting the long journey across the continent to Pennsylvania.

Between 1942 and 1945 the theory was tested, and the results, published in 1947, seemed at first sight to show that the birds were trying to return to the conjugate point instead of to their original home. For a while the mystery of orientation seemed to have been solved. But then, as scientists from all parts of the world began to study the details of the Kearney experiments, doubt crept back into their minds.

These doubts were crystallized at a most important meeting held at the Linnean Society of London on May 13th, 1948. At this meeting the principal speakers were two scientists from Cambridge University—Dr. W. H. Thorpe, the distinguished zoologist, and Dr. D. H. Wilkinson, a brilliant young physicist from the Cavendish Laboratory. Thorpe and Wilkinson attacked Yeagley's theory from two entirely different quarters and virtually demolished it.

Thorpe pointed out that the experiments were not conducted in a conclusive manner. The mobile lofts, each painted bright yellow and surmounted by a captive balloon 150 feet above it, were taken to Kearney and the birds were apparently allowed to remain in the lofts for one day in order to "rest and acclimatize themselves to their surroundings" before being sent out in various directions for release. In spite of this "rest day" and the captive balloons, only three pigeons out of 500 actually returned to the lofts. The results, therefore, were chiefly based on a number of recoveries in the surrounding country, which were judged to have indicated that the birds were *trying* to get back. These results were obtained by a method of plotting which Yeagley called "the combined flight vector". The fallacy of this form of measurement can be shown as follows: if six pigeons are released at ten miles from the loft and one of them flies directly towards home, but proceeds past it and continues for ten times the distance, and if the other five then fly in the opposite direction for less than ten miles, the combined flight vector will indicate that all six flew in the right direction for approximately the right distance. Finally, no bright-yellow lofts with their captive balloons were taken to some quite different place which was not a conjugate point in order to ascertain whether the pigeons at Kearney, Nebraska, were doing something different from any pigeons released at random from any mobile loft anywhere.

Wilkinson attacked Yeagley's theory from the point of view of the physicist. Could the effects of magnetism or Coriolis possibly be large enough to be detected by any sensory mechanism in birds? He was almost certain that they could not, and his arguments convinced a gathering of Britain's most distinguished ornithologists. He considered first the magnetic effects and ruled out the possibility that a bird could respond directly to the magnetic forces which come into play when non-magnetic matter is placed in a field. This would require an organ sensitive enough to detect a change of less than 0·005 gauss, and pigeons have been subjected to magnetic fields of about 1,000 gauss without any visible reaction. It seems likely that any such sensitive mechanism would cause a visible reaction on the part of the bird when subjected to the shock of an application some 200,000 times greater than that which the mechanism was normally called upon to detect.

But there are two other ways in which a bird might be sensitive to a magnetic field, and Yeagley had put forward one of
them as the basis of his theory. He had suggested that the bird
might, in effect, be a conductor, and that if moved in the
earth's magnetic field a potential difference would be induced
between the two ends of the conductor which could be detected
by the bird. No current, however, is created, and Wilkinson
showed that a bird accelerating from rest to 40 miles per hour
would have to make an electrostatic measurement of the order
of one-millionth of a volt. Since the most accurate man-made
instrument for making such measurements—the cathode-ray
oscilloscope—cannot detect differences of less than about 1/10
volt, and since any such minute measurements would be hopelessly upset by the ordinary effects of atmospheric electricity,
whose background intensity could not possibly be gauged by
the bird, Wilkinson concluded that "the induction effect as
conceived by Yeagley is not operative".

Yet another possible means of detecting the magnetic field
might be available to the bird, however, if its anatomy contained a conducting loop which oscillated in the field. This
would create an alternating current, and the measurement of
that current might be easier for the bird than a purely electrostatic measurement. But Wilkinson showed that this current
must be measured to an accuracy of 10^{-10} amps. and that in
view of the much bigger currents of physiological origin which
are present in living matter, it was, to say the least, extremely
improbable that birds could make the desired measurement of
the earth's magnetic field.

Finally, Wilkinson turned to the computation of Coriolis
forces. The effect of the Coriolis forces due to the earth's rotation could only be felt as a minute deflection of the downward
pull of gravity. Its strength, in these latitudes, is less than
1/6000 of the gravitational force itself and the angle of the
deflection would be less than 1 minute. In addition, the effect
would be masked by the irregular influence upon the vertical
component of the force of gravity of land masses such as
mountain ranges and also of the centrifugal component. But
this is not all, since the Coriolis forces due to the rotation of the
earth could only be detected if the bird's course and speed

were almost impossibly true. Any slight alteration, of course, would introduce Coriolis forces not related to the earth's rotation but to the change of course. Thus a bird would have to fly to an accuracy of 1/50 of an inch in 100 feet.

Ising's conception of the mechanism involved in measuring Coriolis forces included a more complicated principle—that the forces caused a swirling in the fluid of the semicircular canals of a bird of which the bird could become conscious. It has the additional significance that the method could be used when the bird is at rest; but once again the effect can be shown to be so minute as to make it an extremely improbable method by which a bird could determine latitude.

Both the magnetic and Coriolis effects vary directly as the speed of flight. Thus a change from 40 miles per hour to 39 miles per hour would be equal to a geographical displacement of 150 miles. Thorpe and Wilkinson have shown conclusively that it is at least very improbable that the Yeagley theory is the answer to the problem, more particularly since the normal perceptions of animals—as, for example, in changes of intensity in light or sound—do not register such minute changes as would be necessary to make use of the Coriolis forces and the earth's magnetic field. But they have not shown that such sensitivity is impossible, and it may well develop ultimately that some part or parts of the theories of Ising and Yeagley will be found to hold good.

Meanwhile, what other hypotheses are available? Wilkinson is thrown back to a visual explanation again. If random search or spiral exploration will not cover all the known facts, he suggests, might not these principles be materially assisted by an appreciation of latitude derived by a glimpse of the sun correlated with the time-sense which has been accepted? If the height of the sun could be estimated to within one diameter of the sun itself, then the necessary accuracy could be achieved.

In my view, this is not enough. But there are other theories, and we must consider in detail the most interesting experiments with swallows which have been carried out by two Polish scientists, Professors Wojtusiak and Wodzicki. Here are the important things which they discovered, the clues, as it were, from which they set forth once more to solve the mystery.

Swallows were taken from their nesting sites and released at various distances and in various directions from home. When released, they circled once or twice and then set off. In two-thirds of the cases the birds set off in the right direction. Some of the others began by following a railway line in the wrong direction. The birds returned as easily from any point of the compass. They returned almost as quickly through rain, thunderstorm, and fog, and their speed was reduced by only half at night, although swallows are not normally nocturnal. The farther the birds were taken away, the higher the speed of return up to a distance of about seventy-five miles, from which they returned at an average of twenty-two miles per hour. At greater distances the speed was much reduced, but remained more or less constant at about seven miles per hour. Four swallows were tried over the same course a second time. One took a fraction longer on the second run, one did it in half the time, and the other two took about a quarter of the time. (This was particularly interesting in view of the training which is normally given to racing pigeons over shorter courses on the same bearing before a long-distance flight.) Finally, experiments were carried out with House Sparrows, and it was found that they could not home over greater distances than about six miles.

The two Polish scientists clung to the fact that the swallows could so often set off correctly both by day and by night, in fair weather or in fog. Here was evidently something outside the range of the conscious perceptions of the senses of man. Professor Wojtusiak put forward the suggestion that birds might have a visual perception of electro-magnetic radiation, for it must be something invisible to man, but existing in darkness and capable of passing through fog. Infra-red rays have those properties. In support of this theory, he called attention to some curious orange or red fat globules found in the retina of birds' eyes and also in those of terrapins and tortoises. If this should enable them to detect infra-red radiations, then by the power of sight they could distinguish between warm masses and cold, between land and water, between the brightness of the south and the darkness of the north. The professor began his experiments at once, and soon showed that tortoises gave preference to areas illuminated with infra-red rays, which may well explain the extraordinary manner in which water-tortoises are able to find their way to the nearest water even if it is out of sight. The experiments extended to birds, and pigeons could apparently be shown to choose to feed from a dish lit by infra-red in preference to one lit by an equal intensity of visible light, even though the positions of the dishes and the lights were frequently reversed.

But to set against these results are some researches by Hecht and Pirenne into the sight of owls. These two scientists failed to find any evidence that the eyes of the Long-eared Owl were sensitive to infra-red radiation. Although owls are for the most part non-migratory, yet the possession of a sense which would react to rays which are present at night would quite obviously be of the greatest advantage to a nocturnal bird. If such a mechanism were present in any birds, it is strange that it has not been developed in the highly specialized eyes of owls. Indeed, the researches of Hecht and Pirenne have put what seem to be almost insuperable difficulties in the way of the infra-red theory.

All these experiments go on, however, and the evidence mounts up, but the answer is not found. To me it seems that the anatomists might now make a useful contribution. Birds which are known to be the most outstanding homers should be studied afresh and compared with those which are bad homers, in order to see if any part of the brain, nervous system, or sense organs can be shown to have become more highly developed in those birds with the best "sense of direction".

I am convinced that the birds cannot keep their secret much longer. Soon an irrefutable theory must emerge. Soon we shall know definitely how the swallows find their barns, how the Great Shearwaters scattered over the Atlantic Ocean find the tiny island of Tristan da Cunha, their only breeding-place, how Anabel found her way back to the lighthouse. Till then, the mystery remains unsolved.

I <u>must</u> get that window-catch seen to.

THE SCARLET BELT

DANIEL PETTIWARD

Illustrations by Anthony Brandt

THERE was a comfortable-looking widow next to Richard Hamming the night he dined with the Prescotts, who turned out to live on the East Coast at Widmouth, where he had been taken almost every summer between the ages of five and ten.

Richard had been back there some years before; he had bicycled over from a T.A. camp nearby, and they talked rather smugly about the vandalisms which had taken place since what they called "the old days". The pier, said the widow, was still in half. The colour scheme of the borders in the Municipal Gardens before she came away was even more incredible than ever—the flowers looked as though they were made of inferior cake icing—and they were starting a vast indoor swimming-pool on the last remaining patch of the old heath. "All the old

75

crowd," said the widow, "have left. The Pedlars have gone and the Curleens and the Hansell-Smiths. Did you know the Hansell-Smiths, by the way?"

"Just," said Richard; "but the Gaymers are still there, aren't they? They were, at any rate, when I went on this famous bicycle ride."

"Oh no!" said the widow. "Oh lord, no! They left very soon after the tragedy. They live at Shipstead now; you know, about twenty miles to the south of Widmouth." She looked at Richard expectantly—hardly daring to hope that he might not have heard about the tragedy.

"What tragedy was that?" Richard asked. "I don't remember hearing of any tragedy. "

"About Rosemary. You knew surely that Rosemary had been found dead—strangled in Merriethorpe Grove?"

"Rosemary—strangled! Good God, no! Of course I didn't know a thing about it. How absolutely ghastly. Wait a minute, though; Rosemary was the youngest, wasn't she? I believe she was just about born the last time I went there as a child."

"Yes," said the widow, "she was the youngest—only nineteen —and the prettiest. Everybody loved Rosemary. It's always the way, isn't it? And to this day they haven't the ghost of a clue who did it."

"I'm fairly certain," Richard said, "that she was at home that time I cycled over. In fact, I'm sure she was. I went and looked the Gaymers up, because old Gaymer used to doctor me, as I invariably came out in spots the moment I set foot in Widmouth. Of course, he hadn't the faintest idea how to cure them, but I used to love going to him because of the parrot and the black-and-white rabbits and all those comical little duck-ponds."

"Oh yes," said the widow, warming to Richard, "I used to adore those duck-ponds."

"I've got a sort of idea," Richard went on, puckering his brow and allowing a piece of disguised boiling fowl on his fork to go quite cold and greasy, "that I played tennis there, though the only thing that definitely sticks in my mind is a long and confusing talk I had with old Gaymer about silage—oh, and a curiously blue blancmange we had for supper."

"It's always the way," said the widow, with whom this seemed a favourite phrase; "the things you'd like to remember you can't."

"And when did you say this frightful thing happened?"

"Oh, nearly two years ago, it would be, possibly three. Mrs. Gaymer took it rather better than he did; it's often the way, you know. Women seem to have more resilience than men. Possibly it's because they get hurt more often," she added with a little crushed look, as though remembering her past injuries.

"Yes, I know," said Richard; "and they have babies and stay in the water longer. I dare say it's all part of the same thing. But Rosemary! I can't get over it! I do wish my mind wasn't such a complete blank about her. Tell me more about it."

"Well, there's not a lot to tell really," said the widow, "though the circumstances were very odd. Rosemary went off after lunch saying she was going to have a picnic tea in Merriethorpe Grove—it's funny how sinister things so often happen in Groves, isn't it?—with a particular girl friend of hers, a perfectly charming creature called Jane Merle. She took tea for two people with her in a basket—they always took it in turns to play hostess—and apparently went off as gay as a cricket. When she hadn't come back by supper-time the Gaymers naturally got a bit anxious, so they got in touch with the Merle girl. At first she made out she'd met Rosemary, but when she realized how terribly worried the Gaymers were and that things might be serious, she admitted that she'd promised Rosemary some days before to say that they had picnicked together supposing any-one should happen to ask, but that she hadn't actually seen her all that day."

"Had she any idea who Rosemary was with?"

"No, none at all, and she swore it was the first time that any-thing like that had happened. She hadn't even heard Rosemary mention any man friend whom she might not have wanted her parents to know about. She did admit, however, and Mrs. Gaymer supported this, that for the last few months or so Rose-mary had seemed a bit preoccupied, as though she had some-thing on her mind, you know, but that was all. Of course, Rose-mary had several boy friends of her own age, but they were all well known to the Gaymers, and naturally there wasn't any need for any secrecy if she was meeting any of them. The whole thing seemed so utterly unlike Rosemary; she was always so frank and open and told her parents absolutely everything."

"But when did they find her?"

"About half-past nine that night. Doctor Gaymer and George Griffin, the young surgeon from the Cottage Hospital, went up to the Grove, though they didn't imagine for a moment that she would still be there, and almost immediately they found her in a little clearing under an oak tree. It was quite near the main pathway, but completely hidden unless you just happened to know of it. It was a spot she often used to go to, apparently. She'd been dead about three hours, they said. There was no attempt to conceal her; she was just propped up against a tree —strangled. The wood is usually full of people at the week-end, and hundreds of holiday-makers," she added, like a newspaper report, "must have passed within a few yards of her."

"Surely there was some indication as to whom she had been with?"

"Not much, so they said. It was clear that two people had had tea, and it was presumed that one of them was a man, partly because she had obviously been strangled by someone very strong, and partly because there was only lipstick on one cup. There was a thumb-mark on the other cup, but it was very blurred. The only other thing of any significance apparently was a large bloodstain which George discovered on a boulder behind some bushes about twenty yards away, but I believe the police decided in the end that it had no connexion. They got thousands of local people to produce their fingerprints—they even took mine—but it wasn't any use."

"And no one saw her with anyone?"

"Apparently not."

"And apart from her usual bunch of boy friends she hadn't any special admirers?"

"You sound as if you were interrogating me," said the widow with a little giggle.

"No, I don't think so," she went on. "At one time George Griffin seemed rather smitten with Rosemary, but I imagine by that time it must have blown over, because he was engaged to Audrey Sellers—you know, from that huge place on the Lingford road beyond the smelly waterfall—and not long afterwards they were married and he went to a practice in Kenya, where his brother is."

"And she hadn't been robbed or attacked or anything?"

"Oh no," said the widow, "nothing like that at all. They came to the conclusion it must have been a schizophrene or whatever you call it."

"I do wish I'd known about it at the time," Richard said; "one always likes to think one would have found something out that the others never spotted."

"I can't imagine, you know, why you didn't hear about it. It was in all the papers."

"Nor can I," said Richard, "though I've been ill an awful lot off and on."

"Oh, what rotten luck," said the widow politely.

By that time dinner was over, and except that between rubbers of bridge Richard got the widow to give him the Gaymer's new address, the matter of the murder was not referred to again that evening. Just before midnight he drove back to his bachelor lodgings in the neighbouring town of Lipcot, where he was a very junior partner in a firm of Estate Agents. Although he had been playing cards for the past three hours, the thought of Rosemary Gaymer was very much to the front of his mind, and later, as he lay in bed in his poky bed-sitting-room, he was still racking his brains for further details of that meeting with her. He could not remember her well enough to feel the horror he might have felt had she been an intimate friend; he felt only a sense of curiosity and of excitement at having met her at a time which could not have been so very long before her death, the sort of fatuous pride one might feel at being an old flame of the bride at a wedding.

He toyed deliciously with the idea that if only he could remember a little more about their meeting he might find that he held some key to the problem of her death which was not available to anybody else. Perhaps the girl might have confided something to him. People were always confiding things to Richard. He had just that mixture of *savoir-faire* and simplicity which fascinated people without frightening them.

He had played tennis that afternoon, he was certain; but with whom? And had Rosemary played too and, if so, what had she worn or, for that matter, what had *he* worn, as presumably he hadn't come prepared for tennis and would have had to borrow racquet and shoes, unless he had played in bare feet? . . . Bare feet! The words rocketed through Richard's brain like an explosive charge. Of course, he remembered Rosemary now, prancing about in her naked feet like a young colt! He could see the swing of her white skirt and the sun on her bare brown arms, and there was another thing he remembered suddenly— her belt; her scarlet belt embroidered with hearts and daisies and things, doubtless made by some distressed gentlewoman in some arts and crafts shop.

He could even remember too a little twinge of jealousy he had felt because she seemed so flawless, the little longing he always felt with flawless people to prove them wrong over something. And at the same time he could remember a sense of triumph, a feeling of self-satisfaction which somehow seemed to be bound up with white heather. There was white heather in the wild garden below the tennis court. Old Gaymer had brought it back from the Isle of Mull, or it may have been Eigg, and planted it there. And yes, of course! He had talked to Rosemary alone in the wild garden. She must have put on her shoes by then, surely, because they had burrowed their way through gorse and brambles in search of a lost ball, a ball which he remembered suddenly he had belted there on purpose so that they could pretend to look for it while they talked together out of sight of her parents. "Out of sight of her parents": that was a significant thought. It showed, didn't it? that in spite of what the widow had said, Rosemary was not above lending herself to a little mild deception, and it showed, too, what had perhaps given him the idea in the first place, that they had in fact talked of matters which might well have been unknown to other people.

But was it wishful thinking merely that made him believe she had asked his advice about some man, some secret lover whom she adored but was half afraid to meet? Was this a genuine memory, or was he just conjuring up in his imagination the sort of person that Rosemary's murderer must have been? That last visit to the Gaymers must have taken place, he realized, almost immediately before his mother died, because he had hurried home a week before his camp was due to finish. After the funeral he had stayed at home off and on for over two years, supposedly to keep his father company, but in reality avoiding him whenever possible except at meals or sometimes in the evening, when they played chess together in the draughty library, the one room which the memory of his mother's presence didn't make it almost unbearable to enter. Richard was meant to be reading for a Land Agents' Society exam., but just when he seemed to be getting over the shock of losing his mother he had been unconscious for many weeks in hospital after a motor crash. It was nearly eighteen months before he was fit enough to get back to his studies, and during most of that time he had lost complete touch with the outside world and with the affairs of all but his oldest friends. It was quite easy to understand how he had failed to hear of Rosemary's death.

After puzzling his brain for a further hour or two, Richard fell into a fitful sleep, but soon after sunrise he found himself again awake. The thought of Rosemary was still with him, as if he had continued to think of her without interruption; only now there was a difference. Now he knew for certain that he had not imagined this curious man friend of hers. He could remember definite facts about him, facts which Rosemary must have told him in the wild garden. She must have been dying to tell somebody, thrilled to find someone sympathetic and a little older than herself to whom she might confide her doubts, because she had doubts of this man even at the height of her adoration for him, Richard was sure of that, and one side of her deplored the secrecy of their relationship which the other side of her found so particularly intriguing.

It was the familiar story of the egotist amusing himself by rousing the untried passions of the adolescent. He would tease and torture her when she fawned on him, and when she failed to fawn on him enough he would become fiendishly jealous and demanding. He gave her presents sometimes. Of course! It was he who had given her the red belt. He had given it to her no doubt to make her forget something he had said, some wounding thing which he would quite certainly say again the moment he had won back her trust. And another peculiar thing he remembered. Their meetings had always, up till then at any rate, taken place at night.

The man had obviously sworn Rosemary to secrecy about himself, and Richard could as yet remember nothing which gave him a clue to his identity, but there was quite a lot to go on, the belt for instance. She had probably told her parents that she had bought it herself, and doubtless no importance had been attached to it, but now, with his fresh information, it might be possible to trace when and where it had been bought and conceivably who had bought it.

There could surely be no doubt that this furtive individual who cast such a spell over Rosemary was her murderer. He must have been a completely uncontrolled type, the sort who would kill on a sudden impulse of pique or hurt pride. He might even be someone well known to the Gaymers or to Richard, someone they had never considered in his true colours.

With such exciting thoughts racing through his head Richard could remain in bed no longer. He kicked himself out of bed and tugged aside the worn curtains to let in the still weak sunlight. Then, pushing his hair back out of his eyes and scrambling into his dressing-gown, he perched himself barefooted and yawning at his desk and wrote a letter to Dr. Gaymer.

He told him everything that he could remember or reconstruct of his encounter with Rosemary; he offered to do everything in his power to help bring her murderer to justice and he finished up by saying:

"I can only hope that I did my utmost to dissuade her from her association with this fiend. Of course, in the light of later events, I feel desperately guilty that I did not take drastic action to break up the relationship or at any rate warn you. I have not gathered exactly how long after my visit the tragedy took place, but I seem to remember that Rosemary was distinctly dreading her next meeting with this man, so I suppose it may well have been the fatal one. . . ."

All that day at the office Richard's mind kept jumping from the matters in hand to the matter of Rosemary and to fresh memories of her which continued to take shape. Although he could never memorize her face properly, he felt fairly sure he could remember her hair, except that it had an annoying habit of changing just when he felt certain he could visualize it exactly. Sometimes he seemed to see it hanging on her shoulders, and then abruptly, just as he hoped her features might follow it into his vision, it altered, and he saw it shorter and tidier and with a blue, or it may have been a white, ribbon in it. At other times his recollection of her and of what she had told him of this man seemed to recede from his mind altogether, and he had a sudden panic that he might be confusing her with someone else, that his letter to old Gaymer might have been complete gibberish.

When Richard reached his office on the following morning, a Friday, after another troubled night, a clerk informed him that a telegram had just come in over the telephone. It was signed "Gaymer" and read, "Believe your information may be of greatest help would appreciate meeting at earliest opportunity." Richard read these words with an almost unbearable feeling of excitement. He had been going that evening to spend the week-end with his father. Instead, he wired home saying he had to go to Shipstead, and might well be delayed until the next day or later. Then he wired Dr. Gaymer saying he hoped to be in Shipstead by six that evening.

Richard attended to a few outstanding matters of business (but with such ill attention that it would have been better if he had left them to someone else) and then caught the mid-morning train to Waterloo. It would hardly be fair to keep old Gaymer waiting a minute longer than necessary, to say nothing of his own impatience and curiosity. It was nearly a three-hour run from Liverpool Street to Shipstead, and Richard arrived at a quarter-past five, having had tea, as much as he could get down, on the train. He went straight off in search of the Gaymers' house. Dr. Gaymer, he gathered, was no longer in practice, and he wondered what in the world had made him move to the unprepossessing little villa he found among dozens of its kind, on the outskirts of the town. The Gaymers were just finishing their tea as he reached their house. They both looked white and strained, and the doctor was so aged and emaciated that Richard scarcely recognized him.

"We didn't expect you quite so soon," he said, when civilities had been exchanged and Richard had refused a cup of tea and one of Mrs. Gaymer's memorable rock-cakes. Old Gaymer spoke slowly and painfully, as though the prospect of reopening investigations into the tragedy was intensely distasteful to him.

After a few minutes he led Richard off into his study, an incredibly overcrowded little room full of objects which Richard remembered with a stab of recognition—the lizard paperweight, the set of blue Manchurian horses, even the parrot cage, no longer occupied. He looked round, as he had done in the dining-room, in the hopes that there might be a photograph of Rosemary, but, greatly to his surprise, there was none. Occupying nearly the whole side of the room were french windows opening on to the usual pocket-size suburban garden with a hideous rustic summer-house in the far corner, and beside this a little cluster of rabbit hutches in which Richard caught glimpses of black and white—so something remained from the old régime.

Even now the doctor seemed strangely reluctant to broach the subject of the tragedy. Instead, he seemed most anxious to hear all about Richard. He questioned him in his slow deep voice about his health, his work and his interests. He talked of Richard's mother and of their visits to Widmouth together when Richard was a child. Richard saw suddenly that the idea of hunting down Rosemary's murderer must long ago have ceased to have any fascination for the doctor, or if it did, was probably outweighed by horror at the thought of having the whole affair revived, together with the reappearance of the police and all the questioning and theorizing and publicity over again, at the end of which some poor maniac might conceivably be brought to book, if he had not already been consigned to an asylum. But none of it would bring back Rosemary. It would only, Richard realized with a sudden feeling of shame which took the edge off his enthusiasm, drag the poor Gaymers back from their retreat into the harsh limelight.

At last, however, with a weary glance at the clock, the doctor said: "I am naturally most anxious to discuss the question of our child with you, but my wife and I have talked it over, and we thought it best that Inspector Claybell, of the County C.I.D., who worked on the case at the time, should be present to hear our discussion, otherwise it would almost certainly mean having to go over the same ground twice. I told the inspector over the telephone all about your letter. He should be here at six."

"Oh," said Richard, a little nonplussed, "I see. Actually I had rather hoped that we might have been able to sort of piece the thing together between ourselves before we went to the police. My memory is terribly unreliable, and until I've heard all the details from your end I'm quite capable of producing a mass of irrelevant and probably inaccurate information. I was very relieved to get your telegram, because, quite frankly, after I'd written to you, I had a frightful feeling that in my anxiousness to help I might have been imagining the greater part of what I wrote."

"The inspector is fairly certain," said the doctor, "from what you have told me and from what we already know that you have definitely put us on the right scent. Ah, that should be Claybell now."

The doctor went to the door, and a minute later ushered in two men. One was a large square man in too tight a suit, an obvious plain-clothes detective whose name was not mentioned, while the other, who was introduced as Inspector Claybell, gave Richard quite a shock. He was a flashy-looking man with a casual, insolent manner, who looked more like a race-course tout than a detective. Richard felt it must have been sheer chance which had put him on the right side of the law. He began to wish more than ever that he had discussed his story with old Gaymer first. The idea of unburdening his mind and Rosemary's confidences to this creature repelled him in the extreme.

At Claybell's suggestion the two detectives sat down opposite Richard at the familiar old wobbly gate-leg table that used to be in the waiting-room at Widmouth. There was a moment's silence while old Gaymer fumbled among the debris on his desk for Richard's letter. When he had found it he handed it to the inspector.

"You do the talking," he said, shuffling about awkwardly by the french window.

"Right you are, Doc." The inspector spoke in a whining voice that for some reason made Richard think of marble slabs swimming with spilt beer.

For a few seconds he contemplated Richard with his mouth and eyes screwed up, as though he had eaten something he couldn't identify; then he continued speaking. "Now, old chap," he said evidently under the impression that he was putting Richard at his ease, "I want you to tell me, as far as you can recall, precisely what occurred on the last occasion that you encountered Miss Gaymer."

Why on earth, thought Richard, furiously, can't he say "remembered" and "happened" and "met" like anybody else?

"Well, the annoying thing," he said, forcing himself to be reasonably civil, "is that each time I try to remember I seem to remember something just a little different from the time before, and that is really why I wanted to talk things over first with Doctor Gaymer before I attempted to make anything in the nature of an official statement."

"Yes, I can quite appreciate that, Mr. Hamming," said the inspector, whose expression made Richard doubt if he was capable of really appreciating anything at all: "perhaps, though, you wouldn't mind telling us something more about this red belt which you state Miss Gaymer was wearing on the last occasion that you saw her? I take it you are certain that she was wearing it on this occasion?"

"Yes," said Richard, "I can pretty well swear to that. You know," he added, "I haven't been able to decide exactly what *was* the date when I went over to Widmouth. I know it was some time in the summer of 1946, and I presume it must have been at the week-end, otherwise I wouldn't have been able to get off camp in the afternoon. I'm afraid I don't know either when Miss Gaymer—when the tragedy happened."

The inspector flicked back the pages of a little pad he was holding. "The visit to which you refer," he said, "*your* visit, occurred on May 17th, 1946. The body was found on September 15th of the same year. Four months later."

"Funny—I thought somehow the dates would have been much closer together."

"No, just four months. You stated just now," said the inspector, with a glance of impatience at old Gaymer who was walking restlessly about by the window, "that you had several

ANTHONY BRANDT.

1950

rather conflicting recollections relating to your last visit to West Widmouth. You are quite certain, I presume, that this is not accounted for by the fact that you met the deceased on more than one occasion?"

"It's odd you should say that," said Richard thoughtfully; "it had also occurred to me that as I had completely forgotten all about the meeting in the wild garden, until something just happened to remind me of it, I might conceivably have met Rosemary—Miss Gaymer—later, in somebody else's house or in London or somewhere, and forgotten all about that too. My mother died on May 21st, you see, almost immediately after that visit to Widmouth and what with that and the motor smash I had in the autumn, I'm afraid my recollection of other events that summer has been pretty well blotted out. As a matter of fact, several times since, people have spoken to me about things that I'm supposed to have done or seen during that time, and I've not had the slightest recollection of them, at least not without terrific racking of my brains."

"I see," said the inspector, sucking his teeth; "now, with reference to this red belt. You say you are absolutely certain that it was not on some later occasion that you saw Miss Gaymer wearing this belt?"

"Well, I thought I was," said Richard; "I mean, I've been assuming that that was the only occasion on which I saw her, but if I *did* meet her anywhere else, I suppose she might have been wearing it then, though I seem to connect it especially with the time she was leaping about the tennis court in her bare feet. I really can't be more definite, I'm afraid, unless you can help me."

"Well, you see, old man," said the inspector, "I don't want to say too much, because it's nearly all theory on our side, and I want to avoid suggesting anything to you which might mislead you. Still, I dare say you've twigged already that according to information in our possession Miss Gaymer didn't receive the red belt until some time *after* your meeting with her on May 17th. So, if you could remember any further details of a second meeting, it would help us considerably."

"Yes, I see," said Richard; "I shall have to think again."

"Perhaps," said the inspector, "just to make quite sure we are both thinking of the same belt, you would describe it to us exactly if you can."

"Yes," said Richard, "curiously enough, it's the one thing I can see absolutely clearly. It was made of scarlet felt with a blue, a brown, a yellow, and I think a purple heart stitched on either side of the buckle with bright green wool, and then there were some clusters of white daisies growing out of more green wool representing grass."

The detective exchanged a brief glance with his assistant, and started flicking back his notes again, and as he did so old Gaymer, from the window, suddenly burst out: "For God's sake, come to the point, can't you, Claybell!"

The detective raised his eyebrows and kept them raised all through his next sentence. "I'm coming to it right now, old chap," he said; "the police-surgeon's report showed that, from traces of felt and wool found on her throat, Rosemary Gaymer must have been strangled with a belt such as you describe. She had, however, never been seen wearing such a belt on any occasion. In fact, she had no belt when she left the house on September 15th. So you see, Mr. Hamming, we may be quite wrong, but it looks as if you must have seen Miss Gaymer on the very day she was murdered and seen her in Widmouth too, because it's been pretty conclusively established that she never left the neighbourhood."

"You see," old Gaymer broke in again, "you must have come to Widmouth on a business trip or something that day, and met Rosemary on her way up to the woods"—there was a fierce note of urgency in the old man's voice—"you must have heard about this other fellow then."

"Yes," said Richard; "I believe I did; it's coming back to me gradually." He looked a little dazed. "She was in trouble, I think—terrible trouble. She must have sent for me or something. She must have told me to come to the Grove in case she needed me."

"Yes, she must have," cried old Gaymer; his voice was eager now, almost pleading. . . . Now that they were apparently on the brink of discovery, his interest seemed to have revived. . . . "You must have seen her shortly before they killed her. Perhaps you saw the man. Perhaps you can remember what he looked like.

4

You see, that day when you came over and we had the tennis, my wife is perfectly sure that Rosemary had plimsolls on all the time. But when we found her that evening she had bare feet. I couldn't look myself, but George told me that, and the police say there was a small patch of soft ground which had her bare foot-marks over it as though she had done a sort of little dance. She often danced when she was happy. . . ." The doctor's voice broke, and for a moment he could not go on. Then he said very quietly, "They said the swine must have tripped her or pushed her over as she danced."

"Danced!" Richard almost shouted the word; "danced! Of course, that was it! She heard the sound of music from some loudspeaker in the valley and she began to dance. That was what maddened him—that she should want to dance when the bottom had been knocked out of his world."

"And you saw her?" old Gaymer cried out, coming right up to Richard and gripping him by the shoulder. "You actually saw her?"

"Yes, I saw them both." Richard had sprung to his feet. His eyes were blazing as the ideas began to surge back from his subconscious. "I heard them arguing after they had finished their tea. I heard pretty well everything they said. . . . I must have been quite close . . . in a tree. . . . Yes, it must have been a tree. . . . She must have told me whereabouts they would be. . . . I must have hidden where I could watch them. . . . He wanted her to go away with him, abroad somewhere. He kept telling her that nothing else mattered. He had planned to marry another girl because she was rich, and he had to have the money, but he wanted Rosemary too. He wanted to get his hands on the money and then come back to Rosemary and take her away. He thought he could still make her do just what he wanted. He made her lie in the river once like Millais' Ophelia with all her clothes on. She lay there in the moonlight for hours until she went quite blue."

"So they met often, did they, these two?" asked the detective in a voice that was scarcely above a whisper, a voice from which all the jauntiness had gone, like flat cider.

"Yes, often, often," Richard answered. His speech was curiously harsh and high like a spirit guide's. "He couldn't bear to be without her for long. She used to sneak out of the house and meet him at night in the Grove. She thought it was a great adventure at first, but at their last meeting she found out all about this other girl he was intending to marry, and that broke her up completely; she was absolutely livid with him. She said nothing would induce her ever to meet him again. She even took care never to be by herself for long in case he should come along and try to find her. He wrote to her, though, pleading and pleading with her, and in the end she consented to meet him just once more in the Grove, in the daytime, just to prove to herself and to him that she could resist him and to say 'good-bye'. She didn't tell him that by that time she had realized she was in love with someone else. She didn't tell him that now that his hold over her had weakened she hated the very sight of him. But he could see it all in her eyes, even in her gestures. He challenged her to deny it and she couldn't. That's what made him so desperate. I suppose he thought if *he* couldn't have her he didn't want her to belong to anybody else. I don't think he meant to kill her at first, though, but when he saw her dancing like that as though she had forgotten his very existence, as though she didn't care how cruel she was being to him, as though she were dancing in her imagination with this other man, then he must have lost control."

Richard paused for a second to collect his breath, then he rushed on: "He took the belt, the red belt he'd brought for her to try to placate her, and he tossed it carelessly round her throat. She thought he was going to dance with her. She never flinched or anything. She must have thought he had caught her mood the way he sometimes did when he forgot himself for a moment, and that he was going to dance a wild, idiotic dance with her. It looked just like that. He made it look like that. At that moment he contrived somehow to look as artless and as care-free as she did. But suddenly he put his foot out and tripped her, and as she fell he crossed over the ends of the belt he was still holding and gave a violent jerk. It was all over in a second. I don't think she felt much, the poor sweet darling. He knew just how to do it." Richard slumped back into his chair and buried his face in his hands, sobbing convulsively.

"Yes, that's all right, quite all right, old man," said the

inspector with a horrible attempt at joviality, though the sweat was running off his forehead like water from a leaky gutter, "we understand just how you felt, old fellow. Now what do you say to a nice little ride in the car with the doctor. You'll be O.K. with the doc."

But Richard seemed not to hear him.

FOGGY BOTTOM

CHRISTOPHER MORLEY

Illustrations by Figaro

Mr. Christopher Morley was asked to write an Anglo-American mystery story. This eminent American writer and broadcaster—whose English audience grew vastly during the war through his part in "Transatlantic Quiz"—obliged in a gay mood with the adventure of "Foggy Bottom". He explains in a letter that "Foggy Bottom" is "the name of a riverside region in Washington to which the State Department (what the British would call the Foreign Office) recently moved". Foreign Offices, he reminds us, are "subject to a good deal of fog". Mr. Morley is a devoted connoisseur of Sherlock Holmes, and is a member of that remarkable American society, the Baker Street Irregulars.

YOU may be right, said Dove Dulcet, the literary detective. Unifying the armed services may eventually iron out departmental jealousies, especially under an intelligent Defence Secretary. But as a sentimentalist (Dulcet continued) I'm rather sorry about unification. When I was in Naval Intelligence the best fun we ever had was spying on the Army. The U.S. could have the greatest Intelligence Service in the world if we had time to spy on the enemy instead of on each other. I'm sure the President, the Chief of Staff, even the Un-American Activities Committee, never guessed how zealous was our interior reconnaissance. The only way the Navy or the Army could ever find out what they needed to know was by mutual espionage. Of course the Marines and the Air Corps were hopelessly handicapped. All they had to do was fight.

Obviously we couldn't learn anything through Channels, and Top Secrets never got to the top. There was a kind of embolism in the middle (about the grade of Commander or Lieut.-Colonel) where they didn't trust anything either above or below them. Everything clotted right there. Most of our own Restricted stuff we could only learn by debauching some Englishman to whom it had been told by an American correspondent in London. OPSHAK, that was my superhush project, used to bowl googlies at British Brass who happened to be over here, and feed them whisky. They couldn't get it at home, and their tolerance was worn thin. Also, you know how goofy the Englishmen were, what with food and nylons and the *New Yorker* ads. You should have seen some of them give when they got away from the Embassy and out to a party in some rebuilt stable in Georgetown.

OPSHAK? Oh, that was just our professional cant. Operation Shakespeare. The good old Swan told all the secrets there are, but in such a cunning literary convention that no one but Lord Bacon guessed them. Don't forget that Shakespeare was a secret agent for the British Navy at the time of the Armada. The Armada was only an armadillo compared to what we were handling, say, about '44.

[*I thought Dove was fouling his anchor a little, so I poured him another splice. He got good holding ground and went on.*]

In Naval Intelligence we were so jealous of the Pentagon— we were sweating it out in those beaverboard sheds on Constitution Avenue—we'd almost sooner defeat the Army than the Nazis or Nips. We thought, when we saw all that shoulder-nickel at the cocktail spots, if we could only lure them inland to Bull Run. But they were running it, full and bye, at the Carlton Bar.

We knew something weird was in the works. But Admiral Leahy would not tell us, because Admiral King wouldn't tell Leahy. We planted a Navy captain to wear chickenguts for

Eisenhower, but he had succumbed to Ike's Kansas charm and was in stays. Nimitz and Halsey and Spruance were too busy to be told anything. We set some very keen Australians to tail MacArthur, but whenever they asked Mac questions he couldn't understand their accent. We smuggled dictaphones into the offices of the news-magazines; but they were so curt, clear, concise (and inverted) we couldn't break the code. There we were, fighting to have a chance to fight, but nobody trusted the Intelligence. We even cultivated some of the Cabinet, hoping to winnow a little chaff. They were pathetically grateful, but they were so busy keeping diaries they didn't know what was happening. Very likely the Secretary remembers what Bagehot said of Hartley Coleridge. "His excessive sense of the ludicrous unfitted him for official position." That's probably why the Navy and I parted company. I'll never be invited again.

And the only time OPSHAK was on the edge of a real strike (repeat, Real Strike) we were blasted by tragedy.

2

I had a smart little confidential staff, headed by Lionel Nightwork—you remember him? Brother of Jinny Nightwork. We had inveigled Jinny and her friend Irene Hargreave into the Waves, so they could fox out a certain amount of dope from those masses of mimeograph. It was Lionel who discovered, from a real estate agent who rented an apartment on Connecticut Avenue to an Admiral who hadn't yet paid for his Big Stripe, the Navy's Secret: Put everything dangerous in mimeograph, because no one has time to read it. This agitated Admiral had just hoisted his Broad Pennant over a new flotilla of filing cases, and was a little paper-happy.

Lionel rushed into my office one afternoon. He had been at the airport; I used to send him there disguised as a ground-crew mechanic, to pretend to tinker round incoming priority ships. Actually he eavesdropped the first remarks made by arriving officers. Often they're well fouled up by the long flight and let out something significant.

"There's a priceless old fishball just in from the Elderly

Country," Lionel exclaimed. "If Blimp had grandsons, he's one. He must know something terrific or he wouldn't put on such an act. He comes roaring out from the plane, pips and swagger-stick and British Warm. 'America!' he shouts. 'God Bless Terra Firma! Your jolly old pilot nearly did a wizard prang off Labrador. Stoutfella. What price a whisky-peg? I've been sitting in a bucket all the way from Shannon. Now let me put my head in one. Moel Famma!' "

Only the Welshmen there would have known what *Moel Famma* means, and there weren't any Welshmen there. But it's our business in Navy Intelligence to know the expletives of all nations.

"He was travelling High Anonymous," Lionel continued, "but I got his name off his dispatch case, Colonel ffrogg-Bottington. He was met by one of those smoothies from State; you know how embarrassed they are by anything vehement. But the Colonel put us at our ease at once. We should have had a gout-stool for him, but we picked him up at the bottom of the steps and he bade us Carry On. He said he had a whacking great Gladstone Bag; that baffled the State Department. I found it for him and he gave me half a crown; just as if he'd been the Labour Government giving away India."

He sounds to me, I said, like a Cravat of the Old School.

"The old school," said Lionel, "was probably Stonehenge. You better take over, Chief. He's definitely wizard. He can put you in your place so you like staying there and wouldn't dream to climb out. I heard him speak of the Pentagon as a sturdy little wigwam. Anyone who buffoons like that gives me overtones of suspicion. I think you should track him down."

No can do, I said. I've just got the first thousand pages of Mr. Morningdew's Diary lifted from Treasury files, and I must analyse them to-night. I doubt, and so does the publisher, if there's anything very important. Mr. Morningdew was too hopeful to be a historian; but I might brighten up his prose a little. No, this is on you, Lionel. Trace Colonel Foggy-Bottom to the Carlton, give him the old Taj-Mahal, tell him you're a goodwill-wallah, and invite him out to Jinny's dump in Georgetown. You know the code: tell him it's *burra-pegs* for a *pukka-sahib*, and *chota hazri* to follow. Tell the gals not to get sore if he calls them Wrens, or even memsahibs. Ply him soft-shell crabs and apologize how amateurish we are. Have Jinny or Irene offer to do his laundry. Ask if he wants Sweet or Savoury. Cut down as much as you can on your vowels. Give him a *sola topi*, a *puggaree*, and a *cummerbund*. Above all, hot water in a tin hip-bath and a clean pair of shorts. Give an Englishman hot water and a pair of shorts and he's yours.

I blame myself bitterly, Dove said. (He surmounted a small ventral disturbance.) I had forgotten that Lionel can't drink. He can't coax anyone else to get fried without frying himself. That's something we had to learn in OPSHAK. You mustn't hire historians who love History. You mustn't hire Drinkers who love Drink.

But Lionel did exactly what I told him. He kidnapped Colonel Foggy Bottom away from the State Department man, who loathed the Carlton Bar and wanted to get home to his well-bred glass of all-purpose sherry in Protocol Park. He taxied Foggy out to Georgetown where Jinny and Irene had fixed up their virgin quarters. They straightened the candles (which make U-turns in hot weather), unloaded their Chihuahua dogs on the people downstairs, pushed their private mending under their innocent double-couch, and secured the rubber ballcock in the toilet so it wouldn't rumble. They're smart girls, and well-trained in Navregs. They got out their International Cook Book (one of our most useful weapons in OPSHAK) and stirred up a smashing kedgeree, with sesamum seeds and chutney and split pulse and those little transparent toasted wafers, *poppadums*. They had everything to remind any pukka pandit of the Sepoy Mutiny. Jinna or Nehru would have been absolutely choused.

It was good teamwork. They made salaam, offered to pay the taxi-wallah, called the Colonel *Huzoor*, and spread him little triangles of anchovy toast and even mustard-and-cress sandwiches. It might have been officers' mess at Sandhurst. They poured him incredible pegs of whisky and cried Here's Lucknow!

You're too Middle-West, said Dove, to guess what that sort of routine does to an old cavalry subaltern from Bangalore. A veteran of the Queen's Own Hussars! I gather from what

4*

the girls told me that Lionel put on the heat like an electric
pad. The Colonel was stewed in his own *raj*. Feeling himself
among Old Carthusians he really gave. Nor do I blame him.
He was only telling what some Yank had confided in London.

Lionel always checked up with me at breakfast. In my little
diggings on Q Street I take red-hot coffee while the morning
is still cool.

I could see at once that something was wrong. Lionel's eyes
were injected deep in his head; his scarf not secured in his
blouse; he hadn't shaved. He tottered towards my steaming
percolator, but his hand fluttered like a loose halliard. I pushed
him into a chair and poured for him.

Buen Día, I said. (I had been up all night with Mr. Morningdew's Good South American Doctrine.) So is this what Foggy
Bottom did to you? I hope you handed him Reciprocal Poop?

"Quite," said Lionel. "Oh, very much quite.—Sorry, Chief,
I've still got a King's English hangover.—I floated Foggy back
to his berth at four bells this morning. Then I took a powder
myself."

He groaned, tried to lift his coffee cup, then put his head
down to it and lapped. Poor fellow, he looked ghastly, but I
had to question him. So was the handsome bloater all packed
up with hermetic secrecies?

"He was that," said Lionel. "The gals went after him like
a couple of vixens, they cosied him with double Rob Roys and
a little sofa-sitting. As per instruction I talked Kipling code.
A few *rissaldars* and *dak-bungalows* and *jinrickshas* and he began
to transfuse. I knew he was ripe when he came through with
the immortal compliment: 'You people don't seem like Ameri-
cans at all.'

"Boy, he was certainly loaded with the inside-in. Even
though he was, as he called it, a little tiddly, he would belay
himself somewhat in front of the girls, but after they turned in
he whispered everything. I mean everything. Time-tables and
technologies you wouldn't even dare mention to the C.-in-C.
I realized if we could use what he told me we could win the
War without any Army at all."

Lionel groaned and gasped, panted as though he would
faint. I waited for the dread secret.

"I've forgotten every damn thing," he said. "You know what cocktails do to me. When I woke this morning my mind was utterly blank. I can't remember a single solitary fact. Down the drain. Washed out. You'd better court-martial me. Conduct unbecoming an intelligence officer."

There's no such thing, I murmured, but he was weeping with his head on my breakfast.

3

There was only one thing to do, Dove continued. Reproduce as near as possible, the conditions of the Georgetown binge. If Lionel were to have exactly the same amount of the same drinks, and the conversation were repeated up to the critical point, and someone were to impersonate Foggy Bottom (it would have to be Me), then perhaps—just perhaps—the great revelation would reappear in poor Lionel's stupefied memory.

I sent him back to his quarters to sleep. I called in the girls, who looked a bit hexed, and explained what we must do. They were to spend the day in writing a script, as accurate as they could remember, of everything that had happened the night before. A complete shooting script, not only dialogue, but full stage direction, properties, canapés, drinks, passes, and gestures. They're clever gals (you remember that Irene is a greatniece of Sherlock Holmes) and they did better than I'd have thought possible. I wish that script could be published. Some of Foggy's cracks were wonderful, and when the girls lured him on to Foreign Office limericks——

But what bothered me most was the expense account to pay for such a duplicate supply of intoxicants. Bagehot might have got it through the Paymaster, but I couldn't and in fact it came out of my privy purse. Otherwise there'd have been a Senate investigation.

I'll be brief; it's all too painful.

Lionel had a good rest, and after a raw egg in Worcestershire and a couple of gin fizzes he was pretty near par by six o'clock. He complained of pains in his breast, but his sister poohpoohed it. For me that goes double, she said. She was the one who sat closest to Foggy.

Lionel and I turned up at the girls' place on schedule. I had procured (from our wardrobe department) the proper uniform to simulate Colonel Foggy; and I rouged my face a little to get that curry-and-chutney glow. They handed us each a script, and the same appetisers and snorts they had served before. I sat, as directed in the script, on the sofa with my arms round the girls, but especially Irene, because Jinny was on the side where my glass stood. I admit I was a little embarrassed by some of the corny lines in my rôle; I had to remember that Foggy supposed himself talking to simple colonials who would scarcely understand what he meant. It was being called Wrens —*Jinny Wren* and *Reeny Wren!*—that griped the gals most. There were so many stage directions marked (*Drinks*) or (*Fondles*) I had to check them off with a pencil to be sure I was accurate. The accent wasn't difficult, I fastened a band-aid to my palate so my tongue never touched the roof of my mouth. That gave the burra-sahib effect.

Poor Lionel was superb. He knew, as we others couldn't, how much depended on this experiment. It might make the whole Pentagon Building obsolete. I thought he was rather flushed and jittery, but no wonder.

I won't say we didn't enjoy ourselves, grim as it was. The girls screamed with unscripted mirth at some of my readings. Of course, we were all getting high. Finally, after innumerable drinks, and too much of that starchy kedgeree, and strips of dead fish called Bombay Duck—all of which they had used to bring Foggy to a climax—we reached this point in the script:

Girls excuse themselves, extricate from Foggy's embraces; Foggy just escapes getting his fingers caught in the bedroom door. Foggy sighs heavily, gives a last look at some cheese-cake pictures in *Life* magazine.

LIONEL (weaving a little): Now we don't have to be so protocol. If it weren't for so much official shirt-stuffing, how much quicker we could——

FOGGY: Old chap, you're wizard. It makes me crackers that we have to bung round hiding things from each other. (Whispers.) Let me tell you something—one of your own burra-sahibs told me this in the comfort station at Sloane Square——

At that instant Lionel tottered. He dropped the bottle (he was just pouring what the script called a *lickure brandy*) and shouted:

"I've got it! I remember—Oh, my God!——"

He put his hand to his breast, and fell. He breathed heavily, but his lips turned blue and he never spoke again. We got a doctor there in twenty minutes, but Lionel was dead. The doctor said that a man with a heart like that should never have worked in Washington.

Dove Dulcet reflected sadly, and then remarked:

Lionel Nightwork was a martyr to duty; and of course we know now what the intelligence was that killed him. He was the first victim of the atomic bomb.

ALONG CAME A SPIDER

ALGERNON BLACKWOOD

Illustrations by Luther Roberts

Mr. Blackwood was a very tolerant man, but there was one living creature which inspired him "with a degree of loathing that includes fear, even horror". A few examples of this creature are dangerous to man; but most are so thoroughly harmless that it is difficult to explain why anyone should dislike, still more, fear them.

I SHARE our lovely planet with another inhabitant who inspires me with a degree of loathing that includes fear, even horror. If brought suddenly face to face with this repulsive individual, something akin to paralysis attacks my muscular system, so that for a passing moment I seem unable to act. I stand and stare, fascinated, frightened, and without knowing why.

You have guessed, of course: I'm talking of my private, personal phobia—a spider. Now, phobies are common, especially this one of spiders; and a phobie is a secret fear for which no explanation occurs. The pre-natal theory is discarded, auto-suggestion does not work; it is a groundless yet persistent fear, innate, in the blood. It appears often in the most fantastic forms, but while you can laugh at the fluttering moths that terrify some people, you never can laugh at your own. Spiders, for instance, are not ludicrous to myself.

I dislike their nasty hairy legs, their too-greedy swollen abdomens, their vile way of eating their bound and helpless prey, or when bigger, snatching tiny birds from the nest before they can fly. Their eight eyes, too, are sinister, since you cannot know what they are really looking at, nor what kind of portrait they see. Horrible, too, is the way the female devours her husband even before she has divorced him. All these, however, are surface blemishes: there is something much deeper than all that if I could only get at it. Does a big spider, for instance, radiate something inimical in the way some folk think a cat announces its near presence long before it is seen! The mere idea is comic. Yet if I see a big spider on the ceiling of my bedroom—say, on a country visit—I cannot go to sleep until I have persuaded the monster to leave.

Naturally, friends declare a fright in early childhood explains my phobie, though it is wholly untrue. Yet I recall a recurrent nightmare in childhood and youth that haunted me, but it was an after-effect rather than a cause.

In my sleep I first heard something creeping cautiously across the carpet towards my bed. On reaching the sheets it began to climb stealthily. With its fantastic eyes it picked out available hand- or footholds. Once on the counterpane, I could hear its nasty scrabbling feet as it crawled along the edge of the sheets and blankets where these lay against my cheeks. And then it paused, eyeing me no doubt from fantastic angles with its horrible, queer eyes. A feathery touch brushed my skin. I woke—or thought I woke in the nightmare—and there, staring at me, perched a big dark spider.

The nightmare broke, I shot out of bed. No sign of a spider anywhere. Had it been a fly, a beetle, a caterpillar, I would not have cared tuppence. The horror of the nightmare clung for some minutes. But, anyhow, this nightmare was not the *cause* of my phobie.

I have often asked myself why this beast is so repulsive and frightening to people like myself with a form of spider-phobie; but asking questions has not cured me. Spiders often have lovely colouring. Also they have no teeth to bite you with, and very few carry poison glands. Their legs may be unpleasant to look at, I know, yet those legs are provided with an ingenious contrivance that constructs faultlessly the geometrical wonder of their web. With the morning dew sparkling on that taut, elastic structure, few sights are more lovely. The tiny kind that adventure gaily for great distances on barely visible strips of gossamer contribute an authentic touch of fairyland. Yes, I stand with hat off in admiration and respect to their amazing skill and ingenuity, from the trap-door spider onwards. Thus, I have tried to see both sides of the horror, as it were; my hate is not just blind hate. Moreover, spiders possess yet another distinction I am sure they are proud of: they are not insects. They have eight legs, not six. They have their own family name which they share with scorpions—Arachnidæ. So there it is! The more I study them, the less can I understand why this acute form of phobie can remain in my blood all these years of my long life. Nor has any doctor I have asked given me any clue.

I recall an unpleasant incident with a tarantula once— in Toronto, where long ago I shared a ground-floor in a boarding-house with another English boy. Folding doors divided us. One afternoon he greeted me with an expression of rapture: "Oh, I say, what do you think I've got?" With immense pride he opened a small box he held. I saw inside a full-size, hairy-legged tarantula. Big as a mouse! He had bought a bunch of bananas from some Southern State. The tarantula was a stowaway. I watched him stroke the devil— yes, actually *stroke* it. I saw the pride and happiness in his eyes. He was seventeen. I was over eighteen.

I concealed my ludicrous phobie. He could not detect my icy shudder. I begged him to be careful. "It's dangerously poisonous," I mentioned, "but won't attack unless frightened." Oh yes, he knew all that. . . . I went out while he kept repeating, "Isn't it a beauty? . . ." An hour or two later I came in to bed. He greeted me. "Oh, I say—it's escaped!" It had. A search of the two dingy rooms, with so many dark corners, was a waste of time. . . . I went to bed.

When I opened my eyes in the morning I saw the monster stuck to the wall facing me across the small bedroom. It was close to a hot-air pipe in the wall. Adrenalin poured into my blood, but I knew enough not to attack. If left alone it would

merely watch me out of its fantastic eyes, all its horrid legs ready to leap, but otherwise quiet. I wriggled out of bed and crawled inch by inch, covered by sheets and blankets, lest even a toe might stick out, and reached the door. At the door, however, I was compelled to stretch out an uncovered arm to turn the handle. Once safely in the passage I turned—the monster, of course, hadn't moved. My young friend later picked it off with his ungloved fingers.

It is not always easy to establish what is, or is not, a genuine phobie, but at any rate the obvious fears—tigers, poisonous snakes, fire—common to all of us, conceal no secret cause. Is, for instance, a bat in the phobie class? Some people I have asked say at once, "Oh, yes, bats, of course! I'm terrified of bats!" A bat, we know, may specially alarm women if it darts by chance through an open window into the room; but that is no mystery; it is perhaps because they fear it may get entangled in their long hair. The wonderful radar wings, of course, makes such a disaster extremely unlikely, for every object in the room sends its message instantly and the bat immediately avoids striking it. The long hair is quite safe. If the lights are turned out, since bright light distresses it, the bat will dart out again into the dusk in a moment or two. They are mysterious creatures, none the less, possessed of very unusual powers.

The large blood-sucking vampires, for instance. These have been carefully studied in Bolivia, where their feeding habits do great harm to cattle in the fields at night. And this particular group of scientists established that a vampire would never touch a human being before he was genuinely asleep. And no pretence of being asleep could ever deceive them. The white men under their blankets might snore, lie motionless, breathe deeply, and assume all the posture of profound slumber, but no bat would come near them. Sooner or later, of course, they would slip off into genuine slumber—and in flitted the bat noiselessly, having spotted a toe or finger not under cover, and next morning they would have lost a quantity of blood. Moreover, this creature's very sharp incisor teeth have been thoughtfully equipped by Nature with a minute gland of some kind that injects a drop of some soothing mixture so that the pain of the prick is not even felt. The man slumbers on undisturbed.

Anyhow, I don't think either bats or cats can be regarded as genuine phobies that exercise their strange gifts on us by way of foolish and quite unnecessary terrors.

I remember reading of a remarkable case of a woman's acute spider-phobie: apparently, she knew a big spider was in her room before she saw it. I read this in a medical journal of repute, though without editorial sanction. It was either an article or a letter. Her own spider-phobie was too acute to be laughed away; her temperature went up, there were genuine hysterics, even the heart was affected. Her husband, who treated these outbursts with sympathy and understanding, heard her scream for help one afternoon and dashed up to her bedroom where she had gone to rest.

"A big spider in the room," she cried. "I haven't seen it. For goodness' sake get it out! . . ." She was in acute distress. He searched in vain, soothing her as best he could. Presently his brother joined in the search—and later, his eye picked out a large garden spider lying motionless among the toilet articles on the dressing-table, cleverly camouflaged by chance. Without saying a word, he quietly squashed it. The woman, on the sofa at the end of the room, could not possibly have seen this, but instantly cried out in a voice of intense relief, "Oh, it's gone!" And she soon recovered her equanimity. Now, I know, that many haters of cats claim to know if there is one about long before they see it. I cannot say. A cat, an electrical beastie but a great pal of mine, may conceivably radiate a warning message, but I find it hard to believe a spider has any gift of that sort. But who knows? I certainly do not.

An odd incident comes to my mind, where a woman with a real spider-phobie, though not acute, paid a morning visit to her garden in the sunshine and chatted with her gardener. A huge garden spider sat in the centre of its beautiful web. She made some unkind remark about spiders to the gardener. "They're not bad to eat, you know, madam," he observed, as he picked it out of the web, gave a quick chew, and swallowed it. "A bit on the sweet side, I always think," he added, selecting another one even fatter and juicier.

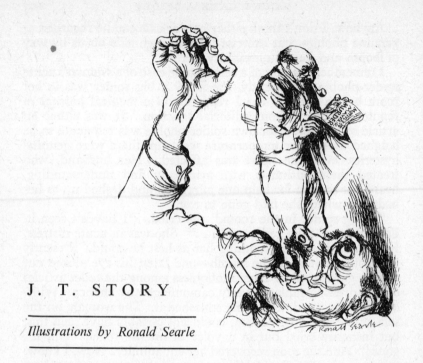

J. T. STORY

Illustrations by Ronald Searle

FAME FOR FERDINAND

MR. FERDINAND POTTER decided on murder. He heard some third programme philosopher say that if a man hadn't made his mark in the world by the time he was fifty, he would never make it. So Mr. Potter decided to make his mark.

He came to his decision by way of the Sunday papers. By diligent reading Mr. Potter was able to ascertain that most murderers made the same mistake—the mistake of getting caught. Mr. Potter thought if he could commit a murder and not make that mistake, that would indeed be something. More, how many ways were there of getting into the newspaper headlines these days? Not many, by heck, not with the wonderful things that were happening every day. Mr. Potter could not think of one single friend of his who had ever got into a news-paper headline. Not even Jack D'Aintree, who had risen from errand-boy to director and snubbed him in the street only yesterday, had ever got into a newspaper headline. You had to achieve something really amazing, and what more amazing than murder? With a good murder you were certain of a head-line for at least three days. That would be something to look back on with relish. Something to savour with a pipe on wet Sunday afternoons. He would be able to sit and read of other murders, and with some authority criticize and judge where they had gone wrong.

At first Mr. Potter considered killing his old school chum Jack D'Aintree, who had risen so sickeningly in the world and become such an insufferable snob. But second thoughts told Mr. Potter that it would be a first and probably fatal mistake to kill somebody he disliked. That was a mistake so many murderers made. It was an elementary mistake. The first question a detective asked was, "Did the dead man have any enemies?" Mr. Potter groaned aloud when he read case after case of a man killing because of this or because of that. They did not seem to learn by others' mistakes at all. Why on earth, if they had to kill, didn't they kill somebody of whom they were inordinately fond? Better, why did they not choose to kill some-body with whom they had no acquaintance whatever?

So Mr. Potter decided to kill a stranger. About the method of killing he was not particular. Firearms were out of the ques-tion, of course, being easy to trace and the missile being prone to nark under the scientific manipulation of Scotland Yard. Bullets innumerable had sent confident killers innumerable to the scaffold. Buy a bullet and you like as not bought a witness for the prosecution. Mr. Potter considered using his hands. It was not a nice thought. Indeed, Mr. Potter felt slightly shocked at the thought, but it had to come under consideration. He dismissed it as an impracticable method. He was not a strong man, nor large. If anything, he was small. After much deep deliberation, for there was no hurry, Mr. Potter decided on that old standby of the murderer, the knife. There was, he felt, something classical in the use of a knife—not that he was a snob like Jack D'Aintree.

Then there was the question of whose knife to use? Obviously it must not be his own, and just as obviously he must not buy one specially for the job. Those also were mistakes painfully common in current murders. He might steal one from a multiple store, or from one of those trusting hardware shops that display goods in boxes on the pavement. Then, again, a double risk was involved. Where perhaps nobody would see him commit the major crime, somebody might witness the minor one, and what unbearable chagrin he would suffer! The problem was a very real one. Happily, an ingenious solution came to Mr. Potter when he was sharpening a pencil.

So late one Saturday evening Mr. Potter boarded a bus which took him right across the town. Besides the extra risk of being recognized in your own neighbourhood, there was something distasteful about having a murder in the vicinity of your home, besides which it tended to lower the land value. Mr. Potter decided to kill in Mayfair. He chose the district carefully. He chose it because he clearly saw how imposing it would look in a newspaper screamline. He would be called "The Mayfair Murderer". How much better this than, say, "The Kilburn Killer", or "The Surbiton Slayer"!

Mr. Potter strolled the dark streets in the proximity of Berkeley Square. He wore a sporty sports coat, striped flannel trousers and a yellow scarf, this being quite out of character with the usual back-street murderer, and likely to put his victim completely at ease for the few important moments before the crime.

Mr. Potter felt nervous, as was only natural, it being his first murder. He whistled a few bars of "A Nightingale Sang in Berkeley Square" and then modulated to "Knocked Him in the Old Kent Road". On his third perambulation along the same street he met a man. This man, he thought, would in all probability be the victim. In a way Mr. Potter felt that he was doing him a favour, for perhaps he was some unsuccessful nonentity like himself who otherwise would never stand the least chance of appearing in the newspaper headlines.

"Excuse me, sir," said Mr. Potter, "but could you lend me a pocket-knife?"

The other was a fat man with small, beady eyes that seemed

to bore right into Mr. Potter's soul. Mr. Potter felt vaguely irritated. Right at that moment he was in no state to have his soul explored.

The other fumbled in his coat pocket and brought out a pocket-knife. Mr. Potter held it up so that the light of a distant street lamp gave him an idea of its size.

"It isn't very big, is it?" grumbled Mr. Potter.

"It's all I've got," said the other.

"I suppose it will have to do," said Mr. Potter, and opening the large blade he drove it through the other's throat.

The fat man's eyes goggled at Mr. Potter as though they had seen the blackness of his soul a shade too late, and he sank to the pavement without a murmur, while Mr. Potter walked back to his bus stop.

The newspapers did Mr. Potter proud. They got an extra "M" in the headline. "Motiveless Mayfair Murder," it said.

Under the headline there was a picture of the street with reporters and police walking about and a crowd of people standing wide-eyed at one end. It said that the man's name was Montague Round, and so far as the police could discover there had been no robbery. Further, the man had no enemies or poor relations. He was unmarried, with no children or dependants, and Mr. Potter could see that the victim was, in fact, in circumstances very similar to his own. He felt that he had taken this unknown man up into the world of headlines with himself. They had made their mark together, so to speak. On the whole, Mr. Potter congratulated himself on having done a good job.

His first impulse on seeing the affair in print was to dash out and buy a copy of every newspaper, to see how they had treated it. Fortunately this impulse was stillborn. That was something the successful murderer could not afford to do. How many murderers owed their early morning stroll to vanity? More than Mr. Potter cared to remember. He must not visit the scene of the crime either, or tell his best friend—and he had no best friend, anyway—or air his views on how the murder might have been committed. He must just contain himself and read the headlines as they dwindled, and try to gain some satisfaction out of the fact that in some great offices on the Embankment some great brains were being paid tremendous sums to solve the crime of which he alone held the solution. And surely that was satisfaction enough?

Mr. Potter followed the progress of the police with great interest. By the third day the murder had got to a small paragraph on the front page, while on the fourth day it had quite a big headline on the inner page, and later on it disappeared altogether, only to pop up next to the stop press on the back page, by which time the police had decided that the crime had been committed by a gang of crooks who had mistaken Montague Round for a notorious vice chief. Mr. Potter was intrigued to read that the murder had borne all the hallmarks of a certain much-wanted criminal and in a matter of days they hoped to apprehend him.

Three weeks later "The Motiveless Mayfair Murder" again made its appearance under a heading which said the murderer

had escaped to the Continent and the French police were col-
laborating and hoped for an early arrest.

Mr. Potter was tempted to write to Scotland Yard an anonymous post card and tell them they were barking up the wrong
tree. But this struck Mr. Potter as a ghastly mistake as he was
picking up the pen. Very obviously it was just the very thing
at which the newspapers were aiming. It was a hideous trap.
Mr. Potter was shaken. Surely a murderer, more than any
other man, was his own greatest enemy. Mr. Potter decided to
read no more newspaper reports, but simply to let the crime
mellow and age in his mind, wherein he could dip when the
mood bade him and savour the glory of that one great achievement.

But there was one more pitfall that Mr. Potter had not
reckoned on. One of those subtle dangers that are not so
common in the Sunday papers, and which only a connoisseur
of murder could hope to avoid. It was lucky, indeed, that Mr.
Potter had become something of a connoisseur, or he must have
fallen to the temptation.

The temptation came to him cunningly disguised as a flash
of inspiration. The temptation to feel again the intoxicating
tension of that bus ride, that stroll in dark places, that query
for a knife—that great moment of the thrust . . . the feel of the
blood on his hand, the joyous ecstasy of something accomplished, something done. More, the immense satisfaction of
going into print again. The banner headlines, the reports, the
bewilderment of the police, conjectures, theories. . . . Little
wonder that Mr. Potter almost succumbed to the temptation.
Almost.

When he had finally pushed the thought aside, he felt that
at last he had rid himself of every danger. He had cheated the
gallows, he had vanquished himself as an enemy. He had
nothing more to fear. When Mr. Potter took himself to the
park one afternoon, nine weeks after "The Motiveless Mayfair
Murder", he knew that he could at last truly regard himself
as having made his mark.

He sat in the late sunshine in a secluded corner of the park
enjoying the bright lupins and quietly conscious of his secret
notoriety. His intense self-satisfaction was tinged with a slight

regret. Thus, had he not demonstrated a curious genius for evil that might, if applied to life earlier, have made him a man of great fame and fortune? But then, was he not far above those poor bunglers who stood in the wax museum? Mr. Potter sighed a happy, somnolent sigh that toned with the bees and merged almost into a snore. There were indeed so many aspects of his achievement that he felt quite confident he would never again feel bored or frustrated or jealous of Jack D'Aintree. As the years passed he would see the braveness of it and the courage; the audacity and the drollness—certainly the drollness. Mr. Potter smiled faintly and his eyes flickered against the pink of the lupins.

It was then that a pair of hands rose from behind the park seat and took Mr. Potter by the throat, throttling his voice, pulling back his head over the seat rail and squeezing relentlessly till Mr. Potter was dead.

The newspapers next day were full of another motiveless murder.

SCANDAL IN ATHENS

KATHLEEN FREEMAN

Pen drawings by F. R. Exell

In ancient Athens the laws of inheritance were complex in detail and gave rise to much litigation; but the main principles were clear. If there were legitimate children, they automatically inherited the property in equal shares, the shares of daughters being regarded as dowries. If there were no legitimate sons, the testator could adopt a son and leave the property to him. But no son not born of free Athenian parents on both sides was legitimate or could have any rights of inheritance. The subterfuges to which these laws gave rise reveal an interesting aspect of Athenian life and provided lawyers with large incomes. Lawyers in Athens did not appear in court: they merely wrote the speech which had to be delivered in person by the litigant. In the following case, reconstructed from one of the speeches written for clients by the great testamentary lawyer Isæus, sex, scheming, and senility create a fascinating story of human folly and greed.

I

EUKTÊMON was a well-to-do Athenian. He had everything in life that could make a man happy, it seemed: an excellent constitution; inherited property which brought in an income more than sufficient for his needs; a wife who had given him five children.

His three sons grew up into worthy citizens, the eldest in particular, Philoktêmon, proving an active partner in his father's enterprises in intervals of military command. The two daughters were given in marriage to two equally worthy and wealthy husbands. The only thing wrong in Euktêmon's life was that his sons, though married, remained childless, and of his two daughters only one had produced sons. These sons—there were two of them—were therefore the only direct male descendants. On their shoulders would one day fall the duty of performing the rites necessary for the welfare of the spirits of their dead ancestors—and to an Athenian this was all-important. His status in the Halls of the Dead, his existence as a shadowy replica of his former self, depended on the reliability and devotion of the coming generations.

Five children—and only two grandsons! Euktêmon sighed and shuddered at the precariousness of his link with the living world. And he was getting on in years. Already he had passed the allotted span.

He looked at his three sons and their barren wives, and despised them. Two of his sons were weaklings. The eldest, Philoktêmon, the General, was strong and fit, but apparently unable to beget a son, and unwilling to divorce his wife and remarry, as was permitted and even usual in such circumstances. His elder daughter could produce only a succession of girls. Even the younger daughter, having given birth to her two boys, seemed to have exhausted her ability to perform a woman's only useful function.

Euktêmon, head of this house of unfruitful vines, compared the prowess of his sons and sons-in-law with his own. Even at his age, he felt, he could do better than that. He wondered sometimes if it were still too late to try.

II

Then came a series of events which increased the deep dissatisfaction gnawing at Euktêmon's soul. His two younger sons both died, still childless, and the eldest, the General Philoktêmon, having decided that he too was destined to remain child-

less, cast covetous eyes upon his sister's elder son, a youth of
nearly eighteen called Chærestratus. Philoktêmon was about
to set off on another campaign, and being afraid lest he
should die without an heir, he decided to adopt this boy, his
nephew, as his own son and heir, as by Athenian law he was
entitled to do. He made out a last will and testament to this
effect, and deposited it with his other sister's husband, Chæreas.
Euktêmon, the grandfather, restless before, was now furious.
It seemed to him that Philoktêmon, his eldest and only surviving
son, had by this act of adoption deliberately relegated him to
the Halls of the Dead already—cut him off from a share in his
own grandson. It was not for Philoktêmon to make a will in
anybody's favour—he had not yet inherited the property. It
was for the head of the house to say how that property should
be distributed if Philoktêmon died.

"I'll show them!" muttered the old man, jealously watching
the transference of his grandson to his new home. "They can
plan for the future as much as they like—but I'm not dead yet
by any means! I've got more life in my limbs still than the
whole lot of them!"

His thoughts turned to a certain house down at the Peiræeus,
and a certain woman who had the power to make him feel
young again for all his seventy years.

III

Euktêmon's property was scattered. He had farms in the
country, a very valuable bathing establishment on the sea-
shore, houses in the suburbs, houses down at the harbour. It
was his pleasant duty at the end of the month to make a tour
of these properties to collect rents and the interest on mortgages.

The houses at Peiræeus were interesting, one of them particularly so. It was part boarding-house, part brothel, as was
usual in a seaport, and it brought in a considerable revenue. As
its manageress he had appointed a reliable woman, formerly
one of his slaves, but freed for this purpose. She, by means of
judicious purchases in the slave-market on his behalf, had set up
a very profitable establishment of girls, each in her own room,
for the entertainment of customers. When they ceased to be
girls—when they were too mature to attract new *clientèle*—they

would vacate their room to a younger girl, and would often stay on as lodgers in the house, perhaps under the protection of one of their former clients. Euktêmon kept an eye on their progress and development, and allowed them to buy their freedom if they could. Some of these superannuated prostitutes were in his own employ elsewhere, as caretakers or in other suitable capacities. They were not old when they retired; Athenians liked their girls young, and the retiring age was usually not later than thirty.

When the next rent-day became due, Euktêmon made his way on an easy-going saddle-mule down to the harbour. He drew the woman in charge into the counting-house.

"Tell me," he said, after the accounts had been inspected and the money paid over, "how is Aktê getting on?"

The woman smiled; she knew her employer's mind.

"Aktê? Oh, beautiful as ever, though it's more than a dozen years now since I bought her for you. But she's too superior for most of our clients. In fact, I was thinking of getting her to give up her room to another girl, who would pay better."

"Yes—do that," said Euktêmon quickly. "I'll see you don't lose by it."

The woman thanked him obsequiously.

"Perhaps you'd like to see Aktê now?" she suggested.

Euktêmon nodded.

IV

The manageress hurried along to Aktê's room.

"The old man's here," she said. "He wants to see you. Now, mind your manners and remember who he is and who you are. Above all, don't let him suspect anything about Dion. If you manage things skilfully, you may be made for life. And I hope you'll remember to whom you owe your good fortune."

"To myself, I imagine," said Aktê with lazy insolence, glancing over her shoulder from the polished metal mirror before which she was arranging her hair.

Her mistress trembled with rage. But the days when she could beat Aktê into temporary obedience were long over. Aktê was a well-made, attractive woman in the late twenties, and she had an ex-lover waiting to take her under his protection when she had saved enough money to buy her freedom. Aktê swaggered out of the room.

What passed between her and Euktêmon nobody knew. The first consequence was that she received her freedom. For a time she was installed in one of the ordinary rooms of the boarding-house, where she did nothing at all except minister to her appearance and wait for her elderly patron. Everybody knew that her real lover was the freedman named Dion. But nobody told Euktêmon. If the old fool wanted to believe himself still able to please a woman, why should anyone disillusion him and receive a thrashing as reward?

A couple of months later, Aktê announced that she was with child. Euktêmon, wild with joy, covered her with presents and caresses. The other lodgers laughed at him behind his back. Dion the freedman smiled. Aktê lay on her couch and ate dates and sweetmeats. The manageress of the establishment, Aktê's former mistress, scolded her and gave her advice, but she too had profited from Euktêmon's satisfaction and she was well-pleased.

v

Euktêmon had no intention of allowing his son to be born in a house of ill-fame. He removed Aktê from the Peiræeus to the Potters' Quarter, a suburb of Athens where he had an inn just outside the city, near a small entrance not far from the Dipylon Gate. He installed her here as landlady, and seven months later her child was born. It was a boy.

Euktêmon was triumphant. He, a man in the seventies, had begotten a son! True, the mother was a freedwoman and an ex-prostitute; but she was an Athenian and she was his. He could never marry her according to Athenian law, but he could do much for the child. Aktê was content. Her son's future was secure. It so happened that Dion the freedman had had to leave Athens owing to trouble over an unpaid fine. He regarded this boy as his, and would have been willing to bring him up if the old man hadn't recognized it. He would be back, he promised her, to produce other sons for the old dotard. Meanwhile, Euktêmon was a rich man and could keep the boy and Aktê in luxury. Dion had no wish to interfere.

VI

Before this, the whole family knew about Euktêmon's goings-on with Aktê. Everything he did was noted and watched by the outraged relatives, and reported to his wife. Philoktêmon, as the eldest and only surviving son, was urged to take strong measures. But what could he do? The old man, they knew, went off regularly under the old pretext of collecting the rents; but now, deserting his own home, he spent most of his time with Aktê at the inn; he even ate his dinner there with her—an unheard-of thing for an Athenian gentleman, to eat with a woman, even in the home, and when the woman was of servile birth and low life, it was an irremediable disgrace.

Eventually both his wife and Philoktêmon remonstrated. But did that make him stop? Not at all! The old sinner, hugely delighted at their discomfiture, spent more and more time at the inn, until at last his family hardly saw him at all.

"She has bewitched him!" wailed his wife. "To think that I, the mother of his five children, should live to see this day! An occasional lapse—well, every wise woman learns to shut her eyes to that. But at his age, and in his position, to consort with a low creature, an ex-slave from a brothel! A man on the social Register of Three Hundred, who has fulfilled many public functions—whose son is a general and whose son-in-law commanded a trireme in the Sicilian expedition—who has a grandson reaching man's estate! Either he is ill or she has bemused his intellect with drugs and charms! What can we do?"

She, poor woman, could do nothing, legal wife though she was. If she left him, where, in the sixties, could she go? She nagged, she made scenes. Philoktêmon the General gravely added his admonitions. The old man laughed in their faces and went back to his mistress, to whom by now he was completely enslaved.

VII

After the birth of Aktê's son, the family watched with painful anxiety to see what Euktêmon would do. They need not have wondered: the old man soon left everybody in no doubt as to his intentions.

Reports began to reach them.

First, the olive-wreath hung out at the inn door had proclaimed that the child was a boy. If it had been a girl, a mere woollen fillet would have announced the misfortune. When the baby had been safely delivered and laid on the ground, to gain strength from Mother Earth and its buried ancestors, Euktêmon had been present to lift it up and so acknowledge it. The baby, bathed in water mixed with oil and laid in a winnowing-basket for cradle, had roared lustily, showing that there was nothing effete about it. The women waiting on Aktê had hung its body about with the usual charms to keep off evil spirits and had set the pointed cap on its dusky head. One of them, gossiping with a servant of Philoktêmon's, said the boy didn't look to her like a seven months' child. . . .

But it wasn't until the fifth day, when the first formal rite was performed, that they could be quite sure of Euktêmon's plans.

The fifth day came. House, mother, and attendants were purified. The old fool, stripping himself naked like any youthful father, was not ashamed to expose his withered frame to the company. He carried the child three times round the hearth, the traditional ceremony to make it learn to walk and run quickly.

Even this was a comparatively private ceremony, confined to members of the household. There was still the tenth day to come, the Naming Ceremony when relatives and friends were invited and there was a sacrifice and a feast.

The tenth day came and went. The family were not invited, nor did they acknowledge the occasion with presents in the usual way. They still hoped that if they pretended to see nothing, a worse scandal could be averted. But on the following day, Euktêmon sent for his eldest son, the General Philoktêmon. He said:

"You are aware, perhaps, that I have a son born of the Athenian Aktê, who is living under my protection at my inn in the Potters' Quarter."

Philoktêmon swallowed hard, but he dared say no more. In Athens, a father was a father no matter what his follies, a son was a son even in his forties and when he was a military commander. Philoktêmon merely bowed.

"I have acknowledged this boy as my son, both at the Running-Round-the-Hearth ceremony and on the Naming Day. You have heard that, too, no doubt?"

"I have," said Philoktêmon, "but——"

"When a man's family gives him no cause for rejoicing, he turns elsewhere. However, I don't wish to treat you unfairly. If you accept my wishes, I shall say no more. I sent for you to let you know that I have decided to ask the clansmen to enrol my son as a member of my family."

"But, Father!" gasped Philoktêmon, "they can't do that! You know it's not legal! My mother is still your wife—and even if she were not, you cannot have legitimate sons by this woman, who was born a slave!"

"Nevertheless," said Euktêmon, "they are your half-brothers, and I intend to enter them as such."

"But that would give them an equal right with me to the inheritance!"

"Inheritance!" said Euktêmon testily. "That's all you and your sisters have ever thought of! You have already disposed of my property in your minds by adopting your sister's son against my wishes! Well, I can't disinherit *you*—the law of Athens doesn't allow it—and I am not proposing that this infant shall share the property. I am well aware that his mother is not and never can be my legal wife. Therefore I am proposing to enter him on the clan roll merely as my son, with a bequest of one single farm. Is that clear? Out of all my property, I surely have the right to leave him that, and you cannot be so grasping as to grudge it, even in favour of your precious nephew, my grandson Chærestratus, whose affections you have stolen from his father and mother and, above all, from me!"

Philoktêmon, convinced that his father was crazy, made no defence. He contented himself with saying:

"The clansmen will never allow it."

"And you?" pressed his father. "Will you oppose it?"

"It has nothing to do with me," said Philoktêmon. "It is illegal, and they won't consult me."

VIII

The clansmen did not allow it. They held a meeting at which this preposterous and unprecedented proposal was discussed, and voted against it. When Euktêmon turned up with his baby son and a sheep for the customary sacrifice, he was sent away.

A few days passed. Euktêmon was in such a rage that even at the ınn, where he was usually good-tempered, nobody dared to speak to him except Aktê. After long discussions with her alone, Euktêmon emerged with a look of fresh determination. First he paid a visit to Democrates, son of an old friend of his, who had a sister of marriageable age. Then he sent again for his son Philoktêmon.

Philoktêmon came reluctantly to the accursed inn. He dared not refuse. Shame at his father's folly made him avert his eyes as the old man began:

"You have opposed the inclusion of my son on the clan register. Very good. Now let me inform you of my plans. First, I intend to divorce your mother. Second, I have arranged to marry the sister of Democrates. Nobody can question the legality of these proceedings, and nobody will be able to doubt the legitimacy of any sons I may have by *her*."

Philoktêmon was staggered. His father's vigour and fanatical determination were unmistakable. No one could stop a man who wished to divorce his wife and marry again; all he had to do, according to Athenian law, was to declare the fact before witnesses, pay back her dowry and send her back to her family. This new marriage would be legal, and any children springing from it could not be refused admission to the clan. Here was a problem indeed!

Philoktêmon went away without attempting to argue. On the way home, he asked himself whether, after all, it was so certain that Aktê's new-born baby was not the child of this vigorous septuagenarian, who looked, acted and thought like a man at least twenty years younger.

IX

Another family conclave was called. Philoktêmon reported the new development. The relatives shook their heads and advised submission. If Euktêmon married this new bride, they pointed out, sons would certainly be produced somehow, whether by Euktêmon or another, and out of this even greater disputes and dissensions would arise. They advised Philoktêmon to accept Euktêmon's terms: give up his opposition to the proposal that the boy should be registered with the clan as his father's son, on condition that he inherited one farm only. Philoktêmon, not knowing what else to do, gave way.

Euktêmon, triumphant, carried through the business of registering the boy and divorcing his wife. He also cancelled his engagement to marry his new fiancée, and went to live entirely at the inn with Aktê.

Philoktêmon, broken-hearted at the public scandal, went off on the projected overseas campaign to Chios and was killed. But as if to compensate, Aktê gave birth to a second son. Was it true, the gossips said, that Dion the freedman had again been seen in Athens? At any rate, the old man made no attempt to register this second boy.

X

The years went by. Euktêmon passed his eightieth year. At this point, a new influence began to make itself felt in his affairs. Two distant cousins, members of his estranged family, named Androcles and Antidorus, saw a chance of profiting by his obstinate folly. They made overtures, first to Aktê, then through her to the old man, disarming his suspicions by whole-heartedly recognizing his paternity and the claims of the two little boys.

"But," said Androcles, "you made a mistake in drawing up a document leaving the elder boy only a farm. He has a right to a bigger share. That document virtually admits that he has no legal title to anything. You should revoke it."

Euktêmon, convinced, sent a message to Pythodorus, the man with whom he had deposited the document in safe-keeping, and asked him to produce it, as he wished to revoke it. The parties met at the court of the appropriate magistrate, and there before witnesses the document was agreed to be null and void and was destroyed.

This done, the cousins had another suggestion.

"While your wealth is in real estate," said Antidorus, "your sons here will never enjoy it. On your death, your daughters and your grandsons will take possession. But if you turn your property into hard cash, you can give it to your boys and no one can take it from them."

Again Euktêmon was convinced. With all speed he proceeded to sell his properties: the bathing-establishment, a town house, a country estate, goats, mule-teams, and the attendant slaves: a considerable proportion of his wealth. All the money thus realized passed into the control of Aktê and the two scheming cousins.

The family waited for Euktêmon to die before all should be dissipated.

XI

But Euktêmon did not die. He passed his ninetieth year, while Atkê grew fatter and lazier and the two boys reached their 'teens. His former legal wife, mother of his five children, was now in the seventies. His three sons were dead, and also one of his sons-in-law. His daughters were both well over fifty. His grandson was a man of thirty-eight. It was possible, they felt, that Euktêmon would survive them all. He seemed to be immortal.

Yet he was weakening. The cousins looked on avidly as he finally took to his bed; they conspired more busily than ever to get control of all the property by pressing the claims of Aktê's sons. The plain fact was that on Euktêmon's death the law would inexorably rule the boys out of the inheritance as bastards, in spite of all Euktêmon's wishes and his legal machinations. There was not much time left. What could they do?

First they tried pretending that the boys had been adopted by Euktêmon's second and third sons before their death, and that they, the cousins, had been appointed their guardians. They demanded an allowance for the maintenance of the boys. They went so far as to appear in court and depose to this under oath, and they might have obtained a court order, but the family got wind of it in time and the decision went against them.

Secondly, Androcles began scheming to marry the younger

daughter of Euktêmon, widow of Chæreas. Now Chæreas was the man with whom the dead General Philoktêmon had deposited his last will and testament adopting the grandson Chærestratus as his son and heir. Androcles claimed the widow's hand on the ground that he was her nearest marriageable kinsman and so had the right in law to marry her. The marriage hung fire—but the result of the courtship was that General Philoktêmon's will and act of adoption disappeared and was never seen again. Androcles later declared with all assurance in court that it had never existed at all.

Thirdly, they began a fresh attempt to legitimize the bastards. What if, now that so much time had passed, they claimed that these boys were not Aktê's at all, but the sons of some other woman, a pure-bred Athenian of good family, whom the old man had secretly married? The eldest boy was now over twenty; could they not manage, by bribery of registrars and witnesses, to concoct a plausible story?

Whom should they allege to have been the mother? Euktêmon for a time had been betrothed to the sister of Democrates, but she was still alive, a respectable married woman, so she would not do. Had there not once been talk of some girl who had been left in Euktêmon's wardship by an old comrade-in-arms killed in Sicily? Kallippê was her name. If they said he had married Kallippê at the time when he finally went to live with Aktê, who would remember? Aktê was quite willing to swear to anything, if it brought her and her boys a monetary advantage—even that she was not their mother!

In the midst of all this scheming, Euktêmon died at last, aged ninety-six.

XII

His death was sudden. The schemers were taken unawares, though he had been bedridden for some time. The first thing was to prevent the news from reaching the family before they had completed their arrangements.

They locked the doors of the inn. None of the servants was allowed outside. Under the supervision of Aktê and the cousins and the boys, slaves carried the cash and the goods from the inn through an inner passage into the house next door, while Euktêmon's shrunken body lay unwashed and unpurified on the death-bed.

The news of Euktêmon's death, however, leaked out somehow. At once his wife and his daughters, his surviving son-in-law Phanostratus, and his grandson Chærestratus, hurried down to the Potters' Quarter and banged on the doors of the inn. The doors were bolted. Aktê and her minions threatened them from inside, saying that they had no right to perform the dead man's funeral rites, as he had repudiated them. All day long the family tried in vain to get in. It was sunset before the doors were at last reluctantly unbarred.

What a clamour arose as the women rushed to the bed and found the old man's corpse, two days dead as the servants informed them! The women, as was right and proper, set to work to lay him out. The men called their friends and the neighbours to witness the disgraceful state of the house, stripped of every stick of furniture, not a drachma to be found anywhere. They began questioning the slaves, and were told that all had been carried next door.

The men of the family then demanded the right of entry and search, but this was refused. The schemers would not even allow them to examine the slaves who had removed the goods. Baffled, they withdrew. The old man had at last departed, and the long-delayed battle for what remained of his property was about to be joined.

XIII

All Athens was agog when the matter of Euktêmon's heirs came before the jury-court. The claimants were on the one hand Chærestratus, grandson of the dead nonagenarian, a man of forty and a distinguished citizen who, like his real father and his grandfather, had performed many public duties. He alleged that he had been created the adopted son and heir of his uncle Philoktêmon, the old man's son and heir, killed on a military campaign long before. Through this act of adoption, he became, so he claimed, his grandfather's only legitimate heir. Opposed to him, on the other hand, were two young men in the twenties, of whom no one really knew anything for certain. An extraordinary situation had arisen in which not only their father but also their mother was now in dispute, and their chief supporters were the two cousins who belonged to the other side, the family of Euktêmon.

Who were the boys? Were they really Euktêmon's sons by the ex-slave and prostitute Aktê? Was it possible that Euktê-mon could have begotten them at the age of seventy-six and seventy-eight respectively? Well, he had lived to be ninety-six, so perhaps he had been different from other men.

Or were they the sons of one of Aktê's clients, or her lover the freedman Dion? The family said so, of course, but that was natural. Aktê had denied this for many years now—but she would say anything that suited her purpose.

And now there was this story that Euktêmon had married his ward, a woman called Kallippê, when he went to live with Aktê. Nobody had ever seen this girl, who, if she had been handed over to Euktêmon as a baby when her father was killed on the Sicilian campaign fifty-two years ago, must have been over thirty when he was supposed to have married her. No Athenian woman could have been a spinster for so long. If her guardian had not found her a husband, the Chief Magistrate would have stepped in and done so for him. Thirty years his ward, and no one remembered her! What sort of a tale was this? Everybody knew the old man's real wife, his sons, his daughters, their husbands, the grandsons and granddaughters. Nobody seemed to have heard of Kallippê until it became necessary to legitimize the present claimants by giving them a mother who was a freewoman, not an ex-slave.

Nevertheless, the cousins persisted in this story, and swore to it before a magistrate.

Chærestratus, on behalf of the family, brought a charge against them of perjury. The family went to Isæus, the expert in testamentary law, for the preparation of their case, which came before a large jury-court sitting under the presidency of the Chief Magistrate of Athens.

XIV

Isæus did not allow the two male representatives of the family, Chærestratus and his real father Phanostratus, to say more than a few preliminary words. It would not do for them

5*

to recount the sordid story of their ancestor's folly. Instead, he arranged that an elderly friend should speak for them. The court was tense as he began:

"I believe, members of the jury, that the majority of you know already of my close friendship with Phanostratus and Chærestratus, who are here as prosecutors. If there are any who do not, I will give you incontrovertible proof.

"When Phanostratus sailed on the Sicilian expedition as admiral, I knew already, as it was not my first campaign, all the dangers that lay ahead; yet at their desire I sailed with them, and suffered with them, and we were all taken prisoners by the enemy.

"In the face of dangers foreseen, therefore, I stood firm because of my friendship towards these men and my belief in their friendship for me. It would be strange if on the present occasion I did not ally myself with them by trying to tell you the facts from which you will be able to derive a true verdict and justice may be done.

"I therefore urge you to look indulgently on my intervention and listen with goodwill. The issue is no trivial matter for them: it concerns affairs of vital importance."

The speaker proceeded to tell the story of Euktêmon's life, happy enough until in old age he conceived his infatuation for a low woman. Skilfully he outlined the deterioration in Euktêmon's relations with his eldest son; his desertion; the birth of the two young claimants, whom he declared to be undoubtedly Dion's; the intrigues of the two scheming cousins; and finally the scene after Euktêmon's death, when the old man lay unburied while the slaves removed goods and money next door.

Thus, he showed, Euktêmon's considerable fortune had been pillaged and dissipated.

It was a convincing story of folly and villainy, as prepared by the brilliant lawyer and delivered by the venerable family friend. The jury of five-hundred-odd listened with delight to the unfolding of the scandalous history: it was an entertainment of the kind they loved best. Inexorably the points were hammered in: the mother a prostitute; her lover a freedman, who had admitted that the boys were his; the old man past the age

when children are begotten, priding himself on his prowess. For Euktêmon undoubtedly had believed that the elder of the two boys, the young men in court, was his son: no Athenian with descendants of his own blood would choose to allow his tomb to be tended by a stranger. His ghost in the Halls of the Dead would suffer unbearable humiliation if such a sacrilege were permitted.

The speaker turned his full invective on Aktê:

"This woman, who undermined Euktêmon's sanity and gained control of much of his wealth, now has the insolence—relying on her two allies—to treat with contempt not only Euktêmon's family but the whole Athenian State. . . .

"Self-acknowledged as a slave, she has led a life of continuous depravity, such that the law debars her from entry into any sacred place. Yet her lawless outlook has emboldened her to take part in the festival of the Goddesses of the Underworld (Demeter and Persephone), to walk in the holy procession and enter the temple and behold the mysteries from which she was debarred.

"*Who are the claimants?* If they are the legitimate sons of Euktêmon, as has been sworn on oath, let them prove it, as any one of you would do! Granting that Euktêmon was their father, for the sake of argument: who was their mother? If it was not Aktê, as they now allege, who was it? They give a name—but that is not enough. Let them produce Kallippê's relatives, the witnesses to her marriage with Euktêmon; let them produce her neighbours and her clansmen, any person who has ever heard or known of any public expense incurred by Euktêmon on her behalf! Do her alleged sons visit her tomb to pour libations and carry out the appropriate rites? If so, where is she buried? Is there anyone, citizen or any of Euktêmon's slaves, who has seen them going there? Facts like these, added together, not abuse and invective, give proof.

"Call upon them to produce evidence in support of this one point to which they have sworn on oath! The result will then be a verdict in accordance with religion and the law, so that justice will be done to the family of Euktêmon!"

XV

Nevertheless, Chærestratus and the family lost the case.

There was one fatal weakness which even Isæus could not entirely conceal. The last will and testament of Philoktêmon, in which he adopted his nephew Chærestratus as his son and heir, was missing. It had never been seen since the day it was deposited with the uncle Chæreas, and now Chæreas was dead, while his widow was, or had been, wooed by the scheming cousin Androcles. On this document depended Chærestratus's claim to inherit the property of his grandfather through the adoptive father, the dead General Philoktêmon, not through his mother and his real father Phanostratus. By an oversight, Chærestratus had neglected, when his adoptive father was killed in battle, to ask that the will should be produced and his claim registered.

So the cousins and Aktê triumphed, and the two young men of dubious origin took their place as heirs of Euktêmon and claimed their full share, as the old man had so ardently desired. And whether they were his real sons or not, his ghost chuckled in the Halls of the Dead at the success of his plans and the discomfiture of the family.

TWELVE PEAKS TO THE SKY

F. E. SMITH

Illustrations by Calvin Grey

This is a tale of mystery and imagination set on a mountain peak four thousand feet above Cape Town. It is a scene sometimes glorious, sometimes terrible, as Nature chooses; and as the author describes the lovely, lonely background of the mountain forest-ranger's life, we begin to understand how swiftly beauty may change to ugliness in storm and fire, and terror take possession of the mind. There is one word in this tale which the reader may not know—Protea. The protea, the author tells us, is "a large, wild flower indigenous to South Africa, and it appears on most mountain-sides and in the veldt in the spring and summer. The Afrikaans name for it is Suikerbosse, which means sugar-bush, so called because of the sweet juices that exude from its stamens, which the birds love to eat. It has become the national emblem of South Africa, in much the same way as the thistle to the Scots and the shamrock to the Irish." Mr. F. E. Smith is a Yorkshireman. He has travelled in India, Ceylon, South-East Asia and central and northern Africa, and is now settled down for a second stay in South Africa.

IT is a strange thing to dwell on top of the world, and I do not think it is good to live there as long as we did. Of course, it is often beautiful, especially in the early mornings, and there is something oddly moving in being able to stand and look down four thousand feet on to a drowsing city, and see it being gently washed in the iridescent light of a new day. We had many beautiful moments, but also there were ones when the great south-easter blew, and the rolling banks of grey cloud swept over us, when we lived in a cold, nebulous world of swirling mist, and when one could see, as if on a screen, many strange sights and hear many unwelcome sounds. Like the time . . . but I must tell you more yet before I explain why we left our mountain and returned back to where men live on each other's doorsteps and where one is never really alone.

I was given the post of forest ranger and reservoir caretaker two years after my marriage, and one year after our son, Ronald, was born. At the time I was jubilant. The pay was good, the work pleasant and easy, and the life of solitude appealed to me, then. Mary was content enough, and we both thought the clean mountain air would give the child an excellent start in life.

We took over our new home when the daisies were white on the slopes of Signal Hill; in the season when the south-easters roar and bellow at the great bulk of the mountain behind. However, we were lucky that summer; the winds never blew for more than four days at a time, and our first year passed peacefully enough.

I think the view from the house gave us both our greatest pleasure. It had been built on the False Bay side of the mountain, which meant that from our windows we could see, far across the Cape Flats, the vast sweep of the bay, its deep blue waters skirted by the golden bracelet of sand. To the right, the mighty backbone of the peninsula lay, its twelve peaks reaching out towards Cape Point, where two oceans meet. High though these peaks were, we were above them, and so could look down on their every mood. In the early mornings, clouds would cover their valleys and summits, following their every contour in the way of a woman's clinging dress. Then, slowly, as the sun rose, the unveiling would commence. First one flimsy piece of ninon would float wistfully away, then another; until at last the naked peaks, in all their splendour, would rise impassionately to the sky; while on their lower slopes, the pine-woods lay like discarded green velvet. The sea, washing their feet, would be green and blue marble from that height, and its milky fringes, surging rhythmically to and fro, would make one believe he saw the very pulse-beat of the ocean.

So those twelve great peaks stood, their feet in the sea, their summits against the sun and sky, and we could never tire of their beauty.

The north view from the mountain was very different. From here, less than an hour's walk across the boulder-strewn plateau one could look down on the city and its harbours, where great ships called; and it was here that sometimes one felt a strange loneliness—particularly in the evenings when the horizon was saffron and gold, and the first few lights below were struggling bravely with the darkness that was slowly welling upwards. . . .

Yet our first two years were pleasant enough, and if, despite our unspoken decision to avoid the places of sadness, we found ourselves being attacked more and more by the strange melancholia, yet its gradual overpowering of our senses was slow enough to be imperceptible.

Of course, I realize now that our spontaneous, almost eager, acceptance of Michael was due to our instinctive fear of the loneliness that was growing on us both. When the sun shone— and it shone often—the days were beautiful, and we would not have changed our home for that of any man's. But on the nights when the mist was upon us, when the wind was coming in great sobs from the vast, empty spaces around, it was then we were lonely and, sometimes, a little afraid. . . .

It was on such a night that Michael came. The winter, our third, had been a hard one, with unusually heavy rainfall, and the clouds that people below call the Tablecloth had been over us for weeks at a time, enveloping us in a desolate world of clinging mist and drizzling rain.

His way of coming was startling and unexpected. Mary and I were sitting in the lounge after supper in front of a huge fire, for outside the mist was clinging and probing, and we were cold. The wind had dropped, which was a relief, for it is strange to have wind and fog together, and all was very still. I thought I heard Ronald cry, and, leaving Mary in the room, I went into his nursery. He was comfortable enough, and I was tucking his

blankets in when I heard a whispered call from Mary. I ran
back to the lounge to see her standing near the outside door,
with her head bent, listening.

My first thought was that there was an animal outside, so
drawn out and plaintive was the cry. As we stood in the porch,
the moan was repeated, followed by a scratching on the wood.
This sound broke the spell, and with a fast-beating heart, I
jerked open the door.

For a moment I could see nothing, for it was intensely dark.
I opened the door wider, until the light from inside shone down
the steps on the pile of sacking lying on them. As the two of us
stared down at it, the heap stirred, and a pair of white eyeballs
rolled upwards.

"Food, baas. Food, asseblief."

So Michael Xaxaba came to us. We had never had a servant
before, because Mary had argued that housework kept her busy,
and that, as natives are intensely human, one kept in such solitude might become dangerous. As this had been my thought,
too, I had not attempted to persuade her otherwise, but Michael
was different, as I found out after hearing his story. There
would be no danger from Michael, he would be only too grateful for his food and shelter.

For the poor wretch had a strange story to tell, after he had
eaten and been given a few of my old clothes, and after his eyes
had stopped roaming fearfully about the rooms as if he were in
constant terror for his life. He spoke little English, but had a
fair smattering of Afrikaans, and it was in this language that we
spoke.

He had, it seemed, come from Bechuanaland, the protec-
torate on the borders of the Transvaal, from a race known as
the Susuta, and from his childhood had known nothing but the
simple practices of his people. So it had been until he was
twenty-two, until the day he had seen T'lusa, whose tribe had
their kraals in the valley next to his own. T'lusa was a maiden,
she had not yet been into the desert with the old women of her
tribe, and had two years to wait, but N'nombi, as Michael was
called by his people, found her beautiful, and she loved him.
Despite the terrible risks, for tribal law is harsh and inexorable
over such transgressions, they contrived to meet, and each time

found it harder to part. And so it was that N'nombi, whose blood was hot for this maiden, declared he would risk all for her, and begged her to run away with him from their people. At first, the very thought terrified her, and she pleaded with him not to dream of such an idea; but, as his strong, young arms held her tightly, a madness entered her blood, and she agreed.

They took to the hills, and, despite the risks from animals, travelled as much as possible by night. They both knew the dangers well, but they knew also that animals kill swiftly and mercifully, and they were not afraid of death, only the manner of it. . . .

It was on one of these black nights that the terror started for N'nombi. He had gone to sleep by the side of T'lusa, and was lying peacefully enough when suddenly he felt a sense of evil creep over him, and a shock of alarm passed through his body. Opening his eyes he gave a great start, then tried to reach the assegai by his side, but to his horror, as if in a nightmare, his limbs would not move, and he could only lie in mortal dread and stare at the painted hideous figure standing over him. His brain seemed to shrink and burn in his skull as the witch-doctor spoke.

"N'nombi, oh, cursed one, heed what I say and heed well. You and that woman beside you have broken the sacred law laid down by the great Moseth, and it has been given to me to deal out your punishment. I could take you both back to our people, where T'lusa would die the death of an immoral woman, over the ant hill, while you, N'nombi . . . you know your fate well. But this thing I shall not do. You shall both die, have no doubt about that, but you shall suffer the pain of a thousand deaths in your mind before you die. To T'lusa I shall be merciful. But you, N'nombi, you shall die when the four elements unite against you; when you are surrounded by earth and water and air and fire, then you shall die. Remember, N'nombi, remember." The hollow voice echoed away, an arm pointed menacingly at the prostrate man, the glaring eyes stared hatefully down, and then the figure seemed to fade into the darkness, and N'nombi could hear nothing more save the rustle of the veldt grass and the distant cry of a wounded animal.

For minutes he lay there, trying to believe it had been a dream, and yet knowing well that his simple, native mind would regard one so portentous with almost as much fear as an actual visitation. N'nombi had heard his death sentence, and it was with heavy heart that, the next day, he continued the journey with his wife. Their progress was slow and difficult now, for T'lusa was heavy with child, but at last they reached a kraal where they were given food, and it was here that T'lusa gave birth to a son. But she died that same night and the child followed her to the grave two days later.

N'nombi's sufferings were now intense. Believing that the deaths were due to the curse of the "Iqira", he fled from the country into the Transvaal, the fear following him like some dreadful shadow. Simple credence made him make for the cities; probably he felt that if he could reach one and live with the white men, the curse would lose its potency. Equally, he wanted to live as far away from his tribe as possible, and so, after crossing the Great Karoo on foot—hundreds of miles of torrid semi-desert—and struggling over the mountain barrier, he had, at last, reached Cape Town. Here, without a permit to leave his reservation, he could find no employment; indeed, he had to keep out of the hands of the police, and so took to the mountain, living in caves and foraging for food. After weeks of semi-starvation, he learned from another nomad about the white man who lived alone on the mountain, and, thinking, no doubt, that employment here would be both a sanctuary from the police and the greater terror from the past, he struggled to the top and found our house.

I told Mary the story, and she said we had to keep him. I was glad, because of all terrified men I know of none more deserving of sympathy than those outcast natives with the witch-doctor's curse upon them. Their terror is with them always, because it comes from their own minds; they are waiting, always waiting for the inevitable, and so there is always a cloud across the sun for them. Perhaps, if I had known what I know now, I would have striven to give Michael more than pity, for I was soon to learn how much more than that he needed. . . .

Once his strength returned, he proved very useful. Every seven days I had to make a trip down to the pumping-station, where reports had to be made, and a list of provisions given in for the next week. Then, with a couple of natives as carriers, the current week's supplies were manhandled to the top, the round trip taking the best part of a day. I had never liked leaving Mary alone, but now, with Michael about the house, I felt a great deal happier. I knew I could trust the boy, for his gratitude was overwhelming; and Mary felt quite safe with him.

Yet the boy was still afraid. I remember coming across him one evening, sitting on a boulder near the mountain's edge and staring out over Table Bay and the sand flats to where the peninsular swept in an arc to the mainland, to where the great massifs of the Drakensbergs were blue against the evening sky. I was wearing sandals, and so my approach must have been silent, because I was within a few yards of him before he sensed he was not alone. He did not turn round, as a white man would have done, but sat motionless, and only by the stiffening of his back could I tell he had heard anything. From where I was standing I could see one side of his face; it was a ghastly slate-grey, and his eyes were protruding as if the sudden terror was twisting a cord round his throat. "Michael, what is the matter?" I called. "Michael." Only then did he move to look at me, and the look in his eyes was something I shall never forget. Try as I did, I could not induce him to speak of what had terrified him.

So the fourth winter passed and the proteas could be seen on the mountain-side again. And with the spring came the first south-easter, bringing with it the Tablecloth that to those below shows as an endless cascade of cloud falling over the mountain. It rolls over in a great majestic wave that seems about to flood the city below, but, as it sinks and meets the warmer air, the mist condenses and mysteriously vanishes, leaving those in the sun-drenched city a clear view of the strange spectacle.

But to us it meant an unnatural mixture of buffeting wind and dense, dripping fog. As walking in the mist was too dangerous, with a wind of gale velocity, we could do nothing in such weather but stay indoors in front of the fire, trying vainly to keep the dampness from our bones. Michael was always afraid of mist and rain; through the winter this had been noticeable, and it had been our practice to let him stay in the lounge on such evenings and to use an indoor bedroom instead of his servant's quarters.

On one particular evening he seemed unusually afraid; indeed, his fear was something we could both feel—it blew in tiny draughts down one's back, and whispered of unspeakable things, while outside the wind whined and snarled and then leapt at the walls so that they trembled and shuddered at the impact. And that fear—it was like an evil smell in the room. It was impossible to read. I sat and watched him as he squatted in the corner, his arms crossed and hands gripped under his armpits, his body rocking gently, and occasionally a faint whimper breaking from his lips.

"What is it, Michael? Why are you so afraid to-night?" Mary spoke, the strain becoming too much for her.

The poor wretch's lips trembled as he tried to speak, his faltering glance wavering from her to me.

"The baas knows," he moaned. "It is the wind . . . the rain. Oh, baas, baas." His head dropped into his hands as he rocked in misery. I do not think I have ever seen a man so afraid. Giving him a stiff brandy, I tried to drive the terror from him, and was talking patiently to him when the telephone rang.

"Hello. Yes, headquarters, I can hear you. Can I what? I can't see two yards up here. Rosebank side, you say? I'll be over right away. Yes, yes, I'll do that."

There was a fire above Rosebank, a big one, and they wanted to know what I was doing about it. I had to let them know if there was any chance of it crossing the fire belt into the Devil's Peak plantation, and also my estimate of the number of men required to hold it in check. I called Michael, and was so occupied that I did not notice the look on his face when I mentioned fire. Mary told me about it afterwards. . . .

It was a fire. The intense heat had burned a hole in the mist, and through it we could see the whole eastern perimeter of the blaze. The western boundary was hidden behind a ridge on the plateau, but this was the one I had to see, for the plantation lay in that direction, and the same wind that was holding the fire in check to the east would be urging it on at fearful speed towards the last fire belt. And if that were crossed, the whole plantation would go. As we clung to a stunted tree, in a wind that seemed determined to throw us back the way we had come, we saw the flames advancing upwards in bright spurts towards the remaining trees and bushes on the timber-line, seven hundred feet below. They reached a clump of pines, over to our right, the wind dropped for a moment, and we heard the dull explosions as the trees, their oily wood hissing from the pressure of released gases, burst like great, kerosene-drenched torches.

I waited no longer. Shouting at Michael to move over a little to the right, and to check carefully that the fire was making no progress against the wind, I struggled up the ridge, clinging to the rocks as the wind tore at me. Reaching the top, I saw with surprise that the flames had not yet encountered the fire belt; instead, the whole flank was burning red, a sure sign the advance had been held in check for some time. Fires do strange things on mountain-sides; there was probably a rock face somewhere causing a back draught, but a sudden shift in wind direction could set the blaze moving again. I started back to Michael.

A warm rain was now falling, the rising heat causing condensation of the cloud immediately above the fire, and stinging drops, lashed into my face by the wind, almost blinded me as I fought my way back down the ridge. At first, I could not find Michael, although I reached, and clung to, a rock not twenty yards from the tree where I had left him; but then, remembering my last instructions, I looked over to the right, and finally saw him, silhouetted against the red sky. I waved, but as he did not seem to observe me, I went forward again, clawing my way from rock to rock. Pausing for breath, I looked once more. He seemed dangerously near the edge, and appeared to be crouching with his back to the fire. There was something peculiar about his posture, and I shaded my eyes against the glare to take a better look. I stared for a moment in unbelief, while a shock of fear sent the skin tight across my temples.

For there was a dark something in front of Michael, something like a gorilla, short, squat, horrible, something that moved as he moved, and was slowly driving him backwards, backwards . . . towards the edge and the fire. I ran, staggering from boulder to boulder, while the ghastly tableau swayed redly before me. Then, catching my foot in a bush, I fell, winding myself badly, but I was near enough to shoot, at something that now looked like a great bloated snake as it swayed in front of the helpless boy.

There was little time left. He was on the edge and the flames were below. Steadying my revolver on a rock, I fired three times. I could hardly have missed, for the range was not more than twelve yards, and I can use a revolver, but it had no effect on this thing. Again I fired, and again, and still it moved on the tormented boy, whose agonized face, shiny with perspiration, appealed to me. Firing my last shot, I ran desperately towards the vile thing, and at that moment the wind, which had been quieter during this time, suddenly came in a great gust that struck me on the chest and hurled me over. My head struck a stone, and for a few moments I lay half-stunned. Then, hearing a shrill scream above the wind, I rolled over to see Michael swaying on the brink of the cliff, with his arms held stiffly out to the thing in front. For a moment he poised there, the wind at his back holding him upright against the sky, while the pencil lines of rain, like a vast curtain in the background, swung inwards towards him, and the mist above glowed evilly from the fire. Then, as if at a given signal, the rain-curtain fell away as the wind suddenly dropped, the awful thing seemed to spring forward, and, with a final and terrible shriek, the boy toppled over and down the precipice. I must have lost consciousness then, because, as the shapeless creature of the cliff edge hesitated and then turned in my direction, the mist seemed to suddenly close in on me, and all went dark.

I do not remember finding my way back to the house.

By the afternoon of the next day the fire had burned itself out. I waited until the following morning, for the ashes to cool, before setting out to look for Michael's body. Thinking I would be able to find it more quickly by discovering a few landmarks, I walked along the mountain's edge to where Michael had fallen, two nights before. The cloud had lifted now, and the sun was shining, yet as I passed by the stunted tree, I imagined I saw ahead the same nightmare creature, staring down to where the boy had died. I stood still, my heart hammering in my throat, and cursed the fear that was turning my knees to

jelly. Driving myself forward, I felt cowardly relief welling inside me as the squat shape turned out to be a boulder, standing a few feet from the edge. I drew nearer, feeling sure that it was about here that Michael had gone over, and then the skin across my shoulders went tight and stiff. I know my face went very pale, and I wasted no time in leaving that accursed place.

For there were four newly-made scars on that rock, and I knew they had been made by bullets. I had not missed the thing, after all. But, after my search for Michael's body, which I never found, I went back and told Mary we would be leaving shortly. She asked no questions, and I gave no reasons.

So now we live in a smaller house, at the foot of the mountain; and now, when the south-easter is blowing, we can look up and see the great mist cascading down and falling into strange oblivion below. We can also raise our heads and see the blue sky above, and feel the sun on our backs. And, although it is a small house, and people are for ever on our doorstep, it is comforting sometimes; especially on the night when the wind is howling taunts from the swaying trees, and the rain is murmuring of strange, forbidden things. For when one has seen the elements brought together, and a curse come true, it is better not to be alone.

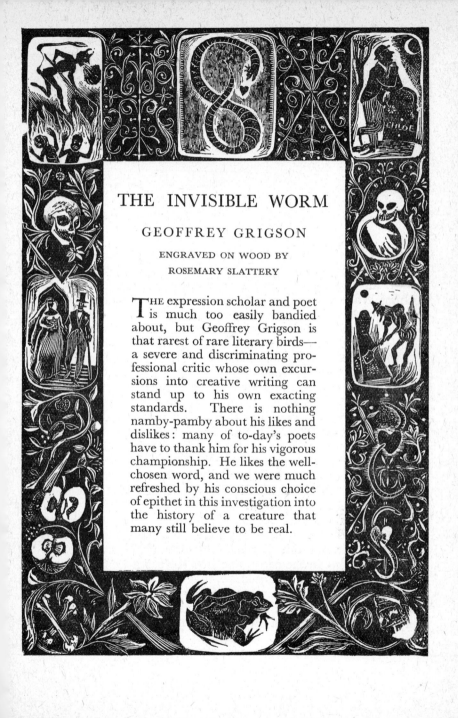

THE INVISIBLE WORM

GEOFFREY GRIGSON

ENGRAVED ON WOOD BY
ROSEMARY SLATTERY

THE expression scholar and poet is much too easily bandied about, but Geoffrey Grigson is that rarest of rare literary birds— a severe and discriminating professional critic whose own excursions into creative writing can stand up to his own exacting standards. There is nothing namby-pamby about his likes and dislikes: many of to-day's poets have to thank him for his vigorous championship. He likes the well-chosen word, and we were much refreshed by his conscious choice of epithet in this investigation into the history of a creature that many still believe to be real.

Do you believe that when you die you will become meat for worms? Not long ago I went into the abbey church at Tewkesbury and saw there the stone cadaver of Abbot Wakeman which is crawling with worms. He had no doubt of becoming worms' meat, so with stone worms and toads he ordered this reclining figure of himself while he was still alive. Go to Tewkesbury, I told a friend of mine, who is an obstinate champion of the fallacies of common belief, if you want to see what grave-worms are like. "I don't want to see them," she replied. So I added that she need not worry, because grave-worms do not exist. "Nonsense." "Well," I went on soothingly, "they don't exist, and you really needn't bother about Golders Green and clean ashes." "Of course they exist."

She gave way to argument, not believing in them quite so firmly as Abbot Wakeman in early Tudor days; yet I have found that Grave-wormers, even now, are more common than Flat-landers, and it set me digging for the Invisible Worm, or at least the truth about him.

The wormiest of soils, I soon found, are the fourteenth, the fifteenth, and the sixteenth centuries. You could not think then of death without thinking of the worm. Natural enough. Worms wriggle in the earth, and into the earth we go. People did not observe, and no one knew, that earthworms like nothing to eat but earth. And what did Job pronounce in the Old Testament? "If I wait, the grave is mine house: I have made my bed in the darkness. I have said to corruption, Thou art

my father: to the worm, Thou art my mother, and my sister."
So the grave-worm was just a fact, like the rising or the setting
of the sun. It did not matter *that no one had seen a grave-worm.*

Luckily, though, we are not always thinking about death.
In the Middle Ages, in the thirteenth century, there was a time
when people thought a great deal more about life. You have
only to go into Southwell Minster, in the Midlands, and into
the chapter-house. All around you are the most delightful, and
life-full, carvings of fresh buttercups and hawthorn, symbols of
spring and not of winter. Life predominates, and the world
feels young. Then, in Northern Europe, there comes a change,
as the Middle Ages wear out. Paintings and windows go up in
churches to warn you of the rewards of wickedness. The blessed
go upward into light, the wicked fall into scarlet flames, and
devils with pronged forks hasten their upside-down descent. In
the last of the thirteen-hundreds, a monk, John Bromyard, who
was Chancellor of the University at Cambridge, preached a
celebrated sermon on the rewards after death of good and evil.
All the sins of the evil-lovers of this agreeable world are cata-
logued. The end of everything comes; and "instead of a great
retinue and throng of followers, their body shall have a throng
of worms and their soul a throng of demons."

The years pass. Men begin to delight rather too much in the
life and activities and lusts of the world, bold with all the fresh
courage of the Renaissance; but—they cannot forget the
pictures, the carvings, the sermons, the worms. So in Queen
Elizabeth's time every poet thinks about death and decay in the
midst of all his so brave delights. The fair body the poet or the
courtier enjoys, may to-morrow be blotched with the plague.
The fair shes are clothed in silk. To-morrow they may be
clothed in corruption. In all the energy and the courage, in
the conquest of new worlds, among the lyrics and the madrigals
and the high jinks, the worm rears his nasty head. There is
much of love with naked foot stalking in my chamber, but death
in the Queen's reign is always pushing a bald face through the
petals or through the flowered curtains of the four-poster. Even
the street women of London wore death's-head rings.

It was not, I think, that the brave Elizabethans were scared
so much of the devils as of the worm, which was the end of joy

and vanity. The link of vanity joins beauty and the worms.
There were no convenient rhymes for worm; but three words
jingled together excellently—lust, and dust (which follows the
worm), and *must*, that short word of ineluctable compulsion.
The poets made these words thin with use. They liked to mix
them with Helen of Troy, whose face launched the thousand
ships. Even Helen had to die:

> *Where is become that wight*
> *For whose sake Troyë town*
> *Withstood the Greeks till ten years' fight*
> *Had razed their walls adown?*

> *Did not the worms consume*
> *Her carrion to the dust?*
> *Did dreadful death forbear his fume*
> *For beauty, pride or lust?*

That was written when Thomas Nashe, one of whose poems
everybody knows, was a small boy. Nashe grows up, the plague
in the foetid streets of London full swift goes by, and he writes:

> *Brightness falls from the air,*
> *Queens have died young and fair,*
> *Dust hath closed Helen's eye,*
> *I am sick, I must die . . .*

And the worms are not missing. In 1594, in some of his wildest
prose, Nashe explained to pretty women exactly how they
would become meat for worms and toads: "Your mome-like
christall countenances shall be netted over, and (masker-like)
cawle-visarded with crawling, venomous worms. Your orient
teeth, toads shall steale into their heads for pearl; of the jelly of
your decayed eyes, shall they engender their young." And the
next minute Nashe writes with delightful loveliness of the meeting of girls and men. Without any trouble you could make a
vermicular anthology coming down to Shakespeare, and from
Shakespeare to Webster, the last inebriate of death in his terrible plays. In the ballad, the murdered Clerk Saunders tells

the maid Margaret that he slept among the hungry worms.
There are worms in hundreds of epitaphs in country churches.
I used to stare at such an epitaph in the church I went to as a
boy:

> O what a nest of worms,
> A lump of pallid earth,
> Is mud-walled man . . .

And that was the epitaph on a man who ventured his money in
the enterprises and wonders of the New World, who knew
Drake, and probably went to the New World himself in one of
the ships out of Plymouth.

Do you remember in Shakespeare the Hamlet worm—"my
Lady Worm"—who owns the skull the grave-digger throws up?
Or Mercutio turned into "worms' meat"? Or King Richard
talking of "graves, of worms, and epitaphs", making dust our
paper, and writing sorrow on the bosom of the earth? Or Rosa-
lind, the Duke's daughter, remarking, "Men have died from
time to time and worms have eaten them, but not for love"?
The situation is usually the same. The worms are in the mouth
of kings or queens, dukes or duchesses; or they are soon going
to be.

"Though we are eaten up of lice and worms," says Bosola in
Webster's *Duchess of Malfi*,

> And though continually we bear about us
> A rotten and dead body, we delight
> To hide it in rich tissue.

And when the Duchess asks who she is, Bosola replies savagely,
"Thou art a box of worm-seed, at best but a salvatory of green
mummy."

And yet the invisible worm, in whom even now so many of
us do not trouble to disbelieve, was nearing the end of his meat.
It would soon be possible to degrade him into a joke. If you
made a joke about the worm in Tudor times, it was a wry joke
or a defiant one. But after the Civil War things were changing.
The Royal Society was formed. Long-nosed scientists were

taking nothing on trust and were upsetting tall tales, and the worm could not escape any more than notions that elephants had no bones or that bears licked their shapeless cubs into the proper likeness of bears. In 1658 a sceptical doctor in Norwich, Sir Thomas Browne, began to look for grave-worms. He opened graves in Tombland in Norwich, and he could not find them. His idea—and everyone else's perhaps—was that grave-worms were common or garden earthworms. His conclusion was, "Few in churchyards above a foot deep, fewer or none in churches, though in fresh decayed bodies."

This is the point for rather more explanation of how the concept of grave-worms came about. It was not only that earthworms are universal or that if you leave a dead dog about, wormy maggots soon appear in it. What made the worm so easy to accept (without ever seeing one) was an old notion going back to Pliny, and from Pliny to Aristotle. This was the idea of "spontaneous generation". You, your dead flesh, bred the worms. That was the point. That was what Bosola meant when he called the Duchess "a box of worm-seed". And the worms would be in you and at you even if you were lapped in lead. This notion of spontaneous generation was universal. Samson's dead lion producing bees which yield honey (as you see it still on treacle tins) produced them spontaneously. There were maggots in cheese. They were spontaneously generated by the cheese. Grubby boys who did not wash had lice. The lice were generated from their sweat. Eels appeared in ponds from which there was no stream: they were generated spontaneously in the mud. Toads, so it was believed, were found inside rocks; and why not if spontaneous generation was a rule of life!

It was just after the Tudor and Jacobean triumph of the worm that spontaneous generation began to be tested and ridiculed. Did maggots just occur in a piece of meat with no outside help? For the first time in human history, in a new age of scepticism and inquiry, the answer was given by the simplest of all experiments. An Italian, Francisco Redi, in 1668, took two pieces of fresh meat. One was placed under a screen of wire gauze, the other was unscreened. In the second there were soon maggots, after the attention of bluebottles; in the first there was none. So the principle was announced that all living things come from the egg, that every living thing comes from a living thing of its own kind. By 1713 an English Fellow of the Royal Society could say in one of his books, "Spontaneous generation is a doctrine so generally exploded, that I shall not undertake the disproof of it"; which was vermicide to the worm.

We might go on keeping him sentimentally, traditionally, and conveniently alive, but it has been only the preservation of an old habit of mind.

LAST NIGHT I DIED

MORRIS COOPER

Wood engravings by John Buckland Wright

F OOLISH, *isn't it? I mean, filling out these forms and everything. After all, I know I'm dead. . . . Sorry, but it is rather difficult to break the habit of a lifetime. No, I'm not complaining, I'm just . . . what am I doing? Guess I'd better start on these forms.*

Name?

Lytton Bennett Reid.

Race?

White, Amer—— Oh, I am sorry. I erase.

Race?

Man.

Age?

Fifty-eight.

Cause?

The reason I'm here? Drowning, I imagine you would call it. Oh, you mean the cause of my drowning? Well . . . it's not too clear. . . . I'd like to think about it for a while, if I may.

Requests?

Requests? Do you mean, I can ask for something? May I see my wife? . . . Oh! . . . no, I'm not blaming you. After all, you're only doing your job, and rules are rules. But your question sounded so. . . . I see. I'm to stay here until I'm used to it. A cigarette? Thanks. I didn't think they'd have any in . . . here. You want me to go back to the cause? About anything that happened while I was—er—before I came here. I'm free to tell you about it. But I thought everything was recorded. My version? Sort of plead my own case. Well, I'm not certain talking will help . . . it's not necessary to talk? Just think . . . think about what happened . . . and why . . . and how. . . .

I stood at the foot of Market Street, looking at the big clock on the Ferry Building and thinking that it hadn't changed in twenty years. The hands were the same hands that had clicked off the hours each long day and each immeasurable night I had spent behind prison walls.

Now they were ticking off the first hours of my freedom. The gulls drifted lazily overhead, a silent grey against the bright sunlight. A few pigeons strutted pompously across the Embarcadero, impervious to the thunder of traffic that rolled past the docks. The busy toot of a chugging tugboat came from the waters that lay out of my sight.

San Francisco Bay had been smooth that lifetime ago when I had crossed on a ferry-boat, manacled to a husky deputy, convicted on the charge of second-degree murder—the murder of my wife.

This morning I had returned across the bridge that had been born while I was out of this life. I had seen the distant grandeur of the Golden Gate Bridge; looked down at man-made Treasure Island. Nothing had waited for me while I lay in prison . . . nothing . . . no one.

And now I was looking at the clock . . . wondering if any of its time belonged to me. Or was I already dead? Could a man live when his heart was dead?

The touch on my shoulder was light, but I straightened up and turned guiltily: the prison years lay over me like an invisible pall. Even before I saw his face, I knew it was Sutton Garney. There were a few more lines under his brown eyes and his lips looked thinner; but his hair was still bushy and black, save for the tint of grey at the temples—the same grey that at twenty-five had given him that distinguished look.

He held out a soft hand and I took it silently. We stood there, the two of us, and I knew the thoughts that were whirling through his mind. The same thoughts that filled mine; the same thoughts and the same dead hopes.

Sutton broke the silence. He nodded towards a sleek convertible. "I thought you might like to see—Grace." There was no warmth in his voice, and he turned on his heel without waiting for my reply.

The ride was long, and we were too busy with our memories to make conversation. Once, after we had left Daly City, I asked, "How did you know where to find me?"

"It wasn't difficult. You always liked to wander around the Ferry Building when . . . you had something on your mind."

That was where I had surrendered to a policeman a little over twenty years ago; dazed . . . befuddled . . . the D.A. had called me "a drunken, homicidal maniac".

The entrance to the cemetery was wide and flanked by ivy-softened columns. Sutton stopped in front of the administration building. "I'll wait for you here," he said. He pointed the directions without getting out of his car.

I stood on the sun-warmed grass, and wondered if any of the roots were deep enough to twine around her earth-rotted coffin. The headstone was small: I remembered she hadn't liked anything ostentatious.

GRACE REID

Born 1897.   *Died* 1929

The woman who had been my wife; the woman I had loved and killed. The woman who had been the wife of Sutton Garney before she was mine.

I was sorry I had forgotten to bring her some roses. I remembered the hat on my head and I took it off.

Is this . . . ? I mean, I'm ready to pay for my sins. Unless this is my payment: to eternally relive the moments of horror, the moments of sadness. Think about something else . . . about Grace? . . .

I met her when she was working as a waitress in a small restaurant near the Cliff House. She refused to accept a cent from Sutton Garney, even though the court had awarded her a generous alimony. Of course, I didn't know any of this at the beginning. She told me about it the evening I asked her to be my wife.

"I'm afraid," Grace finished. "I'm afraid of what he might do."

"That's silly," I laughed. "You're divorced, and Garney hasn't any more claim on you than the man in the moon."

We were quietly married a week later. The morning after our return from a short honeymoon, Sutton Garney knocked on the front door of the stucco bungalow I had bought.

It was the first time I'd ever seen him, though I recognized his face from the newspaper pictures.

"So you're the man who broke up my home." The words were soft, but they held the power that had made him a famous trial lawyer.

"That's not true," Grace protested. "I didn't even know——" But Sutton Garney was walking down the three front steps. I watched until he turned the corner.

I turned to Grace and laughed. "He's nuts."

Grace smiled, but there was a strange look of despair in her eyes. "He's a terrible man when he hates. And he hates you— and me."

I lost my job a month after our son was born. There was a mix-up in the office and a lot of half-veiled accusations, though nothing could actually be proven. But the bonding company cancelled my bond, and I found that there wasn't a firm in town that wanted an accountant that . . . well, of course, no one actually believed . . . but I had no job and no prospects of finding one.

I started to take more than an occasional drink. Whisky had the faculty of letting me forget, for the moment, all the troubles that had plagued me. But it also brought my temper to the fore, though I could seldom remember all that happened—and then only vaguely.

Then one day Sutton Garney looked me up, and though I hated his guts, I couldn't refuse his offer.

Garney had some estate work in addition to his criminal practice, and he managed to find enough to keep me fairly busy. But I kept on drinking and hating myself, and feeling lost.

I remember that evening Grace talked to me about Garney. "I heard you've been seeing . . . him." She made me feel foul and unclean.

"He's evil!" Grace cried. The look on her face made my stomach knot, and I put my arms around her.

"Please, Grace—if it worries you that much, I won't see him any more." Me and my promises. If I didn't see Garney I wouldn't work. And if I didn't work . . .

I met Grace the next day as I was coming out of the building that houses Garney's suite of offices. Her eyes were blazing, and there were red spots on her cheeks, as though I had slapped them.

"You promised," she accused. "You promised."

"Grace!" I called after her as she turned and walked away from me. "Let me explain." But she kept on walking, and a few passers-by stopped and stared at me curiously. One of them snickered.

The hell with it, I thought. And I bought myself a bottle freshly scraped off the bottom of a boat. It was late when I came home. My eyes were bleary, but I had a bunch of roses under my arm. The door to our bedroom was locked, and Grace refused to answer my repeated knocks.

I threw the roses on the living-room floor. Then I finished what was left of a second bottle and passed out.

It was still dark outside when the throbbing pain in my head woke me. The lights in the bedroom were on and my son was crying. I lay on the carpeted floor, my outflung right hand across Grace's throat. Her eyes bulged, and there was a bluish tint on her lips.

A single red rose lay on her bosom.

How long I stayed in that room I'll never know. But when I left, I had my son in my arms. The crushed rose I had taken from Grace's bosom lay in my pocket.

I left my son with Sutton Garney. "We both loved Grace," I

said. "No matter what you think of me, he's still her son. I haven't anyone else to leave him with."

"And you?"

"I don't know. I don't know."

For a long time I stood on the edge of a pier, watching the darkened waters of the bay swirl and beckon to me. Then I took the crushed rose from my pocket and tossed it into the bay.

I surrendered to the first policeman I saw.

Why can't I see Grace? Why can't I talk to her and tell her how much I love her? What was the point in my dying if I have to go on living?

Sutton Garney acted as my counsel and made a deal with the district attorney's office. I pleaded guilty to a charge of second-degree murder and threw myself on the mercy of the court. I saw Sutton once after I was sentenced.

"My son," I asked him, "how is he?"

"You"—Sutton spoke carefully, and each word was a blow on my heart—"have no son."

I stared at him with incredulous eyes, and waited for an explanation.

"He's being well taken care of," Sutton told me. "But you're not to know where he is—or how he is. That"—his voice dropped and I had to strain to catch the words—"is your punishment. As far as you are concerned, when you killed Grace, you . . . murdered your son."

I lost my wife and I lost my son. Now . . . must I keep losing them through all eternity? Must I serve my sentence until Judgment Day . . . as I served the twenty years in prison . . . never once seeing anyone from my past . . . never hearing . . . living alone with the memory of the wife I had murdered . . . the son I had never known . . . dying each day . . . seeing again in my sleep those bluish lips . . . the red rose on her bosom . . . ?

Before we left the cemetery, I gave some money to a grave-digger, and asked him to bring some roses for Grace's grave when he came to work the next day.

He folded the note carefully, tucked it into a pocket of his earth-coloured dungarees, then ran a sweaty forearm across his chin. "How many?" he asked.

"Just one. One red rose."

I could feel his eyes follow me as I slid into the seat of the convertible. Sutton turned the car around; I watched him manipulate the wheel gear-lever with a half-interested curiosity. It was something that had not belonged to my world twenty years ago; most of to-day's commonplaces were to me part of an alien civilization.

Sutton asked the question that I had not dared let pass my lips. "Aren't you interested in . . . him?"

I stared ahead at the winding highway; the white marker in the centre was like a coiling serpent, twisting . . . ready to leap at my throat if I once relaxed.

"I didn't know if you would——" I left the sentence unfinished.

"I adopted him." Sutton's voice had the same interest that he would have given to the purchase of a pound of fish. "I gave him my name and my home. In a few more years, when he finishes law school, he'll become my partner. He's the principal beneficiary in my will."

A pound of fish, a head of cabbage, a loaf of bread. This was my son he was talking about . . . but I had no son.

"Thanks," I said. It wasn't the right word, but I felt I had to say something to keep from choking.

"There is no need for thanks." Sutton's hands on the wheel were quiet, relaxed. "I've done nothing for you."

"Then for Grace," I mumbled.

The fingers on the wheel tightened slightly. "Least of all for her."

"Then for a memory?"

"The only memory I have of Grace is lying on a bedroom floor . . . strangled . . . with a red rose on her bosom."

The road rolled on and the world twisted by, and I wondered how long it would be before my heart would start beating again.

"You went to my house . . . that night . . . with the police," I said.

Sutton nodded his head.

"There was no red rose on her bosom . . . then. Only I saw that rose . . . *and you?*"

For the first time since I had known him, I heard Sutton laugh. There was a bitter mockery in his voice. "You saw the rose when you woke up. I put the rose there after I strangled Grace."

I didn't shout, I didn't rant. My voice was quiet, controlled. "How do you know," I asked, "that I won't kill you—or turn you over to the police?"

He twisted the wheel slightly to avoid a car that was straddling the centre white line.

"The police would laugh at you. And if you kill me—well, how do you think *your son* will feel when he finds out who you are? He thinks both of his parents died, a long time ago. He doesn't know his father was jailed for killing his mother."

"Then why," I asked, "did you tell me? It was no accident."

"Of course it wasn't, you fool. I hated her as I hate you. She repulsed me that night when I came to her; when I offered to give her back my name. She laughed in my face." His cheeks grew taut with the memory, and his hands clutched convulsively at the steering-wheel, the same hands that had wound themselves about Grace's neck, strangling her . . . killing her . . . then leaving a red rose. . . .

He struggled to compose himself, and when he spoke again, his voice was flat, emotionless. "I'm going to make you suffer as I've suffered. I'm going to make you regret stealing Grace's love. I'm going to make you hate the day you were born."

I remembered the words Grace had used so long ago when she spoke of the man who was sitting next to me. . . . *"He's evil!"*

"Let me out!" I shouted. "Let me out of the car!"

Sutton braked to a stop and I got out. His voice followed me. "Come to my office before you leave town—or do anything. I've something to tell that will interest you."

I cut across an open field and began to walk.

*Do they have roses . . . here? Red roses? I'd like to have some when
I . . . if I see Grace. . . .*

There was a gun in my pocket, but I kept my folded hands
on my lap. The back of the leather chair seemed to be sucking
me in as I sat facing Garney. The softly panelled office, the
discreet volumes of richly bound law books, the circular walnut
desk, the inch-deep rug—all these seemed to be distant props
for an audience that had not arrived. The only important thing
in the world was Sutton Garney's lips; his lips and the words
he was twisting through them.

"*My son*," he mocked, "is at an eastern school. But we can
get him here quickly . . . whenever you say the word."

"What do you want me to do?" I asked.

"Nothing," Garney said. "Not a thing. Just wait."

"For what?"

"Until *my son* has everything he wants. Until he's sitting on
top of the world. Until he finds out that he is *your son!*"

"I—don't understand!"

"You will." Garney pointed an accusing finger at me. "You
took away the one thing in the world I loved. Now I'm going
to teach you the meaning of heartache. For every minute I
suffered, you'll suffer a year. For every day that was taken from
my life, you'll lose an eternity."

"You're mad," I said. "You don't think I'll sit by idly and
let all this happen?"

"No?" Garney leaned back in his chair and folded his hands
into a praying pyramid. "Do something. Tell him. Tell the
world. See if anyone will believe you. Or"—he held his breath
for a moment—"you can tell him the truth. You can make him
believe that way."

I began to unfold my hands, and Garney read what was in
my mind. "There's a buzzer under my foot. All I've got to do
is touch it——"

The leather chair in which I was sitting twisted backwards,
and I crashed to the floor. My neck felt as if some gigantic shoe
had stepped on it. I looked up, and saw Garney standing over
me, an automatic in his hand.

"I had that chair specially constructed a long time ago," he said. "Some of my clients are—er—resentful at times." He motioned me to my feet. "Don't come here again. If you do, I'll kill you. The district attorney will probably pin a medal on me if I do.

"One thing more," he said, and my hand hesitated as it reached for the door-knob. "To-morrow I'm going to put a little sealed envelope in a safety deposit box. Insurance. In the event that I should be the victim of an unfortunate accident, I want the world to know who *our son* is."

I left him standing there, next to the overturned chair, the automatic in his hand, a look of hatred on his face.

I walked up behind Garney when he came out of the sea-food place on Fisherman's Wharf. I prodded a gun in his back.

"It won't do you any good," he said. "I've already put that note in a safe deposit box."

"Uh-uh," I said. "I've watched you all afternoon, ever since I left your office. You never went near a bank, and I'm certain you sent no messenger."

"What do you want me to do?"

"Just walk. Keep on walking."

"And if I don't?"

"I don't think you want to die—just yet."

I prodded him along a long wharf. Small fishing-boats floated at anchor; in the early morning fog they would slip out for their catch of fresh fish and crabs and lobsters. In the daytime men and boys and women fished off the wharf we were treading, but now it was deserted.

Sutton stopped when he reached the end, turned and faced me. "I'm listening," he said.

The gun in my hand was steady. "You'd promise me anything I wanted," I told him. "Anything. But you'd never keep your word. Your brain is twisted and cracked. You killed Grace because she loved me and hated you. I never knew Grace when she was your wife, but that didn't matter to you. You sent me to prison, you let me spend twenty years of torture thinking I'd killed my wife. Then you tell me you've given my son everything a young man could ask for. You're going to build a full life for him, and then bring it down with a crash. To taunt me. To show the world your hate for Grace."

"Neatly, if rather violently, put," said Sutton Garney. "Of course, I won't be as crude as you say. When he finds out about your—ah—relationship to him, it'll be an accident. But it will come at a most inconvenient time. Like that little mix-up you had long ago."

I remembered the business about the bonding company. "So that was some of your work." My finger tightened on the trigger.

Sutton nodded his head of bushy hair. "Rather neat, too. I thought for a time I might make Grace leave you, if you were no longer able to support her." He shrugged his shoulders. "It seemed to make her love you all the more. But you helped me when you started to drink. A man like you should never drink. And never plan. You haven't the intelligence or the guts for either."

I lifted the gun.

"What are you going to tell the police," he taunted. "Or do you want to go back to prison. I don't think they'll give you the gas chamber. They'll reason that you've become mentally unbalanced, and you'll spend the remainder of your life in an institution for the criminally insane. And what do you want to bet that some smart boy—maybe some newspaper man looking for a Sunday feature—doesn't get to wondering why you should want to kill me. He'll begin to dig and dig—and maybe he'll come up with something."

I listened to the long speech, to the power of Garney's words. He was convincing, and I felt the walls of frustration close about me. I was beaten and he knew it. No matter which way I turned, Garney had won and I had lost. *My son had lost. . . .*

He laughed again, for the second time, and I threw myself at him. We tumbled off the wharf and sank below the murky waters. He clawed at my hands, and there was a pounding in my eardrums, and Garney's laughter twisted and echoed through my brain. . . .

What more is there to think about? I drowned. But Garney? Did he drown? Or is he still alive? If he's dead, will someone begin to worry why I killed him? Will they nose about and ferret out the story of my son? And if he's still alive? Who is there to stop him? What is there to stop him? How he would laugh if he could see me now. He thought his revenge would last for only a lifetime. But it will last through all eternity. And I'll never know. Will I ever know?

Request granted. This is a story that will appear in a San Francisco newspaper to-morrow:

"Sutton Garney, prominent attorney, died this morning without regaining consciousness. Last night Garney attempted to save a man from committing suicide near Fisherman's Wharf, but he was unsuccessful. In the struggle both men fell into the bay.

"Police were summoned by passers-by, and Garney's unconscious body was brought ashore. The body of the unidentified man whom Garney attempted to save has not been recovered. Police believe there is a possibility that his identity will remain a mystery, since there was a strong current, and his body may have been swept through the Golden Gate and out to sea. . . ."

THE PARCEL

JOHN PETERS

Illustrations by Joan Hassall

*John Peters is a pen-name. In his (or her) own name Mr. Peters is a
Fellow of the Royal Society of Arts, holds an Honours Diploma for a
history of art, and was awarded the Gilchrist Medal by the University
of London for original theses on art. Mr. Peters has written plays,
pantomimes and stories for children. This was his first attempt at a
mystery story.*

JUST a bundle of sodden brown paper tied precariously with
thick string—such was the parcel. It is a wonder it ever got
to the gatehouse without falling to pieces. Yet it did somehow arrive intact into the hands of Andrew Aimes, who took it
straight to his young wife, Emily.

Emily was sitting on a settee in the stone-flagged kitchen
before a heaped log fire.

"Who was it, Andrew?" she asked as he entered the room.

"The postman with a parcel. At least, that's what he calls
it."

"At this time of night? Where's it from?"

"The wrapping paper's so wet I can't see a postmark. That's
unusual!" He examined the wet package in his hand.

"What is?"

"Why, some red figures—one, seven, six, eight—or is it nine?
—have been written across the address."

"Perhaps the Sorting Office has written them on."

"Why should they do that?"

"Are you sure it was the postman who brought it?" inquired
Emily, getting up from in front of the fire. "It's gone
eleven."

"Oh, it was the postman all right. I'd recognize his walk
anywhere."

"Did you see his face?"

"No. It was too dark in the porch. But it was him. I could
swear to that. We'd better open it. There might be a letter
inside."

The wet outer wrapper and thick string were soon pulled off
the parcel, and its contents laid bare. It was a china ornament,
but there was neither letter nor card to say who had sent it.
It was a porcelain group, possibly Derby, and must have been
nearly two hundred years old. The group was made up of two
figures, a man and a woman, in brightly coloured clothes. The
man was dressed in a dark hat, a coat with frilly cuffs, and a
long chequered jerkin, decorated with brilliant floral patterns.
His legs were encased in light stockings, and on his feet he wore
black shoes with light flower buckles.

The lady's attire matched that of her partner for brilliant
decoration. Her dress, which fell low over her shoulders, flowed
in shiny folds caught to one side, to reveal the rich pattern of
her skirt. Round her throat she wore a necklace bearing a small
gilt cross, that lay a striking contrast to the pale flesh tint of her
bosom. Her light shoes, with their dark flower buckles, acted
as a counter-change to those of the man. To add to the liveli-
ness of the group, the artist potter had put the two figures at
the top of three curved steps, supported at either side by scallop
curves.

In the hands of the man he had put a hurdy-gurdy, and in
those of the woman a bunch of flowers. As if all this were not
enough decoration for one ornament, he had built up behind
the man a cluster of tiny flowers with spiky leaves, and erected
a square pedestal near the woman. Under the light of the lamp
the high glaze of the porcelain broke into a hundred highlights,

accentuating every fold of the draperies, and every rounded form of the figures.

"It's a very pretty ornament," said Emily, and, as an after-thought, "I don't know where we'll put it. We've nothing it would go with."

"It might go on the mantelpiece."

Emily scanned the array of oddments above the fire. Two chromium photo frames, a triangular clock, a nest of wooden ash-trays, one automatic lighter, a perspex letter-rack. No. The mantelpiece certainly wasn't the spot for an old-fashioned china ornament.

"It will have to go in the spare room," she announced at last.

Andrew picked up the ornament and turned it over in his hand.

"That's strange!" he said.

"Strange? What do you mean?" asked Emily.

"That potter's mark. Do you see what it is?"

Emily looked close at it.

"It looks like a forked tail under a pair of curved horns. Do you think it makes the piece very valuable?"

"Perhaps. I know certain potters only mark flawless pieces."

"There's another mark there on the woman's neck."

"Which mark?"

"That one—like a red slash, there." Emily pointed with her finger to the left side of the woman's delicately moulded neck.

"It's a different red from the other reds. It's a sort of scarlet."

"Some accident in the firing, I expect. Such things do happen."

"It's a pity. It spoils the colour of the neck."

Andrew stood the group on a side-table, where the fine dust, stirred up by frequent pokings of the log fire, had already begun to settle.

"Let's leave it here till we decide where to put it."

He sat down in the armchair opposite Emily and lit his pipe. For a while neither of them spoke. Then Andrew took his pipe out of his mouth and asked: "Who on earth do you think could have sent it?"

"I was just wondering the same thing."

"Oh, well, it doesn't matter. We'll probably get a letter to-morrow."

"Yes. How far have you read in your book?"

"About three-quarters of the way through. I'll finish it to-night. You know, it's funny to think of just you and I living in this old gatehouse."

"What made you say that, Andrew? Don't you like this gate-house?"

"I like it, but it's funny all the same. Here we are, living in a great barn of a house, miles away from anywhere."

"It's not all those miles. Why, the village is only a mile and a half."

"And the next nearest houses are six and a half."

"Well, where else could we have got such a well-built house for nothing? After all, Aunt Julia did give it to us."

"I know she gave it to us, and I'm very glad she did. I only said it was funny to think of you and I alone here, so far away from anybody else."

"Don't you like being alone here with me, Andrew?"

"Silly girl, you know I do," said Andrew, and got up from his chair and kissed the top of Emily's head. Then he sat down on the settee beside her. Together they stared into the glowing embers of the fire, peculiarly happy in their isolation, far from the rest of the world in body and in mind. In the warmth of that room, half-formed thoughts drifted idly from one to another, to merge into that dreamy, drowsy state, which is neither sleep nor wakefulness.

Andrew drew Emily a little closer to him. Their eyes were open, and they were quietly content in their own company. He looked up slowly from the red glow towards the forgotten present on the side-table.

"I say! There's something queer about that ornament. I'm positive it was facing this way when I sat down," he said quietly, not fully believing his own words.

"Facing this way?" Emily looked at the ornament. "Why, it looks far away. How queer! It seems remote, as if behind a soft mist, just like the figures of a Corot landscape painting. I remember seeing the two faces, so I suppose it must have been facing the other way. Yet it couldn't have been this way round could it?"

"I suppose it couldn't," Andrew admitted reluctantly. "Though I'm sure the figures were facing this way." He tried to focus them clearly, without the effort of getting up from the settee and leaving the immediate heat of the fire. But his mind seemed incapable of making the attempt. It seemed to him also that the group was, as Emily said, enveloped in a Corot haze.

"Some trick of the light, I expect," he said, and stroked the back of his now closed book with his thumb. Emily poked the fire and put on another log. Outside, the wind began to blow among the tall pines north of the gatehouse. A window rattled as a gust of wind blew under the kitchen door.

"Push the mat up against the door, Andrew."

Andrew got up and pushed a long wool mat against the bottom of the oak door. Then he fastened the sneck, to return to his place at the side of Emily. Gradually the light in the room began to get less and less.

"Something's gone wrong with the electric light. Ah! That's better! That engine's a nuisance. You'd have thought Aunt Julia would have let the electric company supply her, instead of fussing about with that generator."

Andrew felt the same, but did not say so. His gaze was once more drawn towards the figures. He stretched out his hand, and touched Emily on the knee. She looked where he was pointing. The porcelain ornament was slowly moving round. A sudden desire to scream came upon Emily. She stuffed a handkerchief against her mouth, and bit hard on it. When the two figures were facing the fire, the ornament stopped turning, and the electric light seemed even less bright than a moment ago.

A severely practical man, not superstitious, without a trace of nonsense in the whole six feet of him, Andrew Aimes prepared to bestir himself into action. He sat up straight. His hand released the book, and was moving forward in the direction of the group, when the porcelain man with the hurdy-gurdy walked down the three curved steps, and stood on the wood of the side-table. Andrew's stomach turned to jelly. He withdrew his hand to his knee. Emily stared at the porcelain man.

"Andrew," she whispered, "I'm frightened."

"Keep still, dear."

The porcelain man twirled the handle of his hurdy-gurdy. There wasn't a sound, yet the porcelain lady raised her skirt a little higher on one side, and tripped down the steps on to the table.

The clock on the mantelpiece ticked away the silence. Minutes crawled by, with Andrew and Emily almost as still as the figures themselves. Then Andrew, unable to stand the strain any longer, took a deep breath to laugh. There came a faint hollow sort of sigh of a laugh, so completely foreign to his usual laugh, that he stopped abruptly to gaze unbelievingly at the table.

Without preliminary warning, the porcelain lady swung her bunch of flowers across her breast, bewitching the hurdy-gurdy player with her dark eyes and small round face. A subtle movement of her plump little hand raised her skirt just high enough to bring into his full view a dainty ankle. This was a signal. Like lightning the hurdy-gurdy player spun round on his heel, and advanced towards the gaily dressed lady. He got quite close to her, and slipped his arm about her waist. She lifted up her face and smiled. He smiled back, and together they performed a quaint doll-like dance round and round in a clockwise direction. At the pause to reverse, she pouted her dainty lips, inviting him to kiss them. He bent over her. They looked into each other's faces. He parted his lips slightly to kiss her. At that instant she lifted her bunch of flowers till it came between them, a barrier to his attention.

"The minx!" muttered Andrew, hardly knowing he spoke.

Emily sat as one entranced.

Thwarted at the moment of victory, the hurdy-gurdy man flung the lady from him. She stood a little way off, with her back to him, lifted the bunch of flowers shoulder high, and ogled him over the heads of the blossoms. Three quick steps, a drop to one knee, and he held her left hand. Tenderly he raised it to his lips and kissed it. The lady pulled it sharply from his grasp, and smote him in the face with her flowers.

That blow completely shattered the charm of the preceding dance. The would-be lover pointed an accusing finger at her.

Step by step, but without lowering his accusing finger, he backed away from her, ascending the three steps on to the porcelain platform. He tucked his hurdy-gurdy into his side, and commenced to turn the handle. Unheard music must have come from the instrument, for the coquette's feet started to move in time with the rotating handle. Imperceptibly he quickened the speed of the handle. The lady's dancing feet speeded up. Round and round she went, one circle spiralling into the next.

A hypnotic state, induced by this movement, held both on-lookers in its grip. The music must have been racing now, for the tiny figure, forced to keep whirling round below the plat-form, was showing obvious signs of distress. The movements of her body became those of a person already exhausted but un-able to stop.

Unrelenting, the hurdy-gurdy man played on and on, his eyes fixed on the dancer to hold her there, spinning like a tee-totum. The rhythmic turning of the handle changed without slackening speed. The fickle jade, who had slighted her swain, was compelled to mount the steps.

What happened next was so swift that Andrew and Emily could never have seen it but for their rapt attention. From out of the body of the hurdy-gurdy flashed a long, pointed dagger. It followed an arc of the man's arm through the air, and plunged right through the neck of the lady. Her head came forward, her two dainty hands fluttered upwards, and her body slumped down at the feet of the man.

A scream of horror escaped from Emily's lips. There was a blinding flash as the electric bulb glowed incandescent and went out. Andrew jumped back instinctively, and gave his attention to Emily. She was lying across the arm of the settee, her hair hanging close to the flames of the fire. He felt his hands cold and trembling as he heaved her up straight. Beads of sweat glistened on his brow. In his distress at seeing Emily thus, the scene he had just witnessed temporarily vanished from his mind.

He rubbed her ice-cold hands with his own. A little warmth returned to them. Next he patted her white cheeks . . . but there was hardly any response. He pushed the settee frantically

over the rugs to the window. Then he flung the window wide
open. The keen cold air rushing from the pine-woods acted
immediately, reviving Emily. She was now trembling uncon-
trollably, so Andrew closed the window and pushed the settee
back in front of the fire.

Watching her lest anything should happen, he switched on
the standard lamp beside the fireplace. Twelve bell notes struck
by the clock on the tower of the village church sounded
ominously in the distance. An owl hooted.

Andrew stabbed the poker into a partly burnt log, and split
it along a wide crack. Flames caught up and gave extra light
to the room.

There was a bottle of rum on a window ledge, with two
glasses made ready earlier for a night-cap. He poured some
rum into one of the glasses, and drank it down. Then he gave a
sip to Emily.

Walking deliberately over the sandstone flags, he went to the
hall, took out the light bulb, and brought it into the kitchen.
To avoid looking at the side-table, he kept his eyes fixed on the
ceiling, and by standing on a chair was able to take out the
fused bulb and replace it with the one from the hall. The light
came on instantly. As he got down off the chair, Emily grasped
his hand. They both looked at the side-table. Andrew made
as if to pick the ornament up.

"Don't touch it!" cried Emily.

He took his hand away. "Shall we go to bed, dear?"

"I don't know. It's so cold here."

"Come on, dear. We'll lock the door and go up."

Andrew switched on the landing light, and Emily went first
up the wooden stairs, leaving her husband to lock up.

He locked the outside door, and when he had gone out of the
door leading from the kitchen to the hall he took the precaution
of locking that one also. This done, he went to bed.

* * * * *

They slept soundly, to awaken late. A letter from Uncle
Ambrose was lying on the mat. Over breakfast of coffee and
hot buttered toast, Emily read out its contents. It was a short
cheery letter of the kind Uncle Ambrose always wrote:

"My dear Emily and Andrew," it began, "I am sending you a small gift which I hope will arrive unbroken in time for the anniversary. As you know, I am not young, and I would specially like you to have this rare piece of porcelain, so am making sure you get it, by giving it to you now. Wills and probates have a way of going wrong.

"The porcelain group has a strange history. It was made, so I am told, by a weird but gifted craftsman, working somewhere in the Midlands about the middle of the 1750s for one of the then famous pottery firms. Underneath it, you will find it marked with this queer fellow's own pottery mark, which he insisted on using, despite much opposition from the firm of potters.

"Beyond this, little else is known about him, except that he had a local reputation for being a little mad, and very wicked.

"He was known as 'The Demon Potter'."

"Does he say anything else?" asked Andrew, sipping his coffee.

"Yes. Listen to this:

"The group I am sending you is probably the last he made, as he was hanged in the late 1760s for murdering a young woman by stabbing her to death in the neck. They say she slighted him. Have a good time, and my good wishes to you both."

Emily put down the letter and looked hard at Andrew, who had drained his coffee cup without even tasting the bitterness of the few grounds at the bottom. He rose silently from the breakfast table, and taking Emily by the hand, led her over to the side-table. Then he looked intently at the pretty porcelain pair, the hurdy-gurdy man and his lady. Emily looked too.

On the table, completely undisturbed, lay the coat of dust from the fire ash.

"They didn't move after all," he said.

"No, they couldn't have, could they?" replied Emily.

To their friends who inquire the reason for an undusted side-table, the young married couple never volunteer an explanation. But when Emily mentioned it to Andrew, he only laughed and said: "We must have been very, very tired, and perhaps a little lonely, or that Demon Potter's work would never have mesmerized us both."

To music's pipe the passions dance.

MATTHEW GREEN: *The Spleen*, 1737.

*   *   *

Hell is full of musical amateurs. Music is the brandy of the damned.

GEORGE BERNARD SHAW: *Man and Superman*, 1903.

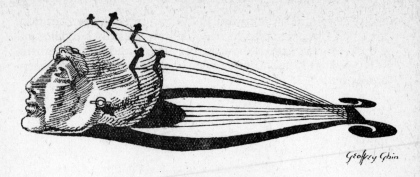

Geoffrey Ghin

MIND TO MIND

KENNETH WALKER

Illustrations by Geoffrey Ghin

Kenneth Macfarlane Walker is not only a well-known surgeon, but also a student of occidental and oriental philosophy. He is here dealing primarily with the mystery of Telepathy, but it is not exaggerating to say that the greatest mystery of all, for us, is also vitally involved—the mystery of Man.

WHEN a professional colleague of mine was asked whether he believed in telepathy, he replied: "Yes, but for heaven's sake keep that strictly to yourself." He was wise to be so cautious. In a religious age medical men carefully hid any doubts they may have harboured on the subject of the doctrines of the Church, for to gain the reputation of being heterodox was damaging to their practices. In a scientific age they must be equally cautious not to offend the canons of scientific orthodoxy, and telepathy is an idea that cannot be fitted into the accepted scientific creed. It is a form of extra-sensory perception that a scientist is unable to recognize unless he is prepared to change a great deal else in his general scheme of thought, so that the doctor who confesses that he believes in it is in danger of being called a crank. He will be accused of being the kind of man who attends spiritualistic séances, and who is as heterodox in his practice as he is in his private life. A doctor is wise therefore to keep his interest in strange and inexplicable psychic phenomena to himself.

The word "telepathy" was invented by the Victorian psychologist, F. W. H. Myers, to denote the transmission of an impression from one mind to another without the intervention of the recognized senses. Myers did not attempt to give any explanation of how this was brought about, but it was assumed by many people that it was by means of "vibrations of thought" transmitted through space. We know now that this is extremely unlikely to be the case, and in order to avoid the implications and associations that have become attached to the word telepathy, two new terms have been introduced—"extra-sensory perception" (E.S.P.) and the "Psi" faculty. As will be seen later, telepathy is closely allied to the other, at present inexplicable, phenomena of precognition, clairvoyance and psychometry, all of which can be conveniently grouped under these two new terms. The first question that has to be asked is, "Do these strange faculties actually exist, or are they merely imaginary?" The second, "If they exist, how are they to be explained?"

Fifty years ago there were scientists who protested that it was an outrage that such questions as these should even be asked. In June 1881 the members of a learned committee published a report of their investigations of certain "thought reading" claims made by a Mr. Bishop, in the well-known scientific journal *Nature*. They prefaced their report with the cautionary words: "From these experiments it is needless to say we did not expect any result." This should have safeguarded their scientific reputations, but one of the committee, Professor Ray Lankester, made doubly sure of his scientific integrity by protesting that it was a mistake even to investigate "so puerile a hypothesis" as the transmission of thought. Fortunately, there were other men of the opinion that the advancement of knowledge was of greater importance than the safeguarding of established beliefs, and who were prepared to accept new ideas, even if acceptance of them were to necessitate rearrangement of their previous thoughts. In spite of the danger of being called charlatans, such men as these began working on psychic problems on their own. Professor and Mrs. Henry Sidgwick of Cambridge made a number of experiments to see whether they could transmit thought to each other while sitting in separate rooms. One of them selected at random a two-digit number and visualized it, whilst the other wrote down the number that came into his mind. Then they calculated how much of the successful results could be accounted for by the laws of chance. The successes proved greater than could be ascribed to accident, and the Sidgwicks accepted this as valid evidence in support of telepathy. As the years passed, more and more reputable people became interested in the subject, amongst others Arthur Balfour, Henri Bergson, William James, Lord Rayleigh, Professor Broad, Camille Flammarion and Professor J. J. Thomson. Even the doctors were now taking an interest in telepathy. The French physician, Dr. E. Azam, discovered that a female patient, whom he had hypnotized, was responding to his unspoken thoughts. He decided to test whether she would be equally sensitive to the sensations that he experienced and, going behind her back, he put into his mouth some table salt. She volunteered the statement that she tasted salt. Janet, the well-known French psychiatrist, even went so far as to claim that he was able to induce hypnotic trances in subjects at a distance sufficiently great to exclude the possibility of sensory communication. At a later date Jung also supported the idea that "telepathy" might occur.

In 1882 the Society for Psychical Research was founded, and the many stories of spontaneous telepathy that they invited and received were submitted to a careful and critical scrutiny. Those who carried out this work came to the conclusion that when all doubtful cases had been eliminated there remained behind a residue that lent strong support to the view that there was a mysterious faculty of the human mind of which orthodox science could give no adequate account. Sometimes the message was received by the mind in the ordinary waking state and in other cases in a state of sleep. Two examples will be given from a volume published by the Society under the title *Phantasms of the Living*. In the first of these cases the percipient was a child of about ten who was walking along a country road reading a book on geometry. She had no cause for anxiety concerning her mother's health, but she suddenly had a vision of her lying upon the floor of her bedroom at home. So convinced was she of the reality of her vision that she went straight to fetch a doctor, with whom she returned home. Here her mother was found lying on the floor suffering from a heart attack and in urgent need of medical attention. In the second case the receiver of the message was, at the time of its reception, asleep. His description is as follows:

> "My brother and father were on a journey. . . . I dreamt . . . I saw father driving in a sledge, followed in another by my brother. They had to pass a crossroad on which another traveller was driving very fast, also in a sledge with one horse. Father seemed to drive on without observing the other fellow, who would . . . have driven over Father if he had not made his horse rear, so that I saw Father drive under the hooves of the horse. Every moment I expected the horse to fall down and crush him. I called out: 'Father, Father . . .' and awoke in a great fright." The incident occurred as the percipient dreamed it, except for one small item. (This is quoted by Rosalind Heywood, in *Telepathy and Allied Phenomena*, Society for Psychical Research.)

*   *   *   *   *

Striking although such stories of extra-sensory perception may be, they cannot be accepted as being scientific evidence in favour of telepathy. Science demands that its experiments should be carried out under strictly controlled conditions, and that when repeated they give the same results. In order to satisfy these needs, J. B. Rhine, professor of psychology at Duke University, U.S.A., embarked on a number of controlled experiments in 1930. He did not seek so much for evidence in favour of the existence of telepathy as for information on the kindred subject of extra-sensory perception, or clairvoyance. For this purpose he prepared a number of Zener cards. The pack was composed of twenty-five cards marked with the following five symbols: star, rectangle, cross, circle, and wavy lines. After the subject to be experimented upon had been shown the cards, and the test had been explained to him, the pack was shuffled, cut, and placed face downwards on the table at which he was seated. He was then asked to name the symbol marked on the top card. His answer was recorded and the card was removed, but not exposed to the guesser. This procedure was repeated until the whole of the pack had been named. The pack was then reshuffled and the whole experiment repeated. Afterwards the results were scrutinized. Rhine's comments are as follows:

"From chance alone the average score expected was 5.25 cards. If a subject scored above 5 on the average, the deviation, the total number of hits above chance expectancy, was measured by means of a mathematical yardstick called the 'standard deviation'. This measure, which has long been in use in the various sciences, tells what the odds are that chance alone did not produce the result obtained. If, for example, a subject were given a test with four runs through the pack and scored 7.5 hits per run, the odds would be about 150 to 1 against the total score of 30 hits, or a deviation of 10 above expectation, being produced by pure luck or chance. . . . Let us turn to the actual scores. The best individual performer went through the deck of E.S.P. cards well over 700 times during the first three years of work covered by my first report, *Extra-Sensory Perception*, published in 1934. This man averaged about 8 hits per run of 25 trials, better than 3 hits above expectation for each pack. Now the odds are 100 to 1 that no one will average 8 or better for three runs in succession by chance alone. To express the odds against averaging a score of 8 or better by chance alone for more than 700 runs would require a paragraph of figures. This performance of one individual is so significant, and rules out chance so completely, that it does not matter what any of the other subjects did. No matter what their scores, they could not nullify the striking extra-chance character of this one man's performance!" (*The Reach of the Mind*, J. B. Rhine.)

In 1934 Dr. Soal, a mathematician of London University, repeated Rhine's experiments, but under even stricter conditions. An independent and critical observer was always present, and Dr. Soal was meticulously careful to eliminate every conceivable sensory clue that might pass from the agent to the percipient. He worked for five years, tested 160 subjects, and recorded 128,350 guesses, but without being able to report any successes that could not be accounted for by chance. It was a dismal conclusion to five years' painstaking work, and then one of those happy accidents occurred that are so common in scientific research. In talking over his disappointing results with Whateley Carrington, who had himself been experimenting on telepathy, the latter happened to use the word "displacement". In his own experiments he had discovered that his percipients did not necessarily score on the target of the moment but sometimes on the one that preceded, or that followed it. In other words there was a displacement of time in his experiments. Encouraged by this, Soal went all through his results again and discovered that two of his subjects had scored in both directions well above what chance could account for. He got into touch with these promising percipients again, and started on a new series of experiments with them. His precautions against chance hints passing from the agent to the percipient were even stricter than before. They were seated in adjoining rooms, but the intercommunicating door was left slightly ajar so that the "ready" signal could be heard. The cards were marked with the five coloured pictures of a lion, elephant, zebra, giraffe and pelican, and were shuffled and placed in a box, the open side of which faced the agent. The outer doors of the rooms were kept locked throughout the experiments and each experiment was recorded on a separate printed scoring sheet. No sensory hint could possibly have passed from the one room to the other. The results of this experiment were of the very greatest interest and importance. *By far the highest scores were obtained for the card at which the agent was going to look on the next occasion ahead!* When the rate of the whole procedure was made twice as quick, it was the card *two* trials ahead that the percipient guessed. To the one mystery of telepathy had been added yet a more startling one, that of precognition. The Psi faculty was playing havoc, not only with the experimenter's previous notions of space, but also of time. It was not obeying the laws that the scientists had established to account for everything in the universe, including the behaviour of the human mind. Here was something of which no account could be given and which, if it were to be accepted, would necessitate a revolution in scientific thought and a fresh beginning to psychology.

* * * * *

I have no personal experience of any of the more elaborate experiments in E.S.P., but I have been present at tests of a much simpler nature. The subject of the experiments was a Czech, well-known in London as a clairvoyant, and the tests to which he was submitted were of a very elementary kind. Five cards were chosen by one of us from an ordinary pack, sealed in thick envelopes and placed on the table. The Czech was then admitted to the room and asked to state the colours of the suit in each envelope. He walked to the table, stretched a hand over each envelope in turn, jerked it about as though he were receiving some impressions from the envelope and muttered rather spasmodically, "red—red—black—red—black." The tests were repeated, and on several occasions he obtained full marks. His ability to guess correctly varied on different evenings, but his total score was well above that for which accident could account.

In the clairvoyant's perception some operation takes place between his mind and the hidden object he perceives. It is reasonable to assume that his mind does "something" to the object and that the object does "something" to his mind. If therefore there is such a thing as extra-sensory perception, why should there not be such a thing as extra-motor response, that is to say, an action of the mind on a material object, or what the parapsychologist calls psychokinesis or PK? The idea that the mind may exert an action on matter is an old one, and if the dualists are right, it is happening every moment of our lives. The notion comes into my mind that I will stretch out my hand, and immediately my brain, nerves and muscles humour my mind's wish. By some means or another the gap between what is assumed to be an immaterial mind and the matter of the brain is bridged.

There are also well-attested accounts of what are called

"poltergeist phenomena". All that can be said about these strange events is that they are usually associated with the presence of an adolescent boy or girl. In *The Personality of Man*, G. N. M. Tyrrell describes such happenings in a blacksmith's shop in Vienna in 1906. These were investigated and reported upon by Mr. W., a member of the Austrian Society for Psychical Research. The blacksmith complained that his tools and odd bits of iron were flung about the place, and because he had already been hit on the head by one of these, he wore a stiff hat for his own protection. On his second visit Mr. W. found that the smith now kept his tools in wooden boxes outside the smithy because one of his heavier hammers had recently whizzed past him. At the third visit Mr. W. met the unfortunate blacksmith outside his own shop. Two oil lamps had tumbled down and broken during the night and he was now too frightened to enter his own workshop. Mr. W. stated in his report that whilst he was actually present certain objects dropped quite close to him and three actually struck him on the head. It is to be noted that a young apprentice, aged fifteen, was working in the black-smith's shop.

Claims have also been made of strange physical happenings in the presence of certain mediums : stationary objects suddenly tumble, a table rises towards the ceiling and some object falls on to the floor. But the mediums insist that they can only work under favourable psychic conditions, and unfortunately the conditions they select for their work are just those that are capable of veiling fraud. However convincing the accounts of séances in darkened rooms and of poltergeist phenomena may appear, they cannot be accepted by any critical mind. Here also experiments under controlled conditions were required, and having concluded his experiments in E.S.P., Professor Rhine started on experiments with psychokinesis, or P.K.

The test he selected to ascertain whether the mind could in-fluence the movement of material objects was a very simple one. The subject was given a pair of dice and a cup from which to throw them. A target was then set the thrower, say, to obtain a run of sevens. He was to "will" to throw as high a score of sevens as possible. Later, refinements were introduced, such as mechanical throwers, and in order to overcome the difficulty

7

of faulty dice, the target was changed, say, from throwing high scores to low scores, and then back again to high scores with the same dice. It would seem to be a naïve and rather foolish experiment, this, in which men and women sat down solemnly in a laboratory to throw dice and "will" that they should fall in a certain way, an experiment from which nothing much might be expected. Yet strange to say, when the calculus of probability was applied to the recorded results, it was found that scoring above chance had been obtained.

There was another point of interest to be noted in the results, namely, that as the tests proceeded, the successes steadily dropped. Scoring tended to fall off in the later runs, and if it was to be kept above the "chance average", frequent changes in the procedure had to be made. It was as though the subject got bored or fatigued. In the high-dice tests, nearly all the hits above chance occurred at the beginning of the test. For example, there were 134 hits above chance in the first 123 runs, only 19 in the second 123 runs, and only 4 in the third 75 runs. What was the cause of this falling off in positive runs? Was it the mind of the subject exerting some "force" on the dice that began to tire? Did attention flag so that he was no longer able to keep his mind on the target that had been set him? The first of these alternatives, namely, that a *physical* force was being exerted on the dice and that this force rapidly flagged was extremely unlikely, for if the mind had been exerting a physical force, its action ought to have been greater when it was concentrated on a single die. Yet it was found that scoring was as good, if not better, when as many as 96 dice were thrown at a time. It seemed clear that the ordinary laws of dynamics were not determining the success or the comparative failure of the experiment. What seemed to be of far greater importance than the number or size of the dice or the material of which they were made was the interest displayed by the subject in the experiment. Results always improved when he had a strong preference for certain numbers and embarked on the experiment with enthusiasm. And there for the moment this problem of how the mind can possibly affect the falling of dice must be left.

*   *   *   *   *

Geoffrey Thrir

What is to be made of all the strange results that have been reported from the laboratories of Duke University and also from parapsychologists working elsewhere? We can adopt the attitude of the late Professor Ray Lancaster and protest that the whole business is based on fraud and that the experimenters deliberately cooked their results. But surely this is a thesis that it is very difficult to support. Those responsible for the planning and carrying out of these experiments are men well known in the academic world, men of established reputation who would not lend themselves to fraud. It should also be noted that after five years of painstaking, laborious work, Professor Soal reported only negative results, and it was only when he went through all his files again that the new evidence in favour of precognition was found. No, the idea that the experimenters were untrustworthy can be dismissed. But perhaps they themselves were deceived and failed to take sufficiently into account the vagaries of chance. This also is so unlikely that it need not be considered. Dr. Soal was professor of mathematics at London University, and he approached his experiments from the standpoint of the mathematician. He was well aware of the possibility that positive results might be due to coincidence and indeed reported that, in the case of his own experiments on telepathy, this accounted for what had happened. So also were Professor Rhine's results submitted to the scrutiny of a mathematician, who reported that whatever the explanation of the positive results might be, it was certainly not that they were due to chance.

It is impossible to explain the results that have been obtained in the laboratories of parapsychology by the hypothesis of chance unless we regard chance as being something of a quite different nature in these experiments than in other experiments. It is, of course, right that a very high standard of deviation from what is to be expected should be enforced when phenomena of this mysterious nature are being investigated. The more unlikely we consider anything to be, the greater the amount of evidence needed to establish its existence, and in the great majority of these experiments the mathematical evidence against positive results being due to chance is overwhelming. But surely there is some weak place in these investigations through which the factor of human error has been able to exert its action?

To this statement it is impossible to return a "No", but it can be confidently said that had all the precautions against error that were adopted in these experiments been adopted in an ordinary scientific experiment, the results would never have been questioned. It is only because the acceptance of telepathy, clairvoyance, precognition and psychokinesis would play such havoc with our accepted views of the nature of man that we struggle to find some reason for rejecting them. The scientists cannot afford to accept extra-sensory perception and psychokinesis, for in accepting them they would also have to recognize the existence of non-physical mental action. Their universe would have to be divided up again into the physical and the mental, and they would have to return to the Cartesian dualism from which they have only recently escaped. It is small wonder that the results of the carefully controlled experiments carried out by the parapsychologists have not yet been generally accepted.

When the word "telepathy" was first coined as a substitute for the older term "thought transference", it was assumed, as was stated earlier in this article, that if it occurred it was brought about by some sort of vibrations travelling through space. It was supposed that the physico-chemical changes occurring in the brain of the sender of the message set up certain vibrations that, impinging on the brain of the recipient, evoked in his mind a similar idea. It was the simplest form of explanation that could be given and therefore the most acceptable. But there are very grave objections to it. In the first place, we know from our experience of radio that a very powerful apparatus is needed to act as a transmitter, far more powerful than we would expect to find within the confines of the human skull. Secondly, all known forms of radiations obey the inverse square law that connects intensity with distance. If therefore physical energy is being transmitted through space in cases of telepathy, we would find a rapid falling off in it as the distance between the sender and the receiver of the message increased. All of those who have experimented with telepathy deny that this is the case. They claim that it is just as difficult, or as easy, to transmit a message across an ocean as through a wall separating two rooms. The third objection to the "vibration" theory of telepathy is even more weighty. The transmission of a message by a physical means entails the use of some agreed-upon code. Unless somebody is present at the two ends of the transmission to codify and decodify the message, nothing can be sent. Language is a code, but it is not words that are transmitted, but ideas, and often ideas in the form of symbols. There are frequent instances of telepathic dreams, and the symbol is of course the language of dreams. The dreamer is warned that something terrible has happened, but the disaster portrayed in the dream may not be the disaster that has actually occurred. At other times the message is accompanied by hallucination, especially when the phenomenon of precognition is associated with that of telepathy. The arguments that can be brought against the idea that telepathic messages are transmitted from one brain to another by some physical means are too many and too weighty to be readily refuted.

* * * * *

What generalizations can be made on the subject of telepathy? Professor Rhine states that subjects who were tested at Duke University for clairvoyance (the guessing of cards) gave good results, and were equally good when they were tested for telepathy. "Eight of the nine principal Duke subjects who took part in the comparison of the P.T. and the P.C. gave quite similar scoring rates in the two types of test. The ninth, however, strongly and consistently favoured telepathy, giving as her explanation a preference for working with a person instead of cards, which she said she thoroughly disliked." From this Rhine deduces that telepathy and clairvoyance are "essentially the same ability" (J. B. Rhine, *The Reach of the Mind*, 1948). There is another generalization that Rhine is prepared to make: that they are not abnormalities and have nothing to do with mental illness. There is to be found what may be called a pseudo-telepathic syndrome in mental hospitals. Patients with persecution illusions believe that they are receiving hostile messages from their imaginary enemies, but this has no bearing on the subject of telepathy. It would appear indeed that the lower the intelligence of the subject, the less likely are his extra-sensory perception tests to yield positive results.

The next question of interest is whether E.S.P. is widely distributed in the community, or whether it is possessed only by exceptional individuals. Those who are best qualified to give an answer to this question say that although different individuals vary greatly in their capacity, most people possess parapsychical ability in some degree. But this statement needs qualification. In the ordinary man clairvoyance and telepathy work erratically, and are not under his direct control; but in the developed man—and by developed man I take as an example the yogi—they are disciplined functions to be used when he wills. E.S.P. in ordinary people resembles such higher functions of the mind as the creative faculty, in that it is uncertain in character and only works under favourable conditions. Like these functions, it is also affected by the taking of drugs; under the influence of narcotics it disappears, and with the help of stimulants it may be revived. It is to be noted also that if satisfactory results are to be obtained, E.S.P. tests must be carried out at the subject's own natural tempo. The subjects in one series of experiments were asked to keep time with the ticking of a metronome, and the rate of this was altered in different runs. When the rate was speeded up beyond the subject's natural tempo, the results of the test always deteriorated. So also did E.S.P. decline when the subject became bored with what he had undertaken to do, or when he approached his tests in a negative attitude of mind.

*　*　*　*　*

It is obvious that all of these mysterious activities of the "Psi" factor are of a very elusive nature. Even the personality of the man who organizes the laboratory experiments to be carried out on them seems to influence the results that are obtained. A minority of experimenters obtain consistently negative results, and some subjects who did well with one experimenter failed completely with another. There is also a tendency for the performance of a given subject to deteriorate as the test proceeds. We hear of people who were formerly star performers giving results very little above the chance-level after they had suffered from an emotional crisis, a nervous breakdown, or even after they had married.

Now, if there is one assertion that can be made with confidence about all these mysterious faculties—telepathy, clairvoyance, precognition and psychokinesis—it is that they work unconsciously. The subject is completely unaware of what is happening, and he has no idea whether he is getting good results or bad, for it is not his conscious, but his unconscious, mind that is responsible for them. It can also be said that whatever the faculty may be that is at work, it is of an emotional nature. When the intellect intervenes, when, in other words, the subject begins to think too much, his performance is likely to fall off. There is another reason for stating that E.S.P. is more allied to "feeling" or "intuition" than to thinking. Telepathic messages, either associated or not with precognition, are sometimes received when the subject is asleep.

Tyrrell records one instance of this in *The Personality of Man*, a case record by Dame Edith Lyttleton. A Miss E. went to sleep between two and three o'clock, and woke up after having had a terrifying dream that "she had been to a place where someone was being mauled by lions", an event that was actually happening that afternoon at Whipsnade. It is, of course, quite possible that this was merely a coincidence, but warning and telepathic dreams are of such frequent occurrence that some explanation must be sought for them. Now, three things can be said about dreams: the first, that they have their origin in the unconscious part of the mind; the second, that they are affective or emotional in nature; and the third, that they are often symbolic. The last of these characteristics has long been recognized, and it was as natural for Pharaoh to send for his trusted servant Joseph to interpret his dreams as it would be natural nowadays for a man to look at the weather report before going away for the week-end.

The existence of paranormal phenomena of the mind having been proved—so exacting a scientist as Julian Huxley has accepted the validity of these proofs—the next step must be to discover something about their nature. What are the conditions that favour the action of the "Psi" faculty? The subjects that the experimenters have used for their tests can give us little or no help with regard to this. They are quite incapable of explaining what has been happening in the hidden regions of their minds, but something perhaps can be learnt from studying the methods of the earlier protagonists of telepathy and precognition—the soothsayers, diviners and sibyls of ancient times. It is noteworthy that all of these exponents of precognition fixed their gaze on some object, such as the entrails of a recently-killed animal, and made use of some ritual, not merely to impress the onlooker, but in order to bring themselves into a state of mind that they had found, by experience, to be favourable to their work. For the same purpose the Mohammedan diviner looks fixedly at the pattern formed by sand in a shallow disk, at a pool of ink, or even at the grounds left behind in a coffee cup. So also in Europe does the fortune-teller gaze at a crystal and the gipsy at the palm of her client's hand. All of these techniques are methods that the clairvoyant employs to induce a certain receptive state of mind. They probably act by engaging the attention and by thus permitting the less conscious parts of the mind to come into action without interference from the intellect.

How does telepathy work? No answer can at present be given to this question. All that can be said about it is that telepathy is not what many of the older experimenters believed it to be, a promulgation of "thought waves" through space, but that it is a relationship between two unconscious minds. Although the conscious parts of our "egoes" seem to be independent and separate entities, it would almost seem that the unconscious parts of our minds are in some mysterious way closely interconnected. Jung has familiarized us with the idea of a collective unconscious, and although he arrived at his conclusions from data of an entirely different kind, the phenomena of telepathy lends his conclusions some support. The "cross correspondence" experiments carried out by Mrs. and Miss Verrall, Mrs. Holland, Mrs. Willett and Dame Edith Lyttleton in Cambridge about the year 1906 also support the idea that there may be such a thing as a "group mind". None of these ladies was a medium, and all of them were highly educated. They found that with a little practice they could produce automatic

7*

writing, and automatic writing is, of course, an activity of the unconscious mind.

It is difficult to summarize the "cross correspondence" afterwards found in the automatic writings of the experimenters, but the authority who examined them described the various contributions as being "not clear-cut, isolated things with a definite beginning and complete in themselves". They were "tiny bits of very complex patterns". Nothing had been pre-arranged between the team of experimenters, no one person knew what the other was writing about, and yet they were producing together a kind of mosaic of complementary ideas. Looking at the collected scripts, it was difficult to avoid the conclusion that a close intercommunication existed between their unconscious minds. What was of particular interest was that one correspondent appeared to be using knowledge that by rights belonged to one of her fellows. Thus, although Mrs. Verrall was the only classical scholar amongst them, it was not she but Mrs. Holland who was selected to make use of Latin words. Mrs. Holland, although well educated, had no knowledge of the classics. It was as though their unconscious minds had been formed into a common pool from which each could select what she needed.

To go further into the subject of telepathy would necessitate an excursion into metaphysics. We should first have to discover the enigma of the mind-body relationship, and if we were dualists, to decide by what means an immaterial entity such as the mind influenced a material entity such as the brain. From this we would have to pass to the action of one mind on another and, before we had got very far, we would find ourselves lost in a fog of words. It would be better therefore to avoid the risk of this and to summarize what can be said about telepathy at the present time as briefly as possible.

It can be asserted that the existence of telepathy has been proven, that it is a faculty which is widely distributed, but that only in a few individuals is it exhibited in any considerable degree. It can also be stated that telepathy is a function of the unconscious mind, or, if we discuss the problem in terms of the brain, that it is a function of the thalamic area of the brain or that part of it that is concerned with the emotional life. Now, phylogenetically, this is the older part of the brain, a part that in man has been overlaid by the enormous development of his cerebral hemispheres. Many of the functions that are discharged by it in animals have been taken over by the cerebral hemispheres in man. It is through his cerebral hemispheres and his special senses that a man takes note of and adjusts himself to his immediate surroundings, but it may well be that the older part of his brain is still capable of giving him some vague knowledge of what is happening elsewhere. According to Whitehead, everything in the universe takes note of, or prehends, everything else; nothing is isolated and self-sufficient, but is affected by, and in turn affects, everything else. It may well be therefore that what in man manifests itself as telepathy is a phenomenon to be found in a primitive form, as a sense of awareness of what is happening at a distance, in all living organisms. Some support would appear to be given to this view by the observation that examples of E.S.P. are said to be very common in primitive races, in other words, in those races in which the higher centres in the cerebral hemispheres are less developed.

MIND TO MIND: BUT HOW?

BANESH HOFFMANN

Illustrations by Alison Welch

A few months after the previous article had appeared, an American walked into the editor's office and handed in this reply to Mr. Walker's article. Our visitor, Professor Hoffmann, is an authority on theoretical physics. He has published, among other important papers, an investigation entitled "The Gravitational Equations and the Problem of Motion" (written in collaboration with Einstein and Infeld), and he is the author of a semi-popular book on the quantum theory of the atom. He was born and educated in England (first-class mathematical honours at Oxford), but finished his schooling with a doctor of philosophy degree at Princeton. It is significant that two men so eminent in their respective spheres should consider telepathy a sound subject for scientific argument.

Is telepathy an established scientific fact, or simply another old wives' tale?

In his persuasive article, Kenneth Walker shows how strong is the evidence accumulated by men like Rhine and Soal in favour of the existence of telepathy and other forms of extra-sensory perception. He shows, too, how strong is the prejudice that most people have against accepting this evidence at its face value. There are probably far more sceptics than believers. And whether one considers this a melancholy or happy state of affairs depends largely on one's own desire to believe or disbelieve.

The existence of extra-sensory perception is still a matter of controversy. But if one blandly side-steps this controversy by assuming, for the moment, that extra-sensory perception exists as an established scientific fact, one may proceed at once to other aspects of the subject; in particular, the question of the mechanism through which extra-sensory perception acts.

Mr. Walker suggests that extra-sensory perception is almost certainly not of a physical nature; that telepathic messages almost certainly do not proceed from one brain to another by physical means, such as a transmission of waves or some other transfer of physical energy of a known sort. He sets forth, in the following words, three arguments to support his thesis:

1. "We know from our experience of radio that a very powerful apparatus is needed to act as a transmitter, far more powerful than we would expect to find within the confines of the human skull."

2. "All known forms of radiations obey the inverse-square law that connects intensity with distance. If therefore physical energy is being transmitted through space in cases of telepathy, we would find a rapid falling off in it as the distance between the sender and the receiver of the message increased. . . . [But] it is just as difficult, or as easy, to transmit a message across an ocean as through a wall separating two rooms."

3. "The transmission of a message by a physical means entails the use of some agreed-upon code. Unless somebody is present at the two ends of the transmission to codify and decodify the message, nothing can be sent. Language is a code, but it is not words that are transmitted, but ideas, and often ideas in the form of symbols. There are frequent instances of telepathic dreams, and the symbol is of course the language of dreams. The dreamer is warned that something terrible has happened, but the disaster portrayed in the

dream may not be the disaster that has actually occurred. At other times the message is accompanied by hallucination, especially when the phenomenon of precognition is associated with that of telepathy."

He concludes this passage with the remark that "the arguments that can be brought against the idea that telepathic messages are transmitted from one brain to another by some physical means are too many and too weighty to be readily refuted". And this is indeed a widely-held view.

The arguments cited by Mr. Walker are apparently conclusive. We may even strengthen the case by adding a fourth— namely, that the extra-sensory message is able to penetrate any obstacle, no matter how thick or dense, or of what material it may be made.

Yet, for all their cumulative weight, these four arguments do not by any means exclude the possibility that the extra-sensory message is, after all, transmitted by a physical mechanism. Indeed, they leave entirely open the question of the nature of the extra-sensory transmission.

To consider the fourth argument first. Certainly it is tempting to believe that anything that can freely penetrate bricks and stone, wood and mortar, air and water, and the solid earth itself is unlikely to be of a physical nature. Yet sound waves can do that. This is not to suggest that the extra-sensory message is transmitted by means of sound waves, whether sonic, super-sonic, or sub-sonic. It is merely to point out that what at first may have seemed like a serious objection to the thesis that a physical mechanism is involved is actually no objection at all. It is true that sound waves often suffer severe attenuation when passing through obstacles, whereas the extra-sensory message seems not to be hindered by any obstacles.

Does this compel the conclusion that a non-physical transmission is involved? By no means. For example, there is a well-known physical entity that possesses precisely this property of passing with perfect freedom through every possible obstacle, from empty space to the densest matter. That entity is the force of gravity. No one would argue that this perfect penetrability of the gravitational influence proves that it is in any sense non-physical. Everyone accepts gravitation as a physical phenomenon, with no mystical overtones of the sort that one instinctively attaches to the extra-sensory process. Gravitation is certainly physical, and, in theory, one could even signal with it. By merely waving one's hand one influences the gravitational field of the whole universe, and a sufficiently sensitive receptor could theoretically detect this change and interpret it as a message.

Thus, while there is no reason to suppose that the extra-sensory message is actually transmitted by gravitational means, the argument that it travels freely through all obstacles is surely not fatal to its being of a physical nature.

* * * * *

But to return to Mr. Walker's three arguments:

1. It is true that in radio a very powerful apparatus is often used to transmit wireless messages over great distances. But under favourable conditions amateur short-wave transmissions of quite modest power have been heard half-way round the earth.

Great *power* is not necessary if the receptor mechanism is of high *sensitivity*. A Geiger counter, or a Wilson cloud chamber, can detect a single electron, for example. Nor is the human body far behind this degree of sensitivity. The sensitivity of the eye is incredible. Hecht has calculated that a few dozen light quanta falling on the eye are sufficient to excite a visual response. And he has surmised that, of these few dozen quanta, but one survives the journey from lens to retina, so that the retina itself is capable of responding to a single quantum of light—the ultimate, indivisible atom of visible light. If the retina can respond to such microscopic stimuli, is it unreasonable to believe that the brain might possess a comparable sensitivity to the extra-sensory stimulus?

If we grant the brain a sensitivity of this order we hardly need to postulate an extra-sensory transmitter of enormous energy, especially since the extra-sensory message passes freely through all obstacles. Perhaps a fair amount of power is needed if the message is to stand out from the confused background of stray thoughts that must always be flying around. But we cannot be sure that there is not some tuning mechanism that automatically rejects unwanted extra-sensory stimuli coming from extraneous sources. Indeed, the rapport that is said to exist between some minds would tend to suggest that such a mechanism exists.

2. The inverse-square argument, which at first glance seems so formidable, turns out on closer examination to have little application to the problem. Extra-sensory messages can be received as easily over hundreds of miles as from one side of a room to the other, while physical energy would diminish rapidly in intensity as the distance increased. But extra-sensory messages, or ordinary messages, do not depend on intensity; they depend on intelligibility.

Consider, for example, a billboard bearing an advertising slogan in large letters. When we move away from the billboard the letters appear to diminish steadily in size. But our ability to read the slogan does not diminish correspondingly. On the contrary, it remains substantially constant over a wide range of distances. The *intelligibility* does not diminish steadily with distance. And it is the intelligibility that concerns us here.

The behaviour of the intelligibility is actually rather surprising. Not only does it remain constant over a wide range of distances, but it diminishes when the distance becomes too *small*; for we cannot read the slogan when our nose almost touches the billboard.

The billboard's message is transmitted by light-waves. The mechanism of transmission is physical, but the message is received with equal facility over a wide range of distances. The fact that a billboard message is two-dimensional introduces complications that need not be entered into here. A one-dimensional message will have the same general characteristics.

Thus a loudspeaker can be understood with equal ease over a wide range of distances. It becomes unintelligible when the distance is so *great* as to render it almost inaudible, and also when the distance is so *small* as to make the sound overwhelming.

This point alone—the distinction between intensity and intelligibility—is enough to show that the inverse-square argument lacks force. But there is a second, equally cogent, point that can be made in this connection. If the distinction between intensity and intelligibility is ignored and the attention fixed solely upon the intensity, even then there is no reason why the response should fall off as the distance increases. For the brain may be equipped with a compensating mechanism analogous to the iris of the eye or the automatic volume control of a wireless set.

The iris adjusts itself to different intensities of light so that, with a slight time-lag, the visual impression remains substantially constant over a wide range of intensities of illumination. The automatic volume control of a wireless set performs an analogous compensating function, and without appreciable time-lag; so that, at a given setting of the hand volume control, near and distant broadcasting stations come in with approximately equal strength.

The extra-sensory receptor in the brain could be equipped with some compensating device of this sort, for such devices perform the important biological function of protecting the organ from excessive stimulation. The eye has its iris, the inner ear its conducting bones, the conscience its elasticity. Why should not the extra-sensory organ have a protective mechanism that would automatically mask variations in the intensity of the stimulus?

3. Is there really need for an "agreed-upon code" between telepathic sender and receiver? All that is needed would seem to be a community of experience between the individuals concerned. If I have seen a sunset and you have seen a sunset, then when I show you a picture of a sunset you recognize it as being a picture of a sunset without our having agreed upon a code beforehand.

Suppose, now, that when you see a sunset certain currents are set up in your brain, some of which affect the extra-sensory organ? Suppose that roughly similar currents are set up in my own brain when I see a sunset? Then you and I possess, in effect, a code based on our common experience, just as we both understand what is pain without our having first had to exchange emotional code books.

If, when I see a sunset, I can set up in your extra-sensory organ the sort of currents that are flowing through my own, then I can transmit to you the notion of a sunset without the intermediary of a consciously contrived mutual code.

In view of all this, surely no definite conclusion can be drawn as to the nature of the extra-sensory mechanism, assuming it to exist? It may be physical, or it may be something strange, obeying laws of propagation transcending space and time and behaving in a way absolutely new to science. The question remains open. But the phenomenon of precognition implies that something is involved that plays havoc with accepted scientific ideas, though whether this has to do only with the brain or extends also to the mode of transmission of the extra-sensory message one cannot as yet tell.

HOW INDEED?

KENNETH WALKER

Illustrations by Alison Welch

We sent a copy of Professor Banesh Hoffmann's article which you have just read to Mr. Kenneth Macfarlane Walker to invite his comments, and luckily for us this distinguished surgeon was able to write more than a polite footnote in reply to his American critic.

THE first thought that comes into my mind after reading Professor Banesh Hoffmann's article, *Mind to Mind: But How?* is that the writer of this interesting contribution and I share a large measure of agreement. We agree that telepathy has been subjected to the most exacting type of laboratory test and that it has been as fully proven as many other accepted "facts" in science. It is no longer possible to dismiss it as a product of the imagination and to attribute instances of the transmission of messages from one mind to another to coincidence. Many so-called examples of telepathy can be explained in such a way, but when these doubtful cases have been eliminated there still remains a residuum for which coincidence is unable to account. Professor Hoffmann and I agree, therefore, that telepathy is an authentic phenomenon, and we differ only in our attempts to explain the mystery.

And how could it be otherwise? A mystery remains a mystery only so long as it defies our efforts to account for it, and so far telepathy has succeeded in remaining mysterious. No satisfactory hypothesis has as yet been put forward in the hope of explaining it, although many have been offered. Professor Hoffmann offers us the favourite answer given to the riddle, but I personally am unable to accept it as a solution. It is to the effect that the brain of the transmitter of the message sends out certain waves of energy, which, passing through space, impinge on the brain of the recipient in the way that Hertzian waves impinge on the wireless valve. With the help of such analogies as a "compensating mechanism" he has answered the objections I had previously raised to the idea that the message was of a physical nature, and he has in general shown great ingenuity in his attempt to drag telepathy inside the narrow framework within which scientists work. No one could have made a more gallant effort to explain telepathy along scientific lines than he, and undoubtedly he will convince many of his readers.

My own attitude to telepathy is a different one. I see no necessity to attempt the, to me, impossible task of finding a place for telepathy within the scientist's chosen framework, in which matter and motion are used as key ideas. Science is skilful in interpreting some of our experiences, but it has to be admitted that it is quite incapable of making sense of others. The great scientists have always recognized the limitations of their methods and have never attempted to make pronouncements on subjects which clearly lie outside their sphere. Consciousness and thought are amongst such subjects. Only the fanatical scientist is foolish enough to assert that consciousness is the product of physico-chemical activities occurring in the brain. It is almost certain that consciousness is associated with such activity, but this does not necessarily mean that they stand in the close relationship of cause and effect.

Indeed, it is quite impossible to conceive how such utterly different phenomena as moving particles and consciousness can be so related unless we make a radical change in our conception of matter. If the matter of the brain is capable of developing consciousness, the seeds of consciousness must lie also in other distributions of matter, for there is no difference in kind between the matter of the brain and that found elsewhere.

And this view of the universe, that it is a vast living organism endowed with thought and feeling as well as with life, is one that appeals to many philosophers, but to very few scientists. They prefer to look upon matter as being dead. For hundreds of years scientists have adopted the machine as their working model, and they have been extremely successful in interpreting phenomena in the terms they have chosen. So well did the concepts of matter and motion serve seventeenth-, eighteenth-, and nineteenth-century scientists that some of them came to believe in time that they would provide an explanation of everything in the universe, from the birth of worlds to the writing of a poem. But gradually the limitations of their working model were revealed to them, and few scientists are now of the opinion that life, let alone thought, will ever be explained in terms of physics and chemistry.

Even in the limited sphere of physics—the science which originally was the stronghold of materialism—the concepts of matter and motion are no longer proving sufficient for the physicists' purposes. Matter itself has all but disappeared, for the modern physicist is no longer able to describe the constitution of the atom in mechanical terms. It has become so elusive as to defy description. A vast amount of rearrangement has therefore become necessary in the physicist's mental equipment. So many changes have occurred in his way of thinking that the popular books written a few years ago by such men as Eddington and Jeans were couched in the language of idealist philosophers rather than of physicists. Why, therefore, should I feel constrained to explain the mystery of telepathy in terms which have now been proved insufficient even for the physicists' more limited needs?

"It (telepathy) may be physical," writes Professor Hoffmann in his final paragraph, "or it may be something strange, obeying laws of propagation transcending space and time and behaving in a way absolutely new to science." With this suggestion of his I heartily agree. Strange things have recently happened in physics and stranger still are likely to occur during the next hundred years. New concepts will replace the old ones, and novel notions be accepted as "scientific". It would be as impertinent as it would be unnecessary for me to point out to so distinguished a physicist as Professor Hoffmann that one of the terms he uses in his own article is already outmoded. He writes of the "force" of gravity, whereas he knows far better than I do that gravity is no longer pictured as a "force", but as a curvature of space.

Much will have to happen before telepathy can be explained, and the language in which the explanation is eventually written will be as strange as it is new. Still more startling will be the terms used by the scientists who give a satisfactory account of precognition. Professor Hoffmann is right when he states that foreknowledge of future events plays havoc with all accepted scientific views. Scientists have generally shown a great elasticity of mind and a good capacity for scrapping old ideas when they no longer prove serviceable to them. And this is indeed fortunate, for when telepathy and precognition are at last admitted to the fold of proven facts, the scientific changes which will become necessary will be immense. That is why so many scientists prefer to assume that both of these phenomena rest on nothing more solid than old wives' tales. It postpones the day when this great overhauling of concepts has to take place.

Can philosophy help us? Philosophy is a word which scares many people, and I know that the slightest hint of a philosophical discussion will make many readers turn quickly away. Philosophy for them is an academic pursuit of interest only to elderly retired gentlemen with time on their hands, and they would rather accept the riddle of the mind-body relationship as insoluble than struggle in a quagmire of philosophical terms. In spite of this danger, I see no reason why a philosophical mystery should not be a fit subject for discussion in a popular magazine.

When the mind-body problem was examined from the point of view of a scientist, no suitable place could be found for the insertion of a mind; when it is examined philosophically, no means can be discovered by which they can interact. The brain is material, it has mass and it is extended in space. The mind is assumed to be immaterial, for if it were otherwise, it would be part of the body. How, then, can two such different entities as a material body and an immaterial mind get together and interact? Mind and body seem to belong to different worlds, and it is impossible to imagine how this twain can ever meet. Philosophers have done their best to get over this difficulty by all sorts of ingenious but, to my way of thinking, unsatisfactory subterfuges. Some, for example, have said that mind and matter do not actually meet, but that they run together on parallel lines, keeping time with each other. They would declare, for example, that the great physical activity occurring in my brain at this moment is not the cause of my having new thoughts, but merely a synchronous event. At my birth—or rather before it—two clocks were set going in me, a material clock and an immaterial clock, and they have kept time with each other ever since. This is one sample of the many efforts made to overcome the difficulties produced by a dualistic philosophy.

If dualism will not work perhaps materialism will. Why should we not get rid of one of these two entities of dualism and see whether we can manage to explain everything by means of the other? Why not eliminate that hypothetical entity, an immaterial mind, and make the brain alone responsible for everything that happens? Many people have adopted this plan and have become materialists. At first glance, materialism appears to have much to commend it. Calculating machines and robot brains have been constructed, and if engineers and electricians can do this, why should not that cleverest of all artificers, Nature, do even better? Surely that most wonderful contrivance of hers, the brain, can manage to get along without the help of an immaterial and hypothetical mind?

How much "intelligence" can a machine show, and how can we try to define its limitations? (By intelligence is meant the ability of anything to react to changes in its environment.) In my previous article *Mind to Mind*, I described what happened in a man's brain when he saw the lights of a car approaching him, just as he was about to cross the road; how the circles of light focused on the retinas of his eyes, set up an agitation which travelled along the optic nerves to the visual centre in his brain, where an electrical pattern was produced and some of the message flowed forward to stimulate the motor area of the cerebral hemispheres, causing the man to step back and save himself. It was an intelligent response to a change in his environment, a response in which a great many events found a place, in addition to those described above.

Is a machine capable of making an intelligent response to changes in its environment? During the war, the Germans made mines which responded to different forms of stimulation, which recognized the approach of a ship by the noise of its propellers, by the pressure-waves it set up in the sea and by its magnetic effects. Having recognized the ship, they responded in the appropriate manner, which, for a mine, is to explode. Far more ingenious machines can now be made, capable of carrying out many of the brain's functions. The rapid increase of such machines has created the need for a new department of science, known as the science of cybernetics. This term is derived from a Greek root meaning "to govern", and all of these machines work on the same principle, the "feed-back" principle, on which the ordinary thermostat works, that self-regulating device which, when the temperature has reached a certain level, automatically switches off heat production. More elaborate machines of this kind can now be made to do a number of things even better than a man, such as those which control the flight of an aeroplane, and maintain the movement of target-seeking anti-aircraft guns.

One of the cleverest machines is the electric computator, erected in Manchester by Professor Newman. Its job is to carry out with rapidity and accuracy many numerical computations. It is fitted with a thousand valves, similar in nature to those used in a wireless set, and it also possesses its own electronic memory. It can calculate many thousand times faster than a skilled mathematician, and if the correct way of playing bridge were to be coded into it, this clever apparatus would make even a bridge champion feel small. From this it can be seen that, with suitable connections, wireless valves are capable of doing much that brain cells can do. They can be so arranged as to receive various messages, to store these for a time, in a kind of memory, and then to discharge these impulses later when they have received another form of stimulus. If a machine can carry out many of the duties of the brain, why should there not be eventually constructed a machine capable of performing them all? This question inevitably arises and can be answered by pointing out that there are essential differences as well as resemblances between the mechanical and the human brains.

The most obvious difference between the human and the machine brain is that the former establishes its own "feed-backs", its own pattern of memories and its own responses, whereas all of these have to be built into the machine-brain by an outside agent, namely, the engineer. Instead of discussing such complicated machines as the electric computator, let us take something much simpler, such as the penny-in-the-slot machine. The ordinary ticket-machine to be found in the Tube yields up its ticket in response to the stimulus of a certain weight of pennies, but it would be quite possible to contrive one which responded to some other form of stimulation, such as the human voice. But in order to bring about this change in its mode of working, the whole of its machinery would have to be taken to pieces and then rebuilt.

It is otherwise with the brain of a man or of an animal. All that is necessary to bring about a change in them is that the man or the animal should be "taught" to respond differently, in other words, should be "reconditioned". A rat can be taught to recognize a triangle. If a triangle is repeatedly exhibited to it and then it is immediately fed, it will learn to associate the idea of a triangle with the idea of food. Having learnt its lesson, it will always display great eagerness and pleasure whenever a triangle is placed in front of it. The rat may then be "reconditioned" to associate being fed with something else, such as the appearance of a square. When reconditioning has been effected, it will look at triangles with indifference and display an enthusiasm for squares. The brains of men and animals are pliable and adaptive, whilst constructed brains are rigid and fixed. Pliability and adaptability are properties of living tissues, and the chief difference between a mechanical and a natural brain is that the one is alive and the other is an inanimate machine.

There is another fundamental difference between the activities of an electrical computator and those of a man. It is that although the former carries out its calculating work more rapidly and more accurately than does a man, it is unaware of what it is doing. Consciousness, or a man's capacity to be aware of his thoughts, feelings, and movements, is the most wonderful and the most puzzling of all man's possessions. It is the mystery of all mysteries, far more difficult to understand and to explain than any other human attribute.

Instead of dispelling mysteries, this attempt of ours to regard mind as a product of the chemistry of the brain has conjured up fresh mysteries. At first, scientific materialism seemed full of promise, but it is confronted by two immense difficulties: the need to account for life and for consciousness in terms of matter. Can the movement of electrons explain the phenomena of life and consciousness? He would be a bold man who answered in the affirmative, and yet there have been men who have had the temerity to do so. It has even been suggested that the day may come when living tissues will be produced in laboratories. And if lowly organisms ever are produced there, why, it is asked, should not higher organisms also be made? The answer is that this will never happen, and that the idea that it may happen is based on an utterly false conception of the nature of life. But the mystery of life is such an important one that it cannot be dealt with here.

CRANFORD REVISITED

IANTHE JERROLD

Wood engravings by Zelma Blakely

W HEN Mrs. Penrose's nephew came to stay in Bridstone after a long sojourn in Los Angeles, where he had been doing something in films, he said that it reminded him of Cranford. Miss Gosling, who lived with Mrs. Penrose, felt flattered, and planted a lavender hedge round the currants.

But Mrs. Penrose, who had lived in Kensington until twenty-three years ago, when her husband had retired to Bridstone for his health and speedily died there, said that she had not realized that Bridstone was *quite* as old-fashioned as *that*! Peter Penrose quickly explained that he had only meant that Bridstone was very, very fragrant. . . .

Peter Penrose's amiable manners, and the glamour attached to one who calls film-stars by their Christian names, soon made Mrs. Penrose's nephew popular in Bridstone, and his aunt enjoyed taking him out to tea, and even gave a sherry party for him, at which a dozen carefully selected guests consumed small

glasses of sherry and saucerfuls of salted nuts, which Miss
Gosling said must surely remind Peter of Hollywood.

In fact, Peter preferred Bridstone to Hollywood. It made
fewer demands on his energies, and held out rosier hopes for his
future; for he was his aunt-by-marriage's sole surviving relative,
so far as he could find out, and although he was only forty-
seven, and therefore a good twenty years younger than the
average inhabitant of Bridstone, he thought that a retired life
in a freehold cottage on a private income would suit him well,
at any time from now on.

Mrs. Penrose said to Miss Gosling that it seemed rather a pity
dear Peter should let his talents go to waste while Hollywood
cried out for him. But it was pleasant to feel there was a man in
the house, and delightful to listen to Peter's stories about his
celebrated friends. And Miss Gosling was captivated by the
way the young man called her "Sylvia", as though the difference in their ages was not worth bothering about.

The only person in the household, or indeed in the village,
who took an adverse view of his presence in Ash Cottage was
Agnes. Agnes was Mrs. Penrose's old treasure, one of the very
few remaining old treasures in Bridstone, and the envy of all
Mrs. Penrose's friends. Agnes was more than a servant; she
was a skilled artist in domesticity, and she practised her art
industriously morning, noon, and night.

Mrs. Penrose frequently said, and meant, that she did not
know *what* they would do without Agnes! Nevertheless, as both
Mrs. Penrose and Miss Gosling knew, Agnes, like most old
treasures, could sometimes be just a *little* trying. . . . It only too
soon became obvious that she intended to be trying over Mr.
Peter.

The ladies supposed at first that she resented the extra work
caused by the masculine presence, and arranged for the daily
woman to come in on two extra mornings a week. But Agnes
continued to convey disapproval.

What she resented was not, in fact, the extra work, but the
disturbance of a long-established routine of life which had become sweet to her. She was seventy-three, and had been in Mrs.
Penrose's service for nineteen years, and she had looked forward

to several more years in it with no changes, except, naturally, a gradually increasing despotism accruing to her invaluable self.

For, like most rare beings, Agnes was aware of her own value. Agnes was considerably put out now that she must light a fire in the little study, which had never had a fire in it except at Christmas; bring whisky into the drawing-room at tea-time; serve coffee after dinner when everybody knew that coffee in the evening kept people awake; uncork wine when the doctor had not ordered wine, and, generally speaking, endure that sense of change which her soul hated above all things. In the well-bred manner of a trained servant, by the omission of permitted liberties rather than by the commission of unpermitted ones, she conveyed, when some weeks were past, and "Mr. Peter" showed no sign of departure, her deep dislike of the situation.

Peter Penrose did his best to reach those genial and patronizing terms with Agnes which Hollywood regards as normal between the young son of the house and the old retainer; but he failed to win from her more than that polite relaxation of the features which the decorum of servitude requires when an employer is making an ass of himself.

So uncomfortable did Mrs. Penrose and Miss Gosling find the domestic scene that after a while, when Agnes showed no sign of relenting, Mrs. Penrose attempted to have it out with her; but Agnes merely replied, when pressed, that no doubt everything was as Madam said, and she pretended to know as little as Miss Gosling's hibernating tortoise.

A month or two after this, the inconceivable happened: Agnes gave notice.

An earthquake at Bridstone would have been less surprising. The shock to the old ladies, who had foreseen nothing worse, though that was bad enough, than the continuance of Agnes's disapproval, can hardly be conveyed in words. Neither of them could see how to continue in Ash Cottage without Agnes. They would have to pack up and live in an hotel, a prospect wretched enough, and they knew that the reality would be worse. They would sooner be dead.

Searching and painful questions were roused between Mrs.

Penrose and Miss Gosling in the privacy of Mrs. Penrose's boudoir. For the fact was that their own feelings about Peter had begun recently to change. Gossip had told Mrs. Penrose that her nephew was running up a sizable bill for liquor at the "King's Head". Miss Gosling now confessed that Peter had borrowed ten pounds from her and had not paid it back.

Talking it over, the two old ladies realized that they were both a little affronted by the proprietary airs which the young man was showing towards Ash Cottage. All sorts of little things cropped up in this boudoir debate on Peter. They agreed, for example, that they were tired of finding the water cold because of his habit of taking frequent and enormous baths without advertising his intentions.

They ended a thoroughly agreeable conversation by a firm decision to ask him what his plans were; and, with trepidation, they did so. When it appeared that Peter had no plans except to stay and to be charming, they withdrew, defeated.

Then they implored Agnes, with tears, to reconsider her decision. She replied meekly that she was sorry but she was not one to change her mind.

Their hopes were roused next morning, when the daily woman reported with proper excitement that Agnes was in tears in the pantry; but all optimism was dashed again by the remote demeanour of their swollen-eyed old treasure as she waited at lunch. Mrs. Penrose and Miss Gosling were now at their wits' end. Domestic catastrophe was clearly immediate.

* * * * *

The next morning Peter Penrose was found dead in his bed. He looked as if he had suffered an uncomfortable end. A tooth-glass beside him contained a small quantity of fluid that looked like pure water.

At the inquest it was established beyond a doubt that Mr. Penrose had died of drinking a solution of oxalic acid crystals, or salts of lemon, and that the poison had been obtained by him from a small unlabelled glass jar in the bathroom. Mrs. Penrose had bought the salts of lemon at the chemist's about six months ago to clean a Leghorn hat; and Miss Gosling had availed herself of some to get ink-stains off an eiderdown.

Miss Gosling could not remember whether or not she had left the jar in the bathroom—with tears, and in a faint voice, she supposed she must have done so! There had been a label on the jar, though, a red label, she was sure of that.

Mr. Penrose had been in the habit occasionally of taking Epsom salts from a jar of similar size, which stood on the bathroom shelf. There was evidence from the "King's Head" that Mr. Penrose had been the worse for drink on his return to Ash Cottage at closing-time, which was after the ladies and their maid had gone to bed. There was no electric light in the bathroom.

No reason appeared why Mr. Penrose should have taken his own life; but it could not be concealed that his financial position was unsatisfactory. All the same, as his aunt plaintively but erroneously observed, he could *easily*, if he had felt in need of money, have obtained a lucrative position as film-producer.

The jury agreed that the poor gentleman had mistaken oxalic acid for Epsom salts. The verdict was death by misadventure, and the coroner gently suggested to the weeping ladies that they should in future be a little more careful about what they did with domestic poisons.

For a few days after the inquest, Mrs. Penrose and Miss Gosling hardly dared to breathe for anxiety about Agnes's intentions. True, the impediment to her peace of mind had now (how tragically!) been removed. But was it not too much to hope that she would overlook the awful upset of their recent experience? However, time went on, and Agnes said no more about leaving. She slipped *gently* back into the old, sweet, mild routine. Yet, as if the ghost of Peter Penrose lingered, the air was not quite as clear as it had once been between the two old friends.

"Sylvia," said Mrs. Penrose, looking not at Sylvia but at the scones, "I didn't say so at the inquest, but *I* took a dose of Epsom salts that evening, and I am quite clear in my own mind that there was *no* other jar on the shelf *then*!" A faint colour rose in her faded cheeks.

Miss Gosling also coloured. "As a matter of fact, Rachel," she replied, on an odd note of defiance, "although I said I didn't remember what I'd done with the salts of lemon, I'm quite sure

I *didn't* leave it in the bathroom! I put it away in the little cleaning-cupboard in the lamp-room!"

"Wasn't it rather extraordinary that you didn't say so, dear?" said Mrs. Penrose, with a slight edge on her voice.

"I didn't want to complicate matters," said Miss Gosling with an unfriendly glance. "*Somebody else* might have put it back in the bathroom!"

"Why should they?" asked Mrs. Penrose defensively.

"I don't know at all. I think it's very strange that if the jar wasn't on the shelf when you took the Epsom salts, *you* shouldn't have mentioned *that* to the coroner!"

"I didn't want to make things difficult *for others*," said Mrs. Penrose pointedly. "You told your story first."

"*Well!*" said Miss Gosling, and went to her room, after only one cup of tea, and did not come down till dinner-time.

"It's *only* the lack of confidence that distresses me!" observed Mrs. Penrose, helping herself to bread sauce. "One *does* expect one's friends to *trust* one!"

"That's *exactly* how *I* feel!" replied Miss Gosling.

All was not well between the two old ladies, and they found themselves unable to dismiss, as they had hoped, the affair from their minds. A cloud came over their life together.

Until one day, when Agnes had her afternoon out, and went to visit her centenarian aunt in Cortell Parva. On these monthly occasions the two ladies took it in turns to make the tea, which Agnes left ready upon the kitchen table. This time it was Mrs. Penrose's turn, and when she entered the drawing-room with the tea-pot, she was surprised to find Miss Gosling looking very flushed and excited over a volume of an encyclopædia.

"Rachel!" said Miss Gosling, in the restrained, triumphant tones of discovery. "Look here!"

Mrs. Penrose put on her glasses, and looking where her friend's trembling finger pointed, read:

"Oxalic acid is very poisonous, and by reason of its great similarity in appearance to Epsom salts, it has been very frequently mistaken for this substance, with, in many cases, fatal results. . . ."

"... *Rachel! Look here!* ..."

"Well, Sylvia?" she asked, somewhat mystified. "One would expect the encyclopædia to know about these things."

"But," replied Miss Gosling triumphantly, "the encyclopædia is not a *cookery book*!"

"Oh!" breathed Mrs. Penrose, for now she recognized upon the margin of the page a faint brownish smear of the kind left by a cook's fingers when making reference to a recipe, a smear frequent in cookery books, and flattering, no doubt, to the spirits of Mrs. Beeton and Signor Francatelli, but rarely observed upon the austere pages of dictionaries and encyclopædias.

"And *this*!" breathed Miss Gosling.

"This" was an unmistakable carraway seed which had lodged against the volume's spinal fold.

"Well?"

"If you remember, Rachel, Agnes made us a seed-cake on the day poor Peter met with his—his *accident*."

"I remember!" exclaimed Mrs. Penrose. "We felt too distressed to eat it——"

"And gave it to Mrs. Bunn for the W.I. lecture."

*   *   *   *   *

A thoughtful silence dropped between the ladies. They settled to their tea. When their eyes met over the rims of their cups they exchanged small, apologetic, affectionate smiles.

It was Miss Gosling's turn to carry the tray out.

"Agnes will be tired when she gets back from Cortell Parva," she observed.

"Yes. It is so good of her to go such a distance. She has such a sense of duty. So devoted."

"Shall I put her out one of yesterday's jam tarts?"

"By all means!" agreed Mrs. Penrose, cosily brushing a crumb from her lap. She patted her friend's plump hand. "Put her out two jam tarts! How well your lavender hedge is doing, dear!"

"I was thinking this morning," agreed Sylvia, "that I really must make some little lavender-bags for the Mission Sale in July. . . . *Two* tarts, then—Agnes likes apricot best. I believe."

TRACKING
HENRY'S
TOMB

by

HUMPHRY
BULLOCK

Wood engravings by Z. *Blakely*

TRACKING HENRY'S TOMB

H. BULLOCK

Brigadier H. Bullock, C.I.E., O.B.E., has served in India since 1916, *first in the Indian Army and latterly under the High Commissioner for the United Kingdom at New Delhi. He has made a special study of the personal history of the British in India, and admits to a weakness for Anglo-Indian ghost stories as well as for historical mysteries generally. Here he tells of one historical mystery which he has been able to clear up by a combination of good luck and persistence.*

O N a hot, sticky monsoon evening in August, I was looking round a little Christian graveyard at Allahabad, close by the Grand Trunk Road that runs a thousand miles straight across India and Pakistan. The graves could not be seen from the highway, and a friend had guided me to them through the high gates of a timber-yard, the owner of which,

Lala Bhagwati Parshad, knew the history of the burial-ground, for his father before him had owned property adjoining it.

After he had told me what he knew, I examined the epitaphs. They commemorated forgotten Britons—mostly army officers, soldiers, and their wives and children—who died during the first two decades of the nineteenth century. The rest of the tombstones were of Indian Christians and of later date. The timber merchant, who had come into the cemetery with me, made a remark that astounded me. As we walked through the rank monsoon vegetation, he pointed to a tall masonry tomb : "*Yih qabr* Royal Family *ka* member *ka hai*"—"This is the tomb of a member of the Royal Family." The trail I had been pursuing for twenty years had come to an end.

*   *   *   *   *

By the actress Mrs. Dorothea Bland or Jordan, King William the Fourth had five sons, of whom three entered the army and served in the East Indies. As a soldier, the most distinguished was Lieutenant-General Lord Frederick FitzClarence, who died in 1854 when Commander-in-Chief of the Bombay Army. Years ago I saw his grave at Purandhar, a Maratha hill-fort, and the little church beside it which was erected as a memorial to him. The eldest brother, George, who was created Earl of Munster soon after his father's accession, rose to the rank of major-general, and committed suicide in 1842. But I could never gather many facts about Henry FitzClarence, the third of the brothers to hold a military commission. Ordinary reference books were silent or vague. A modern edition of *Burke's Peerage*, which purported to list all the children of the William-Jordan connection, omitted Henry, although it gave full details of his four brothers and five sisters. Earlier works were confusing. *Lodge's Peerage* (1832) made him a captain in the Navy who died in India in 1818, but in the 1857 edition this was changed to a captain in the 87th Foot, died 1817. His death—without details—was recorded in the *Gentleman's Magazine* for July 1818 and the *Army List* of May of that year. Strangest of all, the new edition of the *Complete Peerage*, one of the most remarkable compilations in existence both for accuracy and completeness, the place above all where one would expect to find the solution, merely stated that he died in India without assigning any date or place. Since the *Gentleman's Magazine* and the *Army Lists* are amongst the elementary reference sources, surely "1818(?)" might have been hazarded?

* * * * *

My attention was first drawn to the problem of Henry Fitz-Clarence by the late Sir Evan Cotton, who was an authority on the personal history of the British in India. He had noticed a passage in *Scenes and Characteristics of Hindostan*, by Emma Roberts (1837, vol. I, p. 288). "A broken column at Allahabad," she wrote, marked "the resting-place of a FitzClarence," brother of the newly ennobled Earl of Munster. It could only be Henry. Sir Evan pursued the clue with his usual zest. He wrote to the Chaplain of Allahabad, but no tomb could be traced, and there was no entry in the burial register. I had visited the large Kydganj cemetery at Allahabad, and had copied some inscriptions and looked at more; but I had not noted a FitzClarence. The Ecclesiastical Records at the India Office were searched. These contain complete copies of Indian parish registers of baptisms, marriages, and burials back to 1700 in some instances; but nothing could be found.

When Sir Evan Cotton died, in 1939, I pursued the inquiry and found more evidence. The *Calcutta Annual Register and Directory* for 1817 showed Lieutenant H. E. FitzClarence (he seems to have had a second name, Edward) in the 22nd Light Dragoons, a regiment then stationed at Bangalore, in the south of India, and as being an extra aide-de-camp to the Commander-in-Chief at Madras, Sir Thomas Hislop. But his name was not in the index, nor did it appear in the roll of deaths or in the lists of passengers to and from Europe by sea. In a similar compilation, the *Original Calcutta Annual Directory and Bengal Register* for 1818, the name of Lieutenant Henry FitzClarence appears in the "Account of Administrations to Estates in 1817", but not in the list of deaths.

The War Office records were then searched, and it was found that Henry was appointed a Sub-Inspector of Militia in the Ionian Islands on September 11th, 1817, as captain. On Christmas Day following he exchanged to the half-pay rank of captain in the 87th Foot, and on New Year's Day, 1818, was appointed captain in the 87th Foot. The War Office had no record of his death, and the trail now seemed to lead away from India to the Mediterranean. But in the meantime I had learnt why Henry and his eldest brother George had left England. Both had been officers in the 10th Hussars in the Peninsula, and had been involved in a bitter feud which culminated in the trial by court-martial of their commanding officer, Colonel Quentin, in 1814. In my office library—I was then Judge Advocate-General in India—I found a printed copy of the trial. Quentin was acquitted of all the more serious charges, but the Prince Regent had the officers dispersed. Henry and George were banished to India. Henry was posted in 1814 as lieutenant to the 22nd Light Dragoons.

Thus I found the trail leading again to India, and in desperation I made inquiry from the ever-helpful Superintendent of Records at the India Office, though I felt sure that Sir Evan Cotton had already explored this source. While confirming that the records of deaths and burials held no entry, the Superintendent supplied an extract from the *Calcutta Gazette* of September 18th, 1817:

"DEATHS

At Allahabad, on the evening of the 2nd instant, whilst on his progress to the Upper Provinces, in the suite of the Governor-General, Lieutenant H. E. FitzClarence, of His Majesty's 22nd Regiment of Light Dragoons, and Aide-de-Camp to Lieutenant-General Sir Thomas Hislop, Baronet."

An entry in the diary of Lord Moira, then Governor-General of India, under September 2nd, 1817, corroborated this newspaper report:

"I have been pained by the death of Lieutenant Henry FitzClarence, one of my aides-de-camp. He was a mild, amiable young man, earnest in seeking information, and in improving himself by study. He sunk under the fourth day of a fever. . . . This day we have passed the fort of Allahabad" ("Private Journal of the Marquess of Hastings", 1858, vol. II, p. 209).

So it became clear that the postings to the Ionian Islands were mere paper transactions, such as were common in the days when army officers purchased their commissions, and were made in ignorance that Henry was already dead, for news travelled slowly to and from India in those days.

The mystery was now solved—except for the location of his grave, which was presumably at Allahabad, and according to Emma Roberts (unless she was indulging in literary licence) surmounted by a "broken column". My excitement, therefore, can easily be imagined when the timber merchant made that casual remark in the little Christian graveyard: "This is the tomb of a member of the Royal Family."

The monument which he pointed to had no broken column. It may have had one, but such embellishments disintegrate in a century of Indian suns and rains. It was nameless, too: the recess which had once housed an inscribed slab was empty, as is frequent with the older tombs. These slabs, according to Anglo-Indian tradition, were removed for domestic purposes by the local inhabitants: on them the *dhobi* (washerman) flailed his employer's linen, or spices were ground. But the Lala was positive of the identification, handed down by his father.

Though he did not know the name or story of the "member of the Royal Family" who was buried there, he added that about 1914 some English people, whom he had always understood to be relatives of the deceased, had come from England to inspect the tomb. All the same, a shred of mystery still clings to the tomb of Henry FitzClarence.

THE CASE OF THE PROFESSOR'S CHAIR

MARY FITT

Illustrations by Eric Fraser

We treasure the master minds and their faithful attendants in detective fiction, but the genuine article is rare. Imitations of the great original have almost always failed. For though imitation may be the sincerest form of flattery, flattery cannot please unless it is based upon a genuine appreciation of real qualities. The fundamental reason for the enduring popularity of the prototype pair is not that the one is a clever detective and the other is a humble foil; it is because both are delightful human beings, whose virtues, failings, oddities of thought and feeling, are slowly unfolded to the reader during the telling of their adventures. One develops an affection for them, as for one's friends in real life; one accepts, with growing tolerance and even pleasure, the little vanities and boyish pranks of the Master, and the sometimes desperate humility of his constant companion. One feels at home with them. It is our editorial opinion that Mr. Pitt and Georgina show signs of being also the sort of people one can feel at home with. A domestic air surrounds them, as it surrounded that immortal couple in Baker Street: an air which made their London lodgings one of the celebrated addresses in the world. Of

*course, we agree at once that there is no proper parallel between them.
For Georgina is not only that superior animal, a cat, she is a Siamese
cat; and is therefore probably greater than the greatest biped. It seems
possible, indeed, from the following tale, that Georgina is the Master
Mind.*

"Now don't misunderstand me," said Dr. Manners with
a smile, "but I can't help thinking that Georgina's
talents ought sometimes to be employed in the preven-
tion of crime. I've always thought it odd that famous detectives
—at any rate in fiction—allow murders to happen under their
noses, even when they've been fully warned."

Georgina, sitting on the top of Mr. Pitt's arm-chair, gazed
dreamily away across the garden, though one ear pricked in
Dr. Manners's direction showed that she was well aware of the
subject of the conversation.

"Georgina *has* prevented crimes," said Mr. Pitt proudly,
turning his head to give her a confederate glance. "In fact, one
of her first exploits, when she was still quite a young girl, was
to save the life of a very famous man. You've heard of Professor
Kenneth Lauderdale?"

"Who hasn't?" said Dr. Manners. "He's one of the world's
greatest research chemists. He invented Kappalambdathane.
Where should we be without it?"

"Where, indeed?" said Mr. Pitt. "When I think of all the
people who used to spend their lives trying to get relief from
rheumatism—and when I think that the discoverer of the
specific cure was saved by my Georgina—I wonder what testi-
monial could be worthy of her."

"There is none," conceded Dr. Manners gladly. "But do
you really mean to tell me——?"

"I do," said Mr. Pitt. Georgina bowed her comely head in
confirmation.

During my last year in Chode (said Mr. Pitt) I was invited
by the University of Broxeter to give a course of lectures in law.
The classes had to be held in the evening; and so, as the train
service to Chode was awkward, they suggested that I should
stay overnight on these occasions, which recurred once a week.

I wasn't very keen on the idea; Georgina doesn't care for

8*

hotels. But the Registrar pressed me, and when I explained my difficulty, he told me Professor Lauderdale had offered to give me hospitality. It seemed that Lauderdale had a son named Jack who was not doing very well in his examinations, and if I would go there and give the young man a little coaching, I should be doing Lauderdale a great service. He would put a suite of rooms at my disposal—his house was old and large—and of course I could take Georgina.

I agreed. I knew of Lauderdale's reputation, and I thought it would be interesting to make his acquaintance. He was known to be something of a recluse, absorbed in his research-work and inaccessible to most people. He was already famous, but not of course as famous as he later became, when the discovery of Kappalambdathane put him into the select band of the great benefactors, with Jenner and Pasteur and Fleming and the rest.

On the first evening, after giving my lecture at the University, I walked across, with Georgina in her basket, to Lauderdale's house. The night was rainy and gusty, and I was aware of impending adventure.

In a few minutes we reached our destination. The dark, rambling, old house standing among neglected shrubberies might have been in the depths of the country, though it was actually in the centre of the town. As soon as we were admitted, I was shown straight to my quarters. There was no lack of space. The rooms were large and the ceilings were high; the massive mahogany furniture, the deep chairs and heavy curtains, gave an air of Victorian comfort which was accentuated by the warmth which pervaded the house, and later by the excellent meal which was brought to my sitting-room.

I dined alone. So far I had seen no one but servants, of whom there seemed to be plenty; and I was just considering going to bed when there was a knock at the door and Jack Lauderdale entered.

Jack was a handsome, dark-skinned, black-eyed young fellow, very un-English in appearance; but his tastes were all in the direction of fun and games. He sat down opposite me in one of the arm-chairs, and showed his splendid white teeth

in a dazzling smile as he told me about himself: he was afraid
he was a bit of a disappointment to his father, but he really
couldn't concentrate on the law.   What he liked best was
boxing, and next to that, amateur dramatics. He thought he'd
like to go on the stage, but of course his father wouldn't hear
of it.

"I understand his point of view," he said with a laugh. "But,
you see, our tastes are so different: I'm the son of my mother,
I suppose. He met her out in Italy—she was a singer at the
Scala; he was quite a traveller in those days. Now he never
leaves the house except to go to the University; in fact, he
hardly ever leaves his own flat up there." He glanced up at
the ornamented ceiling, and the note of resentment in his voice
became more pronounced: "He prefers to impose his will on
the rest of us from a distance."

After a little more talk, I arranged that Jack should read
law with me for an hour or so after dinner when next I came,
in the following week. Then he went off, quite happy at having
shelved all responsibility. Throughout the interview, Georgina
had sat on the thick rug in front of the fire and contemplated
the flames. She took not the slightest notice of him, nor he of
her, and that was rather unusual: very few people see Georgina
without making some comment, generally of admiration.

I decided that Jack was either unobservant, or too much
absorbed in his own concerns to pay attention to anything else.

It was not until my second visit that I met the other members
of the household. First, I was received in the entrance-hall by
a good-looking young lady who told me she was Ann Lauderdale, the Professor's daughter. She was fair-haired and blue-
eyed, a complete contrast to her brother. She told me that her
father apologized deeply for not having entertained me on the
previous occasion, but he had forgotten the date. Would I do
him the honour of visiting him in his study on the top floor?
He excused himself from coming downstairs to welcome me,
but he was in the middle of an experiment which required his
constant attention.

I noticed that Ann, in spite of a self-possessed manner, was a
little nervous or agitated: when I put the basket down,

Georgina uttered one of her jungle cries—she could no doubt smell the excellent meal cooking for our benefit below stairs— and Ann started back. But when I opened the lid and Georgina stepped out composedly, Ann's alarm changed at once to delight. She talked to Georgina, and Georgina answered with polite purring; the two of them, both blue-eyed blondes, made a pleasing picture. Then I returned Georgina to her basket, and Ann led the way up the stairs.

Professor Lauderdale was an imposing figure of a man. I shall never forget my first sight of him as he sat at his study desk under an enormous gas chandelier, one of those old-fashioned fitments of brass which are kept in position by means of weights hung on chains. His head was noble, with a flowing mane and a curly beard; on his bony hands he wore mittens, though the room was quite warm, and I observed that the hands were distorted with rheumatism. His nose was hooked, and his dark eyes behind his glasses gleamed with a kind of intelligence I had never before seen in anyone. He was actually not old; but he looked a patriarch, and it was difficult to see in him the father of the two young people I had met. Beside him stood a very tall young man, very thin, with a protruding blue chin and sunken eyes—a fanatic, I thought. Professor Lauderdale called out genially:

"Come in, Mr. Pitt! Forgive me for neglecting you, but I'm sure you understand. Jessop and I have become troglodytes, if you can be a troglodyte on the top floor." He gave a dry chuckle. "This is Mr. Jessop, my left-hand man. I say 'left-hand', because my right hand's crippled." Another dry chuckle. "Jessop, go and take a look at that——" He used some technical name I didn't catch. Jessop at once detached himself and disappeared through one of the doors behind his master.

"Well, Mr. Pitt," said the Professor when I had approached and taken a chair, "do you think you can do anything with that son of mine? Or is he quite hopeless?"

I began explaining that I had had as yet no chance to test Jack Lauderdale's capabilities; but the Professor waved me aside.

"I know, I know. Don't put yourself out unduly. He'll never make a lawyer, in spite of his histrionic talents. But all the same, make him work—make him work! The young must be disciplined. They don't agree, of course. Sooner or later he'll break away and do something absurd. But first he must be disciplined. Doesn't matter much in what: the stage wouldn't be so crowded with incompetent actors if they'd been trained to do something else first." Suddenly he peered over the edge of the desk: "What's that you've got in your basket? Ah!"

I opened the basket.

Georgina stepped out, took one look at him, and—you think I'm going to say, she bolted in a fright? Not a bit of it! She fell instantly in love with him. I never saw such a display of love at first sight. She leapt on to the desk, swaggered towards him with all the coquetry at her disposal, rubbed herself against his shoulder, his beard, his mittened hands, while he caressed her gently and cooed at her as some women do over infants in their perambulators.

"A delightful creature!" he said. "What one misses by spending all one's time with inanimate nature!"

They might have gone on admiring each other all evening if Jessop had not opened the door and called to the Professor to come quickly. The Professor left us, saying:

"Come again—and be sure to bring your charming companion."

After I had dined, Jack Lauderdale came to my sitting-room as had been arranged. He had a request to make: might he bring a fellow-student, a man named Carruthers, who'd be grateful for a little help?

"He's not like me," he explained with disarming frankness. "I'm quite clever: I could mug up the stuff easily if I weren't so bored with it and my father didn't keep forcing it down my throat. But poor old Carruthers—he's dumb. He tries quite hard, and perhaps with a bit of help he might manage; but for some reason everybody finds him a joke. They all pull his leg —I do myself sometimes—but one oughtn't to, really. It's too easy. You see, he believes every word he's told, and that makes him fair game, or so most people think." He nodded towards

Georgina—the first sign he had given that he had noticed her:
"If you told him that cat was a monkey, he'd believe you. I've
never seen anyone so credulous."

"Rather a dangerous attribute," I said. "But bring him in
by all means if you wish. He'll hear nothing but the truth
from Georgina and me."

Carruthers was at first sight a typical student of the poorer
class. He was shy and stooping, serious, conscientious, accepting without question all that his teacher said, and carefully
writing it down. His carroty head, freckled skin and immature
features were in strong contrast to the handsome self-assured
Jack, who nevertheless was kind to his protégé and, I gathered,
gave him a square meal downstairs before we began our lesson.
Carruthers' chief fear seemed to be of meeting Professor Lauderdale on the stairs.

"Why is Carruthers so much afraid of your father?" I asked
young Lauderdale one evening after Carruthers had left. "He
seems almost afraid to come to the house. Surely the Professor
would hardly notice him if they did meet?"

Jack gave a laugh, not altogether without embarrassment.

"Well, you see," he said, "I'm afraid we've built up rather
a horrific picture of my father in his mind. It started as a leg-
pull. Carruthers is a nervous fellow, and it so happened, when
he first came here, my father was Dean of the Faculty, and
had to interview new-comers. Somehow he frightened the wits
out of Carruthers; maybe it was his appearance, maybe something he said—he does say rather terrifying things sometimes
for fun. When the fellows found out how Carruthers felt, they
began spinning yarns to him, all about my father's strange
goings on in the laboratory. They made him out to be an
absolute ogre—and Carruthers believed every word."

"I gather you had some part in all this, too," I said.

Jack's embarrassment became acute.

"Well, yes," he admitted. "One night I did get a bit carried
away—he's so tempting, you see, and what's more, he *will* ask
questions. I told him a long yarn about how when I was a
small boy my father had caught me stealing phosphorus out of
a jar in his laboratory and had made me put it in my pocket.

I said he had picked up some of it I'd let fall, and that was why he had to wear mittens, because he'd burnt his own hands in trying to punish me. The truth was, I shoved the beastly stuff into my pocket myself, not realizing it would burst into flames when exposed to the air. I got badly burnt and had to go to hospital, but it was entirely my own fault. Unfortunately, Carruthers believed the other story."

"That was very wrong of you," said I. "But surely you've contradicted it since then?"

"I have indeed," said Jack. "But you've no idea what Carruthers is like. Once he has accepted a notion, nothing makes him give it up again. When I tried to take it back, he decided I was acting out of fear of my father. My sister helped the legend too, by something she said."

"Really?" I said. "I shouldn't have thought she would have been a party to anything so unkind."

"Well, you see, old Carruthers developed a crush on her," he said. "Naturally she had no use for him—for one thing, she's practically engaged to Jessop—but Carruthers kept pestering her, and she let him take her out on the river one afternoon last summer. She says he annoyed her by asking a lot of questions, about Jessop, about my father and his work and so on. She fended him off for a while, but at last he blurted out, 'You're not a bit like Jack!' and that annoyed her, because her mother and mine weren't the same. My mother died soon after I was born, and my father married again, and his second wife—Ann's mother—left him. So she decided Carruthers was prying into what wasn't his business, and she said: 'Naturally. Jack's my half-brother. Rumour has it my father killed off Jack's mother first and buried her in the cellar with a top-dressing of chemicals.' Then she made him take her back to where Jessop was waiting for her on the landing-stage. Of course she had no idea Carruthers would believe it: she just meant to choke him off with a bit of sarcasm. But with Carruthers, you never know."

After that, nothing happened for a week or two. I gave the two young men some coaching after dinner each night, but otherwise I saw no one. I gathered that at the end of the term there would be a boxing tournament in which Jack would be taking part, and that Carruthers was the secretary and had charge of the tickets. Then, one evening, Jessop strolled in while they were with me.

Jessop excused himself for interrupting, but said he wanted to catch Carruthers: the boxing tournament was to take place the following week, and he was afraid of missing his chance to buy tickets for Ann and himself. I asked him to sit down.

Jessop was in good form that evening. His face did not readily express gaiety; it was usually serious to the point of gloom. But evidently something had gone well with him. He consented to talk, and even once or twice to give a short sharp laugh.

The effect on Carruthers was striking. At first he had seemed almost as nervous of Jessop as if he were the Professor himself; then, seeing Jessop's good humour, he began to relax, and eventually to become rather cheeky. He leaned forward, studying Jessop with an air of tiresome curiosity, and finally burst forth with a question:

"Look here, what *is* it the Professor's working at? They say nobody knows except you. It must be something terrific for them to pay him a salary for the amount of work he does at the University. The students hardly ever see him, and when they do, they say he can't carry out the simplest experiment without everything blowing up on him."

I saw Jessop stiffen. He said coldly:

"Professor Lauderdale is the great chemist of this age. What is disgraceful is that he should have to bother with a lot of lubberly students at all, when he might be carrying on with his own research."

Carruthers' shyness had vanished.

"But what is it?" he persisted. "Will it benefit anybody?"

Jessop relaxed. "That depends," he drawled.

"Depends? On what?" said Carruthers.

"On whether you set a high value on the human race. Professor Lauderdale's discovery will mean that one-third of the human race can be destroyed quite easily from the air."

"Oh!" said Carruthers scornfully, "the splitting of the atom! That'll never happen. They've talked about it for years."

Jessop laughed: "Aren't you forgetting that the Professor's job is chemistry, not physics? His discovery has nothing to do with the atom. It concerns—well, I suppose you could call it a sort of insecticide."

"Insecticide?" said Carruthers. "Well, there's nothing very marvellous about that."

"Not if it's directed at the human race?" said Jessop. He leaned forward; his thin blue jaw looked more hatchet-like than ever; his whole face, with its hollow temples and thin colourless lips, wore an expression of mocking cruelty: "All good insecticides are selective, as you know. The trouble has always been to find something that would kill pests and leave beneficial insects alone. Suppose Professor Lauderdale has found an anthropocide (if I may coin a hybrid) that's colour-selective— something that'll single out the whites?"

Carruthers' jaw dropped.

"Do you mean to say," he gasped, "he has discovered a formula that will give a substance destructive of the white races only?"

"Why not," said Jessop, "if he prefers the blacks, the reds and the yellows?" I saw him wink across at Jack. Georgina, who for some time had been staring fixedly at him, winked in answer. "It'll be called Kappalambdathane," he went on. "We hope that a small quantity will be ready by the end of next week. What's the matter? Don't you feel well? You'd better get some air."

Carruthers hurried away, and the other two roared with laughter. But Georgina and I remained thoughtful for a long time after they'd gone.

The following week when I visited Broxeter it was the last day of the term. I gave the final lecture of my series an hour earlier, so that the students could go to the boxing tournament. The coaching-hour with Jack Lauderdale and Carruthers was cancelled for the same reason; but I had been invited to dine with the Professor, so after the lecture I walked across from the University to his house as usual.

The house seemed quiet when I arrived. No doubt even the servants had gone off to a dance which was being held for them;

the woman who opened the door to me was already dressed, and longing to be off. It was all the more startling, therefore, as I climbed the stairs, to hear violent sounds of a door slamming and heavy footsteps as somebody ran down two or three steps at a time. The author of all this noise soon came into sight. It was Jessop.

I stood on one side, in order to protect Georgina whom I was carrying in her basket; but all the same I did not avoid him entirely. His shoulder grazed mine, knocking me against the wall. He seemed not to recognize me: his face was livid with rage, and when I protested, he said furiously: "Oh, get to hell out of my way!"

In a moment he was gone, through the heavy front door which he slammed behind him. As I pursued my way up the stairs, I thought I recognized the pale and anxious face of Ann Lauderdale on the landing. But when she saw me, she whisked herself quickly away to her room and shut the door.

It was a house of closed doors. I went on, past my own rooms, upwards to the Professor's study on the top floor. It was with something of a shock that I saw him standing in front of his own closed door.

"Ah, there you are!" he cried gaily. "Good! And have you brought your charming companion?" A muffled cry from the basket assured him of Georgina's presence. "But what's the matter?" he went on. "You look startled. Oh, of course—that absurd fellow Jessop." His dark eyes beamed at me benevolently through his glasses as he took my arm and began to lead me away along the landing: "Come along! We dine downstairs to-night. I'll explain to you about Jessop when our hunger is appeased. And Georgina—she too is catered for: the best turbot, I told the cook. I hope that's all right. Or would Dover sole have been preferred? Do let her out of her basket, won't you? There's no one else at home, and I'm sure she'll follow us quite safely."

I did as he suggested. We dined excellently. No servant was there to wait on us, but a meal was keeping hot in a trolley-oven beside the table, and the Professor proved a capable host in spite of his poor mittened hands. Georgina sat beside him

on a velvet-upholstered chair, and was treated to the best of all she cared for. He seemed to be thoroughly enjoying his holiday.

"Yes," he said when we came to the dessert, "this is a great day for me. I have at last succeeded in making a capsule of no less than fifteen ingredients, which I believe will prove to be a specific cure for rheumatism. Soon it will be in every chemist's shop. I have called it Kappalambdathane—Kappa Lamba— K.L.—being the initials of my own name. I am glad to have been able to turn my own suffering to good account."

We drank to its success. He sighed.

"What a pity that young idiot Jessop has chosen to behave so stupidly to-day of all days!" he said. "Would you believe it, he came to me just now and said he wanted to marry my daughter!"

"Surely there's no crime in that?" I said. "She's a charming girl, and I'm sure he's an excellent young man. I should have thought the match would have suited you very well."

Professor Lauderdale beamed.

"In good time, my dear fellow! Jessop has a great deal more work to do before I can spare him to marry Ann. I know all about marriage: I've been twice married myself, and I know what a waste of time it can be. In another five years, per- haps——"

I protested. But Lauderdale would not listen.

"He must be qualified to carry on my work after I'm gone," he said. "He's a brilliant man, but undisciplined—undisci- plined. I regard Jessop as more than a son, since my own son is of no use to me. Jessop is my spiritual heir."

"But he may decide to leave you."

"He won't. He can't. He is wedded—to Kappalambda- thane."

After dinner, I accompanied the Professor upstairs to his own floor. He had taken a fancy to me, now, as well as to Georgina; and he leaned heavily on my arm as we climbed the stairs. He wanted, he said, to show me the first capsules of Kappalamb- dathane: it would be something for my descendants to boast of. Georgina bounded gracefully ahead of us, turning at intervals to see if we were coming. She waited for us outside the Professor's door.

"Come, my beauty," he said, flinging open the study door and allowing her to precede him. I was amused at his formal courtesy towards her: she might have been a duchess, and in fact I doubt whether a duchess would have found him so obliging. But when we had entered and the Professor had turned up the lights of the great gas chandelier, Georgina's first act was to leap upon his desk below it. I wondered if she were going too far.

Not at all: evidently she could do no wrong. Even when she began prowling round the desk, gingerly touching papers, pens and inkstand with her chocolate paw and sniffing the edges of the desk itself with a curiously alert air, he still looked on, smiling benevolently. Then, as I came nearer, I noticed with surprise a fact of the utmost significance: Georgina's tail, usually as smooth as a water-rat's, was bristling like a flue-brush!

I stretched out a hand involuntarily.

"Look out, Professor!" I said. "Something's wrong in here! Don't touch anything, for God's sake!"

Georgina was now standing in the middle of the desk, pointing with her muzzle and quivering. She was staring intently at the Professor's chair. He toddled forward a few steps.

"What is it, my beauty?" he said, making for the chair.

The rest happened before I myself could take another step towards him. Georgina sprang from the desk on to the chair, and leapt away again lightly on to the floor; there was a tremendous crash of falling metal and breaking glass; in the darkness the sinister hiss of escaping gas drove us headlong out of the room.

I reached the meter in the hall and turned off the tap. Then I returned; and when we had opened the windows and allowed the gas to disperse, we brought torches and examined the damage. The huge chandelier hanging over the Professor's desk had fallen; one of the brass chains holding the heavy weights had worn through, and the weight had hit the desk, its ornamental spike making a hole half an inch deep, in exactly the place above which the Professor's head would have been if he had been seated in his chair and writing!

At first I thought it was an accident. But a moment later, Georgina's activities enlightened me once more. She was sitting on the floor beside the Professor's chair, elegantly patting with her paw a length of bright copper wire that hung down from the arm.

A brief examination of the fallen chandelier and the chair soon revealed the truth. The breaking of the brass chain was no accident due to corrosion: it had been deliberately engineered. The chain had been half filed through; near the weak link a copper wire had been fastened and conducted to one arm of the chair, across the seat, and then secured to the other arm, so that when the Professor returned from dining with me and took his place once more at the desk, the pressure on the copper wire stretched across the seat would break the brass chain above, and bring down the brass weight on to his head. Then the escaping gas would do the rest. The house was empty: all except myself were at the boxing match, and it was quite possible I would not have heard the noise, or would not have traced it in time. But the plot had been foiled by Georgina. From the first, she had smelt the recent presence of somebody she didn't like; and her leap at the copper wire had sprung the trap before the Professor could sit down.

A cunning plot; but who was the author of it?

At first I thought of Jessop, whose violent exit had startled me earlier that evening, and who certainly had cause to resent his chief's attitude. It might be convenient to Jessop to get rid of the Professor, not only because of his opposition to the marriage with Ann, but for financial reasons also: Jessop alone knew the formula for Kappalambdathane, and he could make a fortune out of it if his chief were not there to prevent him. Jessop was supposed to be at the boxing tournament; but could anyone be sure that he hadn't slipped out for ten minutes or so? Ann would certainly swear against all comers that he had never left her side.

I rang up Mallett, and we went through the house together, discussing the possibilities. Jack Lauderdale also came under suspicion. He was at variance with his father, and chafing under his tyranny. But Jessop remained the chief suspect before alibis were examined, until we entered the sitting-room which had been placed at my disposal and the first thing I saw was an iron file to which fragments of brass still adhered, lying on my table!

Mallett laughed.

"Well, well, Pitt!" he said, wrapping up the file carefully in a cloth and pocketing it. "What grudge had *you* got against the old man, eh?"

I need hardly say it wasn't I who was arrested. It was the student Carruthers, who, in spite of his ingenuity with the copper wire, had left his finger-prints on the file and his foot-prints on the Professor's desk. Georgina, who had never liked him, noticed his scent as soon as she jumped on the desk; it was she who with quick perception detected the bright new wire stretched across the chair, and made her life-saving leap that brought down the chandelier and foiled the would-be murderer.

The motive for the attempt?

Carruthers, as his fellow-students were already dimly aware, had an unbalanced mind: that is to say, he had two qualities abnormally developed, namely, curiosity and credulity. He could not help asking questions, and he could not help believing the answers. He truly believed that Professor Lauderdale was a monster: cruel to his son, a murderer of at least one of his wives, and above all, the inventor of a substance destined to destroy the white peoples. Carruthers throughout the period of his examination never ceased proclaiming himself to be a benefactor of the human race; some day, he told the doctors, his services to the world would be recognized and appropriately commemorated. He is still, I believe, quite happy in this delusion.

"So now you know," concluded Mr. Pitt with another proud glance upwards, "how Georgina prevented one important crime. Whether her leap was due to a realization of consequences or merely to playfulness I leave you to decide according to your knowledge or your prejudice."

Dr. Manners smiled.

"Let us at least agree," he said, "that we owe it to her that the discoverer of Kappalambdathane is still alive to work out other cures for human ills."

Georgina's pale whiskers, sensitive as a prawn's feelers, twitched in acknowledgment.

LONDON'S "MYSTERY" MEN

HANNEN SWAFFER

Illustrations by Nigel Lambourne

One by one, the "mystery" men of London, like the rest of its old-time "characters", are disappearing.

What has become, for instance, of the youthful-looking man who, with long golden hair falling far below his shoulders, used to walk at week-ends from the East End to the Piccadilly Circus area and back, always gloved and with a rolled umbrella? Never did he speak to a soul. Never did he respond to the occasional cry of, "Get your hair cut!"

For years, he was known to all habitués of London's central streets. No one knew who he was, or why, every week-end, he would start on his solitary pilgrimage and return to some unknown home east of Aldgate.

Some said he had been crossed in love—others that he was a journeyman tailor who, stopped from becoming an artist or an architect, indulged his suppressed Bohemian nature in this way.

But, in recent years, he has been missing from his former haunts. Has he died—or merely cut his hair?

Long since, I expect, death has claimed the top-hatted man

who, apparently well-to-do, would challenge passers-by in the Strand with the words, "Are you saved, sir?" and then walk on, not waiting for the answer, often one of ribald words.

Then there is the mystery of E. J. Odell, most famous of all Savage Club "characters". Bearded and fearsome, often violent in speech, he would browbeat into awe any new Savage whose face did not please him. While he boasted that he was an old actor who had performed with Irving in their youthful days— it was because of this questionable fame that he lived on free drinks—no one was able to trace any details of his stage career. He lived on a reputation that no one dared to question and all doubted, but no one could confirm.

Then, where did he live? That was his secret, kept from everyone.

Seeking to discover it, a group of brother Savages determined to follow him home one morning in the early hours. They walked in his wake, by a circuitous route, mile after mile, keeping out of his sight, they thought. At last, when he reached Hampstead Heath, the old man turned round and led them all the way back to the Savage Club. He had known they were following!

Not until, finally, Odell went into Charterhouse as a pensioner was his dwelling-place known. On his arrival there, the curator showed him a long list of rules. "There's not one of these that I don't break regularly," he said. It was in Charterhouse he died, in 1928, aged ninety-three.

For years, I wondered why George Parlby, another well-known Savage, always wore home-made clothes. He was an accomplished designer of stained-glass windows, and he had so many and such varied gifts that I thought his appearance of poverty was because of an oddity in his character and not evidence of his lack of means. So I did not ask the reason.

Then, after his death at the age of eighty-eight, they told me of the bad patches of fortune that Parlby had encountered.

Dickens would have revelled in making him into a character in one of his novels. His fierce moustache hid the good-natured mouth of the gentlest of men, one who delighted in jokes.

The London Sketch Club, where he painted with the other

members every Friday night, were used to his Christmas Eve
surprises. One year, a Carter Paterson van delivered a huge
brown-paper parcel at the door. Opened, it contained—George
Parlby! Every Christmas, he conducted a band of carol-
singers, all brother Savages, for whom he had made mediæval
costumes. Some years he wheeled all the clothes in a barrow,
pushing it from his Shepherds Bush studio to the club premises
in Adelphi Terrace.

When, because of his impoverishment, they raised a fund for
him, he said to a friend: "I wouldn't dream of counting it; but
I made them give it to me in ten-shilling notes. I have nailed
the wad to my easel; and now, when anybody calls for money,
I ask if it's rent, rates, or light. They show the account, and I
tear off as many notes as are required."

When he died, Bohemia lost another of its most fascinating
figures. His self-portrait is one of the Savage Club's proudest
possessions.

For long, too, I wondered about the identity of a clergyman
I often saw hanging around stage doors. Sometimes, when I
approached, he would run away.

The time came when, notorious as "The Rector of Stiffkey",
he got into trouble with the Church authorities because of some
sexual obsession, went to prison in Lancashire, was exhibited
in a barrel at a Blackpool side-show, and, finally, was killed by
a lion into whose cage he had been kidded to enter.

Then there was the tall-hatted individual who seemed to
spend all his time leaning against an iron post at a Fleet Street
corner, friendly-looking but silent. He stood there year after
year, a mystery to all us newspaper men.

"What does he do?" we asked. "How does he live?"

Rumour said that he passed on messages—"When you see
Mr. Jones, tell him I'll see him at three o'clock," or something
like that—getting sixpence or a shilling for keeping his eyes
open. But I never saw him take a message. So I do not know
how he paid his bills.

All these figures have disappeared one by one.

There still remains the silent Chinaman who passes along the
Strand and across Charing Cross Road, as remote and as
inscrutable as the Orient itself. His native costume is multi-

coloured; his silken hat is shaped like a spreading parasol; his gloves, often unused, hang on strings.

"He advertises a Chinese restaurant," someone told me once. But that is impossible, for he carries no sign, gives away no handbills, mentions nothing. He lives, I suppose, in Asia in his mind, carries it around with him, in fact, uninfluenced by the life of the European city around him, but certainly possessing its respect.

The same can be said of an Indian I frequently see going home around midnight. Although in European dress, his scholarly face reminds me of Tagore, always in his hand is a roll of newspapers. Has he come from a Hyde Park rostrum? That can hardly be so, for India to-day is free. Her grievances are no longer our concern. She is at last working out her own redemption.

Then who is the much more mysterious individual who, clad in tight breeches and a jersey, frequently stops suddenly on the pavement, indulges in shadow-boxing for five minutes at a time, and then, stopping it as suddenly as he began, goes on his way?

Another of London's mysteries is the woman who frequently writes me from North London in cultured script, telling me of her mission to redeem Britain, replace the Sovereign with her son, and lead us all into a new social order. Her letters, all of which are of considerable length, tell of signs she has found in coincidences in newspapers, symbols she has read, "guidance" that has come to her.

But, then, I have received communications of the kind from a Portsmouth man who claims to be God, and a Southend woman who declares she has given birth to the New Messiah. I am used to such things.

Years ago, a man who declared he was God called up the newspaper on which I then worked, said he was speaking to Fleet Street, and added that he was riding up from Croydon on a white horse. Some hours later, after being refused admission to the office, he rode the horse over the Thames Embankment, and shortly after was charged at Bow Street with attempted suicide.

One of the cleverest mysteries in my experience was thought out in London, although it was in New York—in 1912—that I first heard of it. There, I met Bill Gavin, former chairman of the National Sporting Club, who used to plot how to make another fortune by going to bed, staying there for months while he planned every detail; and then he would get up to carry out his scheme.

He made his first big money in this way by working out a method of maintaining a service system for bicyclists in the days of the early cycling boom. His men called at the customers' houses, patched the tyres, cleaned the bikes, and kept them in condition.

Then, after another long period of cogitation, he founded the *Throne*, a high-class women's weekly, and even persuaded Queen Alexandra to write something for the first issue.

I found him in bed in the Prince George Hotel, off Broadway, in the last stages of planning his next fortune, first thought of in his London bed.

This he was going to base on the exploits of "The Mystery Golfer".

"Golf is a passion here among well-to-do business men," he explained, "and all of them, unlike our golfers, boast of the length of their drives.

"Now, I've brought with me a British professional who has driven a ball for a quarter of a mile, although not in an official competition, at St. Andrews.

"Next Sunday, wearing a black mask, he will walk alone to the first tee, and, without saying a word to a soul, hit the ball a terrible welt. After completing the round, he will drive to the local hotel and stay in his room, unseen by anyone, except the landlord, until next day, when he will play another round. After some days, he must break the course record—and then 'The Masked Golfer' will be the talk of America.

"Then I shall sell 'The Masked Golfer's driving course' by mail order, by the hundred thousand, and at a high price. It's a cert!"

But when, next Sunday, Bill and I went to Van Cortlandt Park, to see the mystery man's first drive, he foozled the ball and hit it only a few yards! His mask had slipped—something that Bill Gavin had not foreseen. The standers-by laughed. The masked golfer returned to his room.

Next day, instead of putting on the mask, he blacked one, with burnt cork, on his face.

But, although he then played splendidly, the papers devoted to him, not the columns Gavin had foreseen, but only paragraphs. Bill, you see, had not included in his calculations the fact that Woodrow Wilson would be fighting his first Presidential election and that the news of that would fill pages and pages.

So, after some weeks, Gavin returned to London—to think out, in bed, another certain money-maker.

The last time I saw him, still optimistic, still full of ideas, he boasted to me that he had planned "the perfect murder".

"Explain it to me," I said. "I might want to murder someone some day. There are a lot of people London wouldn't miss."

"But I am going to commit the murder myself," he joked. "No one will ever know."

Bill carried his plan for "the perfect murder" to the grave.

Another of London's mysteries is, "Why do the Marxists hide from the public Karl Marx's love of drink?" Did they disclose it, it might endear to the British public a man the translation of whose ponderous tome, *Das Kapital*, makes most of the nation consider him a frightful bore.

During the years that Marx lived in our metropolis, he had frequent drinking bouts, which often ended in his climbing a lamp-post and hanging on the bar while his faithful disciple, Engels, stood by, imploring him to come down and keeping an eye open for the police.

Once, a comparatively irreverent Marxian has told me, Karl made a bet that he would drink a pint of beer in every pub all the way from the Horseshoe, at the southern end of Tottenham Court Road, to Hampstead. He was doing it successfully until he and Engels reached a Camden Town hostelry, in which, he heard, there was a meeting of trade unionists upstairs. As, in those days, working-class reformers included a lot of teetotal Methodists, his alcoholic insistence on addressing them on the coming revolution was ended by a scene of comedy in which Marx was ejected by the assembled company.

It was in the Leicester Galleries, only the other week, that I solved what was, to me, one of London's mysteries. For years

I had seen occasionally, in the National Gallery, which is opposite my flat, a man who must have been by far its most constant
visitor. He could not escape notice because of his intense enthusiasm about the pictures, his long study of them, his obvious
knowledge of art and his unceasing delight in what he saw.
"Who on earth is he?" I used to wonder.

Then, when I went to see the late Sir Augustus Daniel's
private collection of pictures, I turned to the introductory pages
which Sir Kenneth Clark had written in the catalogue.

"Ask which of your friends go alone to the National Gallery
once a week," wrote Sir Kenneth. "Not many do. Sir Augustus
Daniel did. I used to see him there almost every day, usually
in front of the sort of modest picture which only lovers of painting notice—a van Goyen or the corner of a Teniers. He would
look very closely for a few minutes, and then would execute a
little war dance of satisfaction, such as the cassowary is said to
execute after eating a snake."

So was the mystery solved.

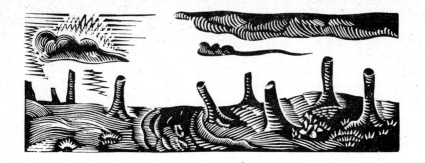

BEHIND THE STUMPS

RUSSELL KIRK

Wood engravings by Luther Roberts

Mr. Russell Kirk is an American, who is painfully aware that his countrymen do not, on the whole, appreciate tales of the supernatural. Nevertheless he here contributes a powerful witch story set in primitive rural America.

"And Satan stood up against Israel, and
provoked David to number Israel."

POTAWATTOMIE COUNTY, shorn of its protecting forest seventy years ago, has sprawled ever since like Samson undone by Delilah, naked, impotent, grudgingly servile. Potatoes and beans grow amid the fields of rotted stumps, and half the inhabited houses still are log cabins thrown up by the lumbermen who followed the trappers into this land. In Potawattomie there has been no money worth mentioning since the timber was cut; but here and there people cling to the strangling farms, make shift in the crumbling villages. An elusive beauty drifts over this country—sprinkled with little lakes, stretches of second-growth woods and cedar swamps, gravelly upland ridges that are gnawed by every rain, now that their

9

cover is gone. As if a curse had been pronounced upon these folk and their houses and their crops in reprisal for their ravishing of nature, everything in Potawattomie is melting away.

Of the people who stick obstinately to this stump-country, some are grandchildren and great-grandchildren of the men who swept off the forest; others are flotsam cast upon these sandy miles from the torrent of modern life, thrown out of the eddy upon the far bank to lie ignored and inert. Worn farmers of a conservative cast of mind, pinched, tenacious, inured to monotony, fond of the bottle on Saturday nights; eccentrics of several sorts; with a silent half-breed crew of negro-and-Indian, and negro-and-white, dispersed in cabins and sun-stricken tar-paper shanties along the back roads, remote from the county seat and the lesser hamlets that serve the languid commerce of Potawattomie—these are the Potawattomie people. Decent roads are few, the normally ubiquitous radio prohibitively costly, even the hand of government almost nerveless in this poverty of soil and spirit.

Yet not wholly palsied, the grip of the State, for all that. Tax-assessments necessarily are moderate in Potawattomie, but there are highways to be kept up, poaching of deer and trout to be kept down, old-age assistance to be doled out. There is a sheriff, intimate with the local tone, at the county seat; there is a judge of probate, also a local man; and the county supervisors are farmers and tradesmen without inclination to alter the nature of things in squalidly complacent Potawattomie. So far, government is a shadow. But now and then the State administration and the Federal administration gingerly poke about in the mud and flotsam of the stump-land.

A special rural census had to be compiled. Down in the capital, a plan had been drawn up, a plan that concerned commodity price-levels and potential crop-yields and tabulated nutritive-values. Acres of corn were to be counted, and pigs and people. Enumerators went out to every spreading wheat-farm, to every five-acre tomato patch; and Potawattomie County could not be omitted.

Always against the Government, Potawattomie; against the administration that ordained this special census most vehemently. This new survey, Potawattomie declared, meant more blank forms, more trips to the county seat, higher taxation, an intolerable prying into every man's household—which last none resent more than do the decently poor. The Regional Office of the Special Census began to encounter difficulties in compiling accurate tabulations for Potawattomie. Doors were shut in the faces of official enumerators, despite threats of warrants and writs; the evasive response was common, violent reaction not inconceivable. Particularly unsatisfactory reports were received from the district about Bear City, a decayed town of two hundred inhabitants. Despite his pressing need for the stipend attached to the office, the temporary agent there resigned in distress at a growing unpopularity with his neighbours; a woman who took the place was ignored by half the farmers she endeavoured to interview. The Regional Office determined to send out a Special Interviewer, and sent Cribben to Bear City. They let him have a car, and a stack of forms, and rather a stiff letter of introduction to the postmaster in that town, and off he drove northward.

Cribben took his revolver with him: he was that sort of man. Once he had been a bank-messenger, and he was wont to tell his associates, "The other messengers carried their guns at the bottom of their brief-cases, so there'd be no chance of having to pull them if there was a stick-up. But I kept my ·38 handy, really handy. I was ready to have it out with the boys."

Tall, forty, stiff as a stick, this Cribben—walking with chin up, chest out, joints rigid, in a sort of nervous defiance of humanity. He looked insufferable. He was insufferable. Next to a jocular man, an insufferable man is best suited for the responsibilities that are a Special Interviewer's. Close-clipped black hair set off a strong head, well proportioned; but the mouth was petulant, the eyes were ignorantly challenging, the chin was set in lines of pomposity. In conversation, Cribben had a way of sucking in his cheeks with an affectation of whimsical deliberation; for Cribben had long told himself that he was admirably funny when he chose to be, especially with women. His wife had divorced him years before—in Reno, since (somewhat to her bewilderment) she had been able to think of no precise grounds which would admit of obtaining her divorce in their own state. He lived chastely, honestly, soberly, completely solitary. He laughed dutifully at other men's jokes; he would go out of his way to write a friendly letter of recommendation; but somehow no one ever looked him up or asked him out. A failure in everything, Cribben—ex-engineer, ex-chief clerk, ex-artillery captain, ex-foundry partner. He told himself he had been completely reliable in every little particular, which was true; and he told himself he had failed because of his immaculate honesty in a mob of rogues, which was false. He had failed because he was precise.

"Corporal, about the morning report: I see you used eraser to clean up this ink-blot, instead of correction fluid. Watch that, Corporal. We'll use correction fluid. Understand?" This is the sort of thing the precise Cribben would say—if with a smile, then the wrong kind of smile; and he would compliment himself upon his urbanity. He did not spare himself; no man ever was more methodical, more painstaking. Reliable in every little particular, yes; but so devoted to these particulars that generalities went to pot. Subordinates resigned and read the "help wanted" columns rather than submit to another week of such accuracy; superiors found him hopelessly behind in his work, austerely plodding through tidy inconsequentialities. Cribben was, truly, quite intolerable. He knew the mass of mankind to be consistently inaccurate and usually dishonest. Quite right, of course. Sensible men nod and shrug; Cribben nagged. His foundry went to pieces because he fretted about missing wrenches and screwdrivers. He thought his workmen stole them. They did steal them, undeniably; but Cribben never would admit that moderate pilferage is an item of fixed over-head. There would have been something noble in Cribben's pertinacity had he loved precision for the sake of truth. But he regarded truth only as an attribute of precision.

So down to that sink of broken men, governmental service, spun Cribben in the vortex of professional failure. Having arrived at the abyss, which in this instance was a temporary junior clerkship, Cribben commenced to rise again in a small way. The assistant chief of the Regional Office discerned in this humourless precision the very incarnation of the second-best type of public functionary, and set him to compelling the reluctant to complete interminable forms. So far as advancement could be accorded him in this capacity, it was: he became a Senior Investigator, with every increase of salary authorized by statute. To entrust him with supervisory duties proved inadvisable; but within his sphere, Cribben was incomparable. It was Cribben's apotheosis. Never had he liked work so well, and only a passion to reorganize the Regional Office upon a more precise model shadowed his contentment. The majesty of Government at his back, the hauteur of a censor in his mien as he queried the subject of a survey or interrogated the petitioner for a grant—a man like Cribben never dreamed of more than this. For Cribben was wholly without imagination.

And Cribben drove north to Bear City.

False-fronted drygoods shops and grocery stores and saloons, built lavishly of second-grade pine when pine was cheap and apparently inexhaustible, are strung along a wide gravelled road: this is Bear City. They are like discoloured teeth in an old man's mouth, these buildings, for they stand between great gaps where casual flames have had their way with abandoned structures. One of these shops, with the usual high old-fashioned window-panes and siding painted a watery white, is also the post office. On Saturday afternoons in little towns like this, post offices generally close. But on this Saturday afternoon, in Bear City—so Cribben noted as he parked his automobile—not only the drygoods half of the shop, but the post office too was open for business. This was tidy and efficient, reflected Cribben, striding through the door. It predisposed him to amicability.

"Afternoon," said Cribben to the postmaster. "I'm J. K. Cribben, from the Regional Office. Read this, please." He presented his letter of introduction.

Mr. Matt Heddle, postmaster, Bear City, was behind the wrought-iron grill of the old post-office counter, a relic of earlier days and more southerly towns; and his shy wife Jessie was opposite, at the grocery counter. They were not lacking in a dignity that comes from honourable posts long held in small places. Mr. Heddle, with his crown of thick white hair and his august slouch, his good black suit, and his deep slow voice, made a rural postmaster to be proud of.

"Why, I wish you luck, Mr. Cribben," said Matt Heddle with concern, reading the letter of introduction. Mr. Heddle

wanted to be postmaster for the rest of his life. "I'll do anything
I can. I'm sorry about all the fuss the other census-men had."

"Their own damned fault," said Cribben, largely. "Don't
give a grouch a chance to make a fuss—that's my way. Take
none of their lip. I've handled people quite a while. Shoot out
your questions, stare 'em down. I won't have much trouble
here."

No, he didn't. Whatever Cribben's shortcomings, he was
neither coward nor laggard. Only six or seven hours a day he
spent in the tourist-room he rented; and by the time six days
had passed, he had seen and conquered almost all the obdurate
farmers around Bear City. Their sheds and their silos, their
sheep and their steers, their hired men and their bashful daughters, the rooms in their houses and the privies behind them—all
were properly observed and recorded in blank forms and check-
sheets. What Cribben could not see with his own eyes he bullied
out adequately enough from the uneasy men he cornered and
glowered at. He was big, he was gruff, he was pedantically
insistent. He was worth what salary the Regional Office paid.
He never took "no" for an answer—or "don't know", either.
He made himself hated in Bear City more quickly, perhaps,
than ever had man before; and he paid his contemners back in
a condescending scorn. His success was due in no small part to
his comparative restraint; for he seemed to those he confronted
to be holding himself precariously in check, on the verge of
tumbling into some tremendous passion like a dizzy man teeter-
ing on a log across a river. He was cruelly cold always, never
fierce, and yet hanging by a worn rope just above a ferocious
hell. What brute would have the callousness, or the temerity,
to thrust this man over the brink? It was easier to answer his
questions and submit to his prying.

Over the rutted trails of Potawattomie County in muddy
spring he drove his official automobile, finding out every shack
and hut, every Indian squatter, and every forlorn old couple
back in the cedar thickets, every widow who boasted a cow and
a chicken-run. They were numbered, all numbered. The birds
were thick this spring in Potawattomie, and some of the lilacs
came out early, but Cribben never looked at them, for they
were not to be enumerated. He was not an imaginative man.

Six days of this, and he had done the job except for the Barrens. Of all Potawattomie, Bear City district was the toughest morsel for the Special Census; and the Barrens were the hard kernel of Bear City's hinterland.

Who lives in the Barrens, that sterile and gullied and scrub-veiled upland? Why, it's hard to say. A half-dozen scrawny families, perhaps more—folk seldom seen, and seldom heard, even in Bear City. They have no money for the dissipations of a town, the Barrens people—none of them, at least, except the Gholsons; and no one ever knew a Gholson to take out a dollar for anything but a sack of sugar or a few yards of cloth or a bottle of rot-gut whisky. The Gholsons must have money, as money goes in Potawattomie; but what they get, they keep.

Cribben came into the post office on Saturday afternoon, a week after his arrival in town, self-satisfied and muddy; Matt Heddle was there, and, Love the garage-man with him—Love already lively from morning libations. "Started on the Barrens this morning, Heddle," Cribben said, ponderously. "Easy as falling off a log. Covered the Robinson place, and Hendry's. Eight kids at the Robinsons', dirty as worms." He looked at his map. "To-morrow, now, I start with this place called Barrens Mill. Not much of a road into it. It's right on Owens Creek. What d'you know about Barrens Mill, Heddle?" He pointed at the spot on his map, his heavy forefinger stiff.

Mr. Matt Heddle was a good-natured old chap, but he did not like Cribben. Potawattomie people said that Mr. Heddle was well read, which in Potawattomie County means that a man has three reprints of Marie Corelli's novels and two of Hall Caine's; but they were not far wrong in Heddle's case. He had not read many books, but he had read them often, in such leisure as he had found in a hard life. He owned a set of Scott, and was your friend for ever if you knew *Rob Roy* and *The Bride of Lammermoor*. These past two years as postmaster had made him comparatively affluent, with time enough to spend many evenings reading. The appetite for knowledge clutched at him as it sometimes does at pathetic men past their prime; and his devotion to the old novelists, combining with some natural penetration, made him rather shrewd. His good nature was unquenchable; so he looked at grim Cribben, and thought he

read in that intolerant face a waste of loneliness and doubt that
Cribben never could admit to himself, from terror of the desola-
tion.

He looked at Cribben, yes, and told him: "Let it go, Mr.
Cribben. They're an ignorant bunch, the Gholsons; they own
Barrens Mill. Let it go. It'll be knee-deep in mud up there,
this week. Look up the acreage in the county office and let it go
at that. You've done all the work anybody could ask."

"You don't let things go in the Regional Office," said Cribben, with becoming austerity. "I've already looked in the
county book: five hundred and twenty acres, the Gholsons own.
But I want to know *what* Gholson."

Matt Heddle started to speak, paused, looked at Cribben
with speculation, and said, "It's Will Gholson that pays the
taxes."

Love, who had been leaning against the iron counter, a wise
grin on his face, gave a whisky chuckle and remarked, abruptly:
"She was a witch and a bitch, a bitch and a witch. Ha! Goin'
to put *her* in the census?"

"Dave Love, this isn't the Elite; it's the post office." Mr.
Heddle said it with courtesy. "Let's keep it decent in here."

"Yes, Will Gholson pays the taxes," Cribben nodded, "but
the land's not in his name. The tax-roll reads 'Mrs. Gholson'
—just that. No Christian name. How do you people choose
your county clerk?"

"Mrs. Gholson, old Bitch Gholson, old Witch Gholson,"
chanted Love. "You goin' to put *her* in the census? She's dead
as a dodo."

"Will Gholson's mother, maybe, or his grandmother—that's
who's meant," Heddle murmured. "Nobody really knows the
Gholsons. They aren't folks you get to know. They're an
ignorant bunch, good to keep clear of. She was old, old. I saw
her laid out. Some of us went up there for the funeral—only
time we ever saw the inside of the house. It was only decent
to go up."

"Decent, hell!" said Love. "We was scared not to go, that's
the truth of it. Nobody with any brains rubs the Gholsons the
wrong way."

"Scared?" Cribben demanded of Love.

"God, yes, man. She was a damned witch, and the whole family's queer. Old Mrs. Gholson have a Christian name? Hell, whoever heard of a witch with a Christian name?"

"You start your drinking too early in the day," said Cribben. Love snorted, grinned, and fiddled with the post-office pen. "What kind of a county clerk do you have, Heddle, that doesn't take a dead woman's name off the books?"

"Why, I suppose maybe the Gholsons wanted it left on," Heddle answered placatingly. "And there was talk. Nobody wants to fuss with the Gholsons. Sleeping dogs, Mr. Cribben."

"If you really want to know," growled Love, patronizingly, "she cursed the cows, for one thing. The cows of people she didn't care for, and neighbours that were too close. The Gholsons don't like close neighbours."

"What are you giving me?" Cribben went menacingly red at the idea of being made the butt of a joke; it was the one thing his humourless valour feared.

"You don't have to believe it, man, but the cows went dry, all the same. And sometimes they died. And if that wasn't enough, the Gholsons moved the fences, and the boundary-markers. They took over. They got land now that used to be five farms."

Mrs. Heddle had been listening, and now she came across the shop and said in her shy voice, "They did move the posts, Mr. Cribben—the Gholsons. And the neighbours didn't move them back. They were frightened silly. "

"It'll take more than a sick cow to scare me, Mrs. Heddle," Cribben told her, the flush fading from his cheeks. "You people don't have any system up here. What's wrong with your schools, that people swallow this stuff? How do you hire your teachers?"

"Barrens Mill is a place to put a chill into a preacher, Mr. Cribben," said Matt Heddle, meditatively. "There's a look to it. . . . The mill itself is gone, but the big old house is there, seedy now, and the rest of the buildings. John Wendover, the lumberman, built it when this country was opened up, but the Gholsons bought it after the timber went. Some people say the Gholsons came from Ohio. I don't know. There's stories. . . . Nobody knows the Gholsons. They've another farm down the

9*

creek. There's five Gholson men now, and I don't know how
many women, but they don't mix down here. Will Gholson
does the talking for them, and he talks as much as a clam."

"He'll talk to me," the complacent Cribben said.

A curious sensation of pity came over Mr. Heddle. He leaned
across the counter and put his hand on Cribben's. This was an
act few ever had done, and Cribben, startled, stepped back.
"Now, listen, Mr. Cribben, friend. You're a man with spunk,
and you know your business; but I'm old, and I've been
hereabouts a long time. There are people that don't fit in anywhere, Mr. Cribben. Did you ever think about that? I mean,
they won't live by your ways and mine. Some of them are too
good, and some are too bad. Everybody's getting pretty much
alike—nearly everybody—in this age, and the ones that don't
fit in are scarcer; but they're still around. Some are queer, very
queer. We can't just count them like so many three-cent stamps.
We can't change them, not soon. But they're shy, most of them;
let them alone, and they're likely to crawl into holes, out of the
sun. Let them be; they don't matter, if you don't stir them up.
The Gholsons are like that."

"They come under the law, same as anybody else," Cribben
said huffily.

"Oh, the law was made for you and me and the folks we
know—not for them, any more than it was made for snakes,
Mr. Cribben. So long as they let the law alone, don't meddle,
don't meddle. They don't matter any more than a wasps' nest
at the back of the orchard, if you don't poke them." Old
Heddle was very earnest.

"A witch of a bitch and a bitch of a witch," chanted Love,
mordantly. "Oh, Lord, how she hexed 'em!"

"Why, there's Will Gholson now, coming out of the Elite,"
whispered Mrs. Heddle from the window. A greasy, burly man
with tremendous eyebrows that had tufted points walked from
the bar with a bottle in both hip-pockets. He was neither
bearded nor shaven, and he was filthy. He turned towards a
wagon hitched close by the post office.

"Handsome specimen," observed Cribben, fretting under all
this admonition, the defiance in his lonely nature coming to a
boil. "We'll have a talk." He strode into the street, Matt

Heddle anxiously behind him and Love sauntering in the rear. Gholson, sensing them, swung round from the horse whose harness he had been tightening. He was a rough customer, unquestionably; but that roused Cribben's spirit.

"Will Gholson," called out Cribben in his artillery-captain voice, "I've got a few questions to ask you."

A stare; and then Gholson spat into the road. His words were laboured, a heavy blur of speech, like a man wrestling with a tongue distasteful to him. "You the counter?"

"That's right," Cribben answered. "Who owns your farm, Gholson?"

Another stare, longer, and a kind of slow, dismal grimace. "Go to hell," said Gholson. "Leave us alone."

Something about this earth-stained, sweat-reeking figure, skulking on the frontier of humanity, sent a stir of revulsion through Cribben; and the consciousness of his inward shrinking set fire to his conceit, and he shot out one powerful arm and caught Gholson by the front of his disintegrating overalls. "By God, Gholson, I'm coming out to your place to-morrow; and I'm going through it; I'll have a warrant; and I'll do my duty; so watch out. I hear you've got a queer place at Barrens Mill, Gholson. Look out I don't get it condemned for you." Cribben was white, white with fury, and shouting like a sailor, and shaking in his emotion. Even the dull lump of Gholson's face lost its apathy before this rage, and he stood quiescent in the official's grasp.

"Mr. Cribben, friend," Heddle was saying. Cribben remembered where he was, and what; he let go of Gholson's clothes; but he put his drawn face into Gholson's and repeated, "To-morrow. I'll be out to-morrow."

"To-morrow's Sunday," was all Gholson answered.

"I'll be there to-morrow."

"Sunday's no day for it," said Gholson, almost plaintively. It was as if Cribben had stabbed through this hulk of flesh and rasped upon a moral sensibility.

"I'll be there," repeated Cribben, with grim triumph.

Gholson got deliberately into his wagon, took up the reins, and paused as if collecting his wits for a weighty effort. "Don't, Mister." It was a grunt. "A man that—a man that fusses on

Sunday—well, he deserves what he gets." And Gholson drove off.

"What's up, Mr. Cribben?" asked Heddle, startled; for Cribben had slipped down upon the bench outside the post office and was sucking in air, convulsively. "Here, a nip!" said Love, in concern, and thrust a bottle at him. Cribben took a gulp of whisky, sighed and relaxed. He drew an envelope out of a pocket and swallowed a capsule.

"Heart?" asked the solicitous Heddle.

"Yes," Cribben answered, as humbly as was in him. "It never was dandy. I'm not supposed to get riled."

"With that heart, you don't want to go up to Barrens Mill— no, you don't," said the postmaster, very gravely.

"She's a witch, Cribben." Love was leaning over him. "Hear me, eh? I say, she *is* a witch."

"Quiet down, Love," the postmaster told him. "Or if you do go to the Barrens, Mr. Cribben, you'll take a couple of the sheriff's men with you."

Cribben had quite intended to ask for the deputies; but he'd be damned now if he wouldn't go alone. "I'm driving to the judge for a search-warrant," he answered, his chin up. "That's all I'll take."

Heddle walked with him to the boarding-house where Cribben kept his automobile. He said nothing all the way; but when Cribben had got behind the wheel, he leaned in the window, his big, smooth, friendly old face intent: "There's a lot of old-fashioned prejudice in Potawattomie, Mr. Cribben. But you know, most men run their lives on prejudice. We've got to; we're not smart enough to do anything else. There's sure to be something behind a prejudice. I don't know about the Gholsons, but there's fact behind prejudice. Some things have to be left alone."

But here Cribben rolled up his window and shook his head and started the motor and rolled off.

After all, there was no more he could have said, Matt Heddle reflected. Cribben would go to Barrens Mill, probably count everything in sight, and bullyrag Will Gholson, and come back puffed up like a turkey. Vague notions. . . . He almost wished someone would put the fear of hellfire into the Special Inter-

viewer. But this was only an old-fashioned backwater, and
Cribben was a new-fashioned man.

On Sunday morning, Cribben drove alone up the road towards the Barrens. In his pockets were a set of forms, and a
warrant in case of need; Cribben left his gun at home, thinking
the devil of a temper within him a greater hazard than any he
was apt to encounter from the Gholsons. Past abandoned cabins
and frame houses with their roofs fallen in, past a sluggish
stream clogged with ancient logs, past mile on mile of straggling
second-growth, Cribben drove. It was empty country, not one-
third as populous as it had been fifty years before, and he passed
no one at this hour. Here in the region of the Barrens, fence-
wire was unknown: enormous stumps, uprooted from the fields
and dragged to the roadside, are crowded one against another
to keep the cows out, their truncated roots pointing towards the
clear sky. Most symbolic of the stump-country, jagged and
dead, these fences; but Cribben had no time for myth. By ten
o'clock he was nursing his car over the remnant of a corduroy
road which twists through Long Swamp; the stagnant water
was a foot deep upon it, this spring. But he went through without mishap, only to find himself a little later snared in the wet
ground between two treacherous sandhills. There was no
traction for his rear wheels; maddened, he made them spin
until he had sunk his car to the axle; and then, calming, he got
out and went forward on foot. Love's Garage could pull the
automobile out later; he would have to walk back into town, or
find a telephone somewhere, when he was through with this
business. He had promised to be at Barrens Mill that morning,
and he would be there. He was within a mile of the farm.

The damp track that once had been a lumber-road could
have led him to the Gholsons, albeit circuitously; but he consulted his map, and saw that by walking through a stretch of
hardwoods, he could with luck save fifteen minutes' tramping.
So up a gradual ascent he went, passing on his right the wreck
of a little farmhouse with high gables, not many years deserted.
"The Gholsons don't like close neighbours." Oaks and maples
and beeches, this wood, with soggy leaves of many autumns
underfoot and sponge-mushrooms spring up from them, clam-

mily white. Water from the trees dripped upon him, streaking his short coat. It was a quiet wood, very quiet; the dying vestige of a path led through it.

Terminating upon the crest of a ridge, the path took him to a stump-fence of grand proportions. Beyond was pasture, cleared with a thoroughness exceptional in this country, not one stump left amid the grass; and beyond the pasture, the ground fell away to a swift creek, and then rose again to a sharp knoll, of which the shoulder faced him; and upon the knoll was the house of Barrens Mill, a quarter of a mile distant.

All around the house stretched the Gholsons' fields, the work of years of fanatic labour. What power had driven these dull and sodden men to such feats of agricultural pride? For it was a beautiful farm: every dangerous slope affectionately buttressed and contoured to guard it from the rains, every boulder hauled away to a pile at the end of the stream, every potential weed-patch rooted out. The great square house—always severely simple, now gaunt in its blackened boards from which paint had scaled away long since—surveyed the whole rolling farm. A low wing, doubtless containing kitchen and woodshed, was joined to the northern face of the old building, which seemed indefinably mutilated. Then Cribben realized how the house had been injured: it was nearly blind. Every window above the ground-floor had been neatly boarded up—not merely covered over, but the frames taken out and planks fitted in to fill the apertures. It was as if the house had fallen prisoner to the Gholsons, and sat in bound and blindfolded shame.

All this was comprehended at a glance; a second look dis-closed nothing living in all the view—not even a dog, not even a cow. But one of the pallid stumps stirred.

Cribben started. No, not a stump: someone crouching by the stump-fence, leaning upon a broken root, and watching, not him, but the house. It was a girl, barefoot, a few yards away, dressed in printed meal-sacks, fifteen or sixteen years old, and very ugly, her hair a rat's-nest; this was no country where a wild rose might bloom. She had not heard him. For all his ungainly ways, Cribben had spent a good deal of time in the open and could be meticulously quiet. He came close up to the girl and said, in a tone he meant to be affable, "Well?"

Ah, what a scream out of her! She had been watching the blind façade of Barrens Mill house with such a degree of intensity, a kind of cringing smirk on her lips, that Cribben's harsh voice must have come like the words from the burning bush; and she whirled, and shrieked, all sense gone out of her face, until she began to understand it was only a stranger by her. Cribben was not a feeling man, but this extremity of fright touched him with something of compassion, and he took the girl gently by the shoulder, saying, "It's all right. Will you take me down to the house?" He made as if to lead her down the slope.

At that, the tide of fright poured back into her heavy Gholson face, and she fought in his grasp, and swore at him. Cribben— a streak of prudery ran through his character—was badly shocked: it was hysterically vile cursing, nearly inarticulate, but compounded of every ancient rural obscenity. And she was very young. She pulled away and dodged into the wood.

Nothing moved in these broad fields. There was no smoke from the kitchen, no cackle of chickens in the yard. A crow flapped overhead, as much an alien as Cribben himself; nothing more seemed to live about Barrens Mill. Were Will Gholson crazy enough to be peering from one of the windows with a shotgun beside him, Cribben would make a target impossible to miss, and Cribben knew it. But there came no movement behind the blinds, and Cribben went round unscathed to the kitchen door.

A pause and a glance told Cribben that the animals were gone, all of them, down to every cat, every hen. Driven to the lower farm to vex and delay him? And it looked as if every Gholson had gone with them. He knocked at the scarred back door: only echoes within. It was not locked; he had his warrant in his pocket; he entered. If Will Gholson were keeping mum inside, he'd rout him out.

Four low rooms—kitchen, rough parlour, a couple of topsy-turvy bedrooms—this was the wing of the house, showing every sign of a speedy flight. A very heavy panelled door shut off the parlour from the square mass of the older house, and its big key was in the lock. Well, it was worth a try. Cribben unlocked it and looked in: black, frayed blinds drawn down over the

windows—and the windows upstairs boarded, of course. He returned to the kitchen, got a kerosene lamp, lit it, and went back to the darkened rooms.

Fourteen-foot ceilings in these cold chambers; and the remnants of Victorian prosperity in mildewed love-seats and peeling gilt mirrors; and dust, dust. A damp place, utterly still. Cribben told his nerves to behave. He went up the fine sweep of the solid stairs, the white plaster of the wall gleaming from his lamp. Dust, dust.

A broad corridor, and three rooms of moderate size, their doors open, a naked bedstead in each; and at the head of the corridor, a door that stuck. The stillness infected Cribben, and he pressed his weight cautiously upon the knob so that the squeak of the hinges was slight when the door yielded. He was in, holding the lamp above his head.

Marble-topped commode, wash-bowl holding a powder of grime, fantastic oaken wardrobe—and a gigantic Victorian rosewood bed, carven and scrolled, its towering head casting a shadow upon the sheets that covered the mattress. There *were* sheets; and they were humped with the shape of someone snuggled under them. "Come on out," said Cribben, his throat dry. No one spoke, and he ripped the covers back. He had a halfsecond to look before he dropped the lamp to its ruin.

Old, old—how old? She had been immensely fat, he could tell in that frozen moment, but now the malignant wrinkles hung in horrid empty folds. How evil! And even yet, that drooping lip of command, that projecting jaw; he knew at last from what source had come the power that terraced and tended Barrens Mill. The eyelids were drawn down. For this only was there time before the lamp smashed. Ah, why hadn't they buried her? For she was dead, long dead, many a season dead.

All light gone, Cribben stood rigid, his fingers pressed distractedly against his thighs. To his brain, absurdly, came a forgotten picture out of his childhood, a coloured print in his *King Arthur*: "Launcelot in the Chapel of the Dead Wizard", with the knight lifting the corner of a shroud. The picture dropped away, and he silently told his unmoving self, again and again, "Old Mrs. Gholson, old witch, old bitch," like an incantation. Then he groped for the vanished door, but stumbled upon the wire guard of the broken lamp.

One's equilibrium trickles away in blackness, and Cribben felt his balance going, and knew to his horror that he was falling straight across the bed. He struck the sheets heavily, and paused there in a paralysis of revulsion. Then it came to him that there was no one beneath him.

Revulsion was swallowed in a compelling urgency, and Cribben slid his hands sweepingly along the covers, in desperate hope of a mistake. But no. There was no form in the bed but his. He hunched against the back-board, crouching like a great clumsy dog while he blinked for any filtered drop of light, show him what it would.

He had left the door ajar; and through it wavered the very dimmest of dim glows, the forlorn hope of the bright sun outside. Now that Cribben's eyes had been a little while in the room, he could discern whatever was silhouetted against the doorway—the back of a chair, the edge of the door itself, the knob. And something *moved* into silhouette: imperious nose, pendulous lip, great jaw. So much, before Cribben's heart made its last leaping protest.

They sit in the Tower, in the dark midnight hour
   They summon before them invisible hosts,
By the guttering taper they write a White Paper,
   The Royal Commission on National Ghosts.
The new regulation for wraith registration
   Is intended to further the State tourist trade—
All ghosts are directed to "walk" where expected
   And some must give reasons for not being laid.

To spectres in residence Members give precedence,
   Monarchs and princes are put at their ease,
Crowned queens on appearing are given a hearing,
   And invited to sit with their heads on their knees.
A king's apparition requires no permission
   For haunting the Tower, a royal demesne;
A sovereign's relation ensures occupation
   By decapitation upon Tower Green.

The spectre manorial with rights immemorial,
   His title may keep to continued access,

But prospects are ominous for phantoms anonymous,
  Like White and Grey Ladies of no fixed address.
A lease residential is henceforth essential,
  Confining to precincts both abbots and nuns;
Black Monks have been called up, but most will be walled up,
  And none may appear in two places at once.

In Tudor-type thatched house or semi-detached house
  No tenant unearthly his presence may flaunt,
If the roof he has jumped off or merely been bumped off,
  A violent end gives no licence to haunt.
Controls will eliminate spooks indiscriminate,
  Ghosts without legends are strictly debarred;
No flibberty-gibbety shade will have liberty
  To gibber without an identity card.

The plan for restriction creates widespread friction,
  And summary eviction draws clamorous crowds,
Banned spirits indignant appear quite malignant
  And mutter and twitter and shriek in their shrouds.
But still in the Tower in the black, witching hour,
  The Members till daybreak remain at their posts,
Making recommendations on manifestations—
  The Royal Commission on National Ghosts.

Sagittarius

Borley Rectory

POSTSCRIPT TO HARRY PRICE

ROBERT FORDYCE AICKMAN

The late Harry Price, the well-known ghost-hunter and detector of false claimants to psychic powers, devoted his life and private fortune to the study of alleged abnormal phenomena. He also formed a library of 17,000 books on the subject, now housed in the University of London. Mr. Aickman writes about Price as one who was intimately acquainted with some of his investigations; and though Mr. Aickman found Price a trying person to work with, he pays testimony to his integrity as a psychic detective. Mr. Aickman, by the way, is a grandson of Richard Marsh, author of that classic example of the mystery story, The Beetle.

OVER one of his famous Reform Club luncheons I remember the surprise with which I heard Price tell me that not only had none of his books been published in the United States, but that no effort had ever been made to publish them. I remember confidently assuring him that a large American market awaited him, though the iniquities of Washington copyright would, of course, deprive him of more than *ex gratia* American proceeds from his past publications. I remember the assortment of articles from varied American papers, most kindly supplied to me by a friend to show how wrong I was: articles which made it clear that the overwhelming American attitude towards the paranormal (to use Price's word) is one of *total* incredulity, and polite or contemptuous anthropological observation from afar.

Despite the work of Rhine and other isolated investigators, who tend to become centres of emotional cults, the American Editor regards the phenomena Price investigated as European, mainly English, and faintly symptomatic of decadence. The American social carapace grows so normally and fits so closely that those who break out towards supernaturalism tend, not towards polite treatises, but towards such violent and frightening creations as those of Poe, Bierce and William Hope Hodgson: creations which find a minority of like-minded readers.

Starting from a remarkable paranormal experience when a child (fully described in his book *Confessions of a Ghost Hunter*), Price resolved to devote his life to the scientific investigation of alleged paranormal happenings of all kinds, from the largest to the smallest, and wherever the story might come from. Most work of value is made possible directly or indirectly by a private income: in Price's case paper was the merchandise from which much of the income came. It is a curious fact that he nowhere records a paranormal occurrence, personally experienced, which equals that first one in his Shropshire boyhood; an even more curious fact is that, despite all his pretensions, he was comparatively unscientific.

A man of the wide interests and varied knowledge indispensable to the pioneer of a new science, he had more than superficial knowledge of many different scientific matters. His wide and various scientific knowledge must, indeed, be the prevailing impression left upon many who read his books; and in his store the predominance of technological information, experience and ingenuity led to his well-known portmanteaux of ghost-hunting equipment (which became before long almost immovable); and to his several ghost-catching and ghost-observing inventions, which were most valuable in his work. No one has ever been so skilful as Price in detecting the fake medium; it is a matter of scientific consequence that one of two mediums did produce results even under Price's elaborate and formidable "test conditions". The Schneider Brothers, and Stella C., whom Price met by chance in the train to Pulborough, where he lived, were

perhaps the most notable mediums whom Price felt able to
certify as genuine; and though none of their manifestations, so
carefully recorded, seems to show the slightest relevance to the
possibility of "survival", yet their cause remains totally obscure
and likely to be of marked importance. But in a larger way
Price's methods were far from those of the best scientists. He
was extremely weak at theorizing, so that he seldom rose above
the level of field worker; he was equally weak at co-opera-
ting with the few fellow-workers in the same field; above all,
he was disastrously lacking in scientific thoroughness and persistence.

The first of these unscientific attributes tended to put his
labours at the mercy of abler theorists who were possibly
negligible field workers, almost entirely lacking in first-hand
acquaintance with the facts. In one of his most important cases,
the noted one of Borley Rectory, where the alleged apparitions
seemed in part to be connected with a seventeenth-century nun,
and in part with the Bull family, two members of which were
Rectors of Borley, it is most noticeable how Price passes from
the emphasis in his first (and better) book on the subject, *The
Most Haunted House in England*, upon what may be termed the
Bull group of supposed apparitions and occurrences, to the
emphasis in *The End of Borley Rectory* upon the Nun group; and
hard not to conclude that he does so, not under pressure of the
evidence, but under pressure of the extremely ingenious theorizing submitted to him by Canon Phythian-Adams, who seems
nowhere to be recorded as having once visited the Rectory. If
this conclusion is incorrect, the fault remains in Price's unscientific exposition. If the two books are read consecutively,
the reader may well be left with so many uncertainties as to
doubt the substance of almost everything recorded. Those with
any knowledge of the authenticated paranormal know how
difficult it is to devise any theory which will cover *all* the cases;
but the suggestions at the end of Price's autobiography, *Search
for Truth*, are notably inadequate. Price's secretiveness could
try the patience. Although I was in full communication with
him when my friends and I made the visits to Borley recorded
in *The End of Borley Rectory*, Price never informed me that he
himself was visiting the place almost immediately before and

after my visits, and in order to carry out the vital excavations in the cellars and well.

And in another matter of great importance, his behaviour to me fell short of the scientific. On inspecting the Rectory in 1943 I was shocked to discover how much farther the structure had deteriorated in the years since the fire in 1939. In particular, the fantastic and unique wall writings were in process of obliteration, and also of submergement among the imitations and random *graffiti* of the hooligan scribblers which such a phenomenon, when left more or less freely open to every passer-by, had inevitably attracted. Price having suggested to me that he lacked precise information as to the ownership of the property at that date, I went to considerable trouble investigating the question, which certainly proved more obscure than could be expected.

Ultimately, however, I traced the ownership, and, indicating that I might be interested in purchasing the place, succeeded in bringing negotiations to a point where, in my opinion (right or wrong), a bargain could have been struck at a quite remarkably low figure. I then wrote to Price, proposing that we initiate a small Trust to acquire the Rectory in the interests of science and for further research. I not only offered a financial contribution, but to undertake free of charge the work of organization. Price was invited merely to make a contribution equal to mine (and, I suggested, to everyone else's); and to sponsor the venture to the extent of becoming its titular head. It may be added that, apart from the absolutely unique scientific value of the Rectory (as the world's best authenticated haunted house), the property was a good commercial investment at the figure contemplated, and included the intact lodge for the housing of future investigators. Price would have nothing to do with the idea, under my management, his own, or anyone else's; and shortly afterwards Borley Rectory, with wall writings absolutely unique in the world, was duly demolished for the building materials it contained. The course of events described in no way prevented Price from lamenting, in *The End of Borley Rectory*, that no public action was taken to preserve the structure from demolition. Yet it was useless for me to put my plans into force without Price's support.

Price's lack of persistence may be briefly disposed of. Repeatedly the reader of his books is driven to maddening speculation why Price did not pursue some particular matter farther in some particularly obvious way. Sometimes the reader wonders whether, in fact, Price did not do so without, for one reason or another (mainly a certain breezy casualness), disclosing the upshot. Could anyone enabled to participate in the almost incredible experience of "Rosalie" (*Fifty Years of Psychical Research*) be so lacking in imagination as to abstain from pressing investigation farther despite all the restrictions and obstacles? Even the crucial diggings at Borley fizzle out, as Price writes about them. It is not that he writes too little; but that much of the matter is merely repetitive, and that obvious lines of inquiry are not only left totally neglected by Price, but to no small extent closed by him to other possible investigators. In both the instances quoted, the matters under inquiry touched more nearly upon the "survival" question than any other Price describes.

It is probable that the gusto, the English boyishness (Price was as totally English as a man can be, a person impossible to think of as other than English) which carried him forward on his quest, made unlikely in a single man the capacity for minute and comprehensive inquiries which the facts and stories needed. In Price the science of psychic research suffered from lack of workers; his vital contribution and initiative should have been followed by auxiliaries of a different, duller type. It cannot be said that Price seemed to encourage such auxiliaries; but as he would presumably have had himself to pay them, he can hardly be blamed. Moreover, after myself meeting Miss Voirrey Irving, the heroine of the "talking mongoose" case (subject of *The Haunting of Cashen's Gap*, by Harry Price and R. S. Lambert), my previous criticisms (obvious enough to anyone who reads the book) of the seemingly perfunctory way in which Price pursued that unusual animal, were modified by a new understanding of the difficulties. Whatever the explanation of such a story, so long maintained by several different people in such a remote place, it must be both out of the ordinary and interesting; but to fathom it, imaginative acquaintance may be required of half a dozen different branches of knowledge.

No one can question that Price worked unremittingly for the recognition by official science of psychic research as a branch of study. In *Search for Truth* he listed the meagre results : a thesis producing a studentship or two (founded, naturally, by private patrons) ; the grudging acceptance by London University of the 17,000 volumes contained in the "Harry Price Library of Magical Literature", undoubtedly the finest collection of its kind in the world. The record throws no credit whatever on official science, which here emerges as incurious and governed by an irrational refusal to consider evidence. It was left to Price to found and run the National Laboratory of Psychic Research from his own resources ; and to put forward the only reasonable legislative proposals yet made for controlling (without persecuting) mediums and their clients. (Accounts of these matters will be found in *Fifty Years of Psychical Research*, one of Price's best books.) The unscientific gaps in Price's work may largely be blamed upon official science, and the continuing failure to "protect the public" (if that is to be desired) from a flock of fraudulent mediums (at least 98 per cent of the total), and upon a cognate attitude among official opinion of other kinds.

To the mainly blank reception by official science of evidence put forward by Price may perhaps be attributed his habit, so inconsistent with his generally sceptical attitude, of making the most of what little evidence withstood his careful testing. A good example of this characteristic (other examples of which are to be encountered at many points in his works) was his frequent (not invariable) claim that the Ghost Club, of which he was the driving force, had been founded in 1862; whereas, in fact, Price, when he himself initiated, in 1938, a new organization for ghost fanciers, he merely adopted the name of an earlier body which had been extinct for generations. When Price had succeeded in demolishing about nine-tenths of the alleged evidence for paranormal manifestations, the discovery that he was building up the remaining one-tenth to its maximum stature inclined the student on occasion to wonder whether there was anything there at all, whether the American Editors were not right; whether perhaps the fraction accepted by Price as authentic might not be proved baseless as the rest by a later investigator. This suspicion must by its nature be ineradicable. Logically Price was justified in doing all he could to mark the distinction between the true and the false (where he considered it to lie). It was the distinction between vulgar fraud and a new world of thought.

To the spiritualists Price was naturally anathema : compared with their ideas his were indeed scientific. However thoroughly he (and the Law Courts) might expose a well-known professional medium, adherents remained and remain governed by stronger motives than respect for evidence. The spiritualists were not the only people who were sceptical : *The Times*, on at least one occasion, doubted whether Price's "laboratory methods" were adequate to deal with "spiritual problems". This very common line of attack upon Price's work was, of course, followed by the large number of critics who were concerned to defend some orthodoxy equally unable to withstand "laboratory methods" ; critics who had as little use for spiritualism as for Price, being, indeed, mainly unable to distinguish the two.

To the vested interests in science and religion which Price disturbed (the paucity of his results being offset by their convincing lack of dependence upon emotionalism) must be added, in computing the opposition his work aroused, the very common habit of imposing upon discussion of the supernatural a taboo as rigid and, in its consequences, as enfeebling as that upon discussion of sex. Nor was Price altogether the ideal advocate. At the outset, and however absurdly, one felt that his first name (by which he had been duly christened) was against his being taken wholly seriously. The academic pointed out that he had no degree. His books are repetitive, his penultimate publication, *Poltergeist over England*, being the worst offender, and inculcate a grossly over-inclusive usage of the word "poltergeist" (probably because Price thought—rightly—that it is the only technical expression in psychics which is generally known). He had his exotic side (readers will recall the Fortnum and Mason hampers taken to Borley, the Chambertin which turned to "jet-black" ink) ; his early taste for black cigarettes persuaded a puritanical medico of my acquaintance that Price was not a person who need be taken in the least seriously. . . . Above all, his badness as a public speaker was only equalled by his love of public speaking.

Price was a man of upright character and regular habits. He dealt single-handed and in his own handwriting, often at the Reform Club, with a daily mass of correspondence. The legibility and vigour of his writing never weakened. The dramatic upsweep of his signature reflected the confidence he felt in life. When I remarked to him that he was the only correspondent from whom I had never failed to obtain a reply by return of post (and surely one of the busiest holograph correspondents in public life), he replied simply that that was the only way to keep level with things.

As time went on, he acquired a special and important position: every significant supposed paranormal happening sooner or later reached his knowledge, and usually because he was directly written to about it. The Press rushed to him whenever a ghost was heard of. Price was the clearing-house for ghosts. Considering the antagonism to psychics, the position he achieved was remarkable and invaluable. More and more, the problem became which ghost to hunt; more and more, it became difficult to hunt any ghost to the end. It was unfortunate that Price, who had so many of the necessary qualifications, was temperamentally unsuited to founding an organization to devolve the work of investigation upon a selection of competent people. Neither the National Laboratory nor the Ghost Club, excellent though both were, attempted anything in that essential direction. It is significant of Price's gifts that there is no longer a psychic laboratory one ever hears of; that the Ghost Club, so successful when he ran it, seems virtually moribund since his death. Above all, no one has succeeded Price even as a clearing-house for ghosts. His hard work to obtain official recognition for psychic investigation found an insufficient response.

There can have been few more interesting lives, though the harvest was so small. Upon the evidence for survival, Price remained completely unsatisfied; nor did he ever find an authentic spirit photograph or séance materialization (with the doubtful and maddening exception of "Rosalie"). Even telepathy he considered non-proven. His advertisement for those able to perform the Indian Rope Trick, *even for anyone who had ever seen it performed*, produced no satisfactory replies. But he saw Anna Rasmussen by psychic agency set in motion pendulums in a glass case under perfect test conditions. Jeanne Laplace by psychometrizing a letter from Dr. R. J. Tillyard, F.R.S., accurately predicted to Price in 1928 the manner of Tillyard's death in a 1937 railway accident. Experiments with "Stella C.", with "a sensitive instrument" which Price designed, a new kind of recording thermograph, suggested to those who believe in the possibility of a genuine séance that in this case the temperature of the room fell when the medium went into a trance, whereas, in a closed apartment full of people, physics required that it should rise. With Willi and Rudi Schneider, "under conditions of control, never", according to Price, "previously imposed on any mediums or sitters in the history of psychical research, were seen examples of floating, levitation and intelligent movements of many objects". There was Borley. There was Kuda Bux's excitingly successful demonstration of fire-walking. There was the occasion when Dr. Julian Huxley "nearly went into the trance state". There was the credit of an important indirect share in the conclusive exposure of that leading modern miracle story "An Adventure" (see *The Mystery of Versailles*, by J. R. Sturge-Whiting: Foreword by Harry Price). To his books, as reliable, often enthralling, guides through what others made to seem a mirror maze, many of us owe an immense debt. Almost alone among writers on psychics, he judged by standards known, clear and dependable; and the best of his writings communicated his own enthusiasm for the search.

Just before Price's death, London saw an interesting and accurate play about psychic research, *The Poltergeist*. To Price must go almost all the credit for the subject having so far intruded into the public consciousness as to make such a venture possible and successful. As already stated, people now know poltergeists when they meet them. "Apports" and "telekinesis" are entering common talk. Price's position was exactly that of the leisured country gentlemen and inquiring, well-sustained village parsons whose careful, devoted field work in the eighteenth century gave modern science its groundwork.

CATSPAW

FRANK STUART

Illustrations by Eric Fraser

Human society unites to hunt the murderer. When on an English farm animals began to die mysteriously, all the creatures made alliance to find and slay the killer. Felena, a Pallas' cat, sacred to the gods, remained a little aloof, as was her custom, until it was time to lead the battle intelligently. Mr. Frank Stuart is a countryman who seems to have developed a talent for understanding animal speech. This is a disturbing tale which, we understand, he overheard being told by an aristocratic Indian cat that recently deigned to come and live in his house, to his neighbour's grey Persian cat.

CATS are afraid of water, and there is a perfectly good reason for their fear. It would be better if certain humans were also afraid of water, especially if cats condescend to live with them.

I am a Pallas' cat, a *felis manul*, a breed that has always been sacred to the gods. I used to be Dan Neal's cat—but then, Dan was not at all afraid of water—until the end, and then he was very much afraid.

My coat is long and soft and silvery grey, marked with tigerish stripes of black, and my thick tail has handsome black rings. But it is my eyes that make people uneasy—the green eyes of our race that for uncounted centuries have blinked in temple darkness at prostrate multitudes.

I was a mewling kitten under the Indian sun when Dan Neal, a soldier then in what people call a war, picked me up and put me in his suffocating pocket. There is wisdom in a system which ordains the existence of people so that cats may have meat and milk and warmth; otherwise, surely, people would seem too stupid to live. In what they call a war, they kill each other that the crows may have meat. But Dan Neal was not even fit for crow's-meat. They could teach him nothing, so in the end they took away his uniform and sent him home to England, and he brought me.

That was how I came to Narlwood Farm, in Gloucestershire, in the flat marshland at the edge of the Severn Sea, where Dan worked as a labourer. Perhaps what they call a war made Dan even more stupid than before. No one liked him, neither horses nor cows nor dogs nor pigs. He was useful to me because I needed meat and milk; I soon learned to catch my meat, slowly killing the flavourless English birds, mice, and rats, but I remained dependent for milk. He provided it. But I hated him.

I hated him because he had brought me from the Indian sunshine to Narlwood, damp and grey and cold. I hated him because he often struck me, until I became so agile and big as to elude his foot with contempt, and dangerous enough not to be picked up and beaten.

One day the farmer, a simple creature in breeches and a tweed jacket, caught Dan beating Punch the cart-horse. He had brought Punch down to the pond to drink, and as it was a hot autumn day, Punch would not come out of the water. Dan hauled on the halter, yelled, swore. Then he got a thick stick, walked into the pond, and started beating Punch over the head.

Punch is a stupid, lumbering beast, and he is used to all sorts of fuss and kindness; in fact, he will seldom work unless they hang flowers in his mane. Cruel beating sent him silly. He backed into the deep water, too terrified to come out.

Dan could still reach him, and was belabouring him on the head when Farmer came. As always when people disagree, there was a lot of useless shouting, and Dan was dismissed.

But Farmer is a soft-hearted man. He did not turn Dan out from his cottage beside the pond. Dan used to sit glowering in front of the empty fire-place, muttering to himself. Sometimes he poached rabbits and pheasants. He dug his potato crop. He did no work that winter, but sat by his fireside growling and sleeping and eating.

One morning in February, there was a din from behind the cottage, and the hens, led by their stringy old cock, came tearing round the house towards the pond, cackling stupidly. I was sitting on a pole by the edge of the pond, in the winter sunshine, dreaming of India.

One of the hens staggered two or three steps, with her bill open, fell over and died.

Farmer, who had been mending a fence-rail where his sheds adjoined Dan's little garden, came round to see what was up. At the same time Dan himself came slouching from behind his house.

"What's all the noise from the poultry?" Farmer asked suspiciously. "Are you trying to steal eggs, Neal?"

Dan jerked his thumb at the dead hen. As Farmer stooped over and picked the body up, Dan grinned. They stood there discussing what the hen had died of; but hens die of such silly complaints, so they gave it up. They were not able to understand the nervous cacklings of the cock and his wives. They were—as usual—all talking at once, asking agitatedly what had happened. The hens gabbled that she had been murdered. The cock flapped his wings and told them not to be fools.

True, the sheepdog, came running up, sliding sideways the way sheepdogs do. He is the warden of the farm animals, and they always report trouble to him. They don't like him—he's too officious—but they trust him in a reluctant sort of way. I think he is an oaf. He sniffed to and fro, back behind the cottage, into the poultry-field, up and down the hedges, and at the dead body which Farmer had thrown down. Dan sulkily offered to bury it. Farmer gave him an odd look, but agreed. Dan *did* bury it; I watched him. I wondered why he didn't cook it—he wasn't fastidious as a rule. I like picking hen-bones myself.

True fancies himself as a detective. He fossicked around, neglecting his farm work, examining every blade of grass, sniffing, moving things with his paws, listening behind hedges, watching my master till Dan roared: "Git out, yer bluddy cur, or I'll drown ye in the pond, wi' a brick round yer bluddy neck!"

I felt the hair rise along my back and my claws unsheathe. The coarse brutality of some humans is disgusting.

The only thing True found out was that the bees were angry because someone had put foul-smelling liquid in the mouth of their hive. But then the bees are always angry about something, usually a smell, and in winter they are too sleepy to do more than roar about it at intervals.

Three days later I was sitting on my post beside the pond. It was misty, frosty weather, the sort you get in this cold, damp land, with a copper sky, every twig on every tree drooped and black, the ground like iron, the flat grass dead with cold, and night seeming near even at midday. Molly the sow, as usual in an interesting condition, was rooting about round the cottage, looking for cabbage-stalks, refuse, anything she could eat. What a stomach! She saw me sitting on my pole. "Don't come grubbing about here," I warned her in distaste. "Remember what happened to the hen."

"Hen!" laughed Molly fatly. "She died from stealing my food, I'll be bound. Niver was such thieves as them hens. They'd bust their sides any day, give 'em the chance." And she rolled round to the back of the cottage. Five minutes later she came staggering back, her mouth opening and shutting, her legs giving way under her weight—not that I blame them for that! She was choking, her eyes protruded. She was trying to tell me something, but I paid little attention, for I am not in the habit of giving fools a second chance. Then she fell dead.

The hens saw her first—if there is anything to gossip about on the farm, it is always the hens who are first. "It's murder!" they shrilled. The old cock walked up, jerked his head about, veiled his eye several times for effect, and said importantly: "This is serious! We'll have to do something about this. We're all in danger. *I'm* in danger!"

True arrived, with Farmer on his heels. True snarled as he saw what had happened, and the sound of the snarl brought Dan out from his cottage. He had his hands in his pockets, and he grinned and said: "Another on 'em dead?"

Farmer stared, pulling his chin. "This is serious, Neal!" he growled. I laughed. It was enough to make a cat laugh, to hear a man repeating what a foolish bird had just said.

Dan Neal said: "If you ast me, that pond water's poisoned."

I shifted on top of my pole and turned to stare at the pond. It was slimy at the edges, but crusted with ice right across, roughened in places where children had broken it with stones before it had frozen. It was quite deep in the middle. When I remembered how deep it was, I stared reflectively at the ice. Something that I had long had in mind began to seem possible. . . .

True pattered round, smelling at the dead sow, at the frosty ground with withered leaves stuck hard in icy mud, and at Dan's trousers, till the man savagely back-kicked like a cow.

True then moved off towards the ragged flower-garden beside the cottage, where the only sign of colour under the gloomy English sky was some yellow-flowered wolf's-bane. True smelled at the ground there for quite a long time, and Dan watched the dog out of the corner of his eye as he talked to Farmer about the sow's death. The two of them walked round the cottage, poking here and there, looking for bad food that the sow might have scavenged up. Of course there was nothing there; I could have told them that.

True went sniffing to the back door of the cottage, and tried to nose it open, just avoiding a kick from Dan.

"Now, then, Neal—haven't you done enough to my beasts?" Farmer snapped.

"Then keep thy bluddy cur out o' my kitchen!" Dan retorted sullenly, swinging inside and slamming the door shut.

It was a week later that Dulcie, the youngest heifer, was found dead in her stall.

They had called in a vet. to see what the sow had died of, and now he was called in again. He was a young man, and while all men are fools, young men are such fools that I cannot bear to look at them; I have to turn my head away. He said she must have picked up something—easy money to get paid for saying *that*! Then he drove off in his old car that emits smells.

By this time the whole of the farm population was in an up-roar. I do not refer to the humans, of course. Their power of smell, taste, sight, touch and hearing is so low that nothing was to be expected from them. The hens had been tearing about screeching "Murder" ever since they provided the first victim. By this time they were frantic. The cows were hardly able to let down their milk. Punch the cart-horse was stupid with fright. I sat on my pole and watched. True running his legs off doing his detective work, peering for footprints, examining broken grasses, haunting the cottage, pattering about the sheds at all hours trying to catch somebody doing something. What a detective!

It was Cackle, the cock, who came to me at last. "I represent all the other animals," he said, stretching his ridiculous little wings. "All of 'em. And I call on you, Felena the Cat, to join us in taking action to protect ourselves."

"Are you bringing in the owl? And the snake?" I asked, half-opening my eyes and stretching out one paw where I could admire its silver softness, and its talons. Everyone knows he hates the owl and is terrified of the snake, but I had to remind him, because these two, and he and I, are the four creatures sacred to Pallas.

"A general meeting of the *civilized* animals has been called, and is now gathering in the barn," he answered importantly. "I call on you, Felena the Cat, by our ancient divinity."

He strutted off. I got up, stretched and followed, for no more than any other sacred beast can I deny that call.

True the sheepdog spoke first.

"I've been watching the cottage. Dan Neal has been there when each of the dead was struck. Now, someone has been moving the wolf's-bane from his garden. Who else but Dan

would do it? Some had gone the day the hen died. More was missing when Molly was found dead. More when the young heifer died. More is missing to-day. Someone else has been marked to die."

An instant cackle, stirring, quacking, shoving, stamping broke out in the cold barn, and I had to jump to miss Punch's great clumsy hooves.

"I've smelt the wolf's-bane in the cottage!" True added. "Dan Neal is the killer, but none of us have seen him at work."

It was time for me to intervene. "*I* have seen him at work," I said calmly.

Every animal turned to look at me. When I had savoured their surprised attention, I added: "He squeezes the juice from the wolf's-bane roots in a basin, with a wooden ram. Human beings do such idiotic things that I took no notice, beyond smelling my food more carefully before I tasted it. But when Dulcie the heifer died, he had been working on the table with cow-cake just before."

There was quite a sensation. I looked at their unintelligent faces: the hens chattering, the cows mooing with shock, Punch angry, True bursting with injured vanity. "Why didn't you tell *me*?" he demanded shrilly.

"You're the detective," I said. "Why didn't *you* ask *me*? A detective ought sometimes to ask sensible questions as well as silly ones."

They all talked at once—it was almost as bad as people. I watched them intently, though I pretended to be indifferent. Inwardly I was quivering. This was the moment I had waited for. Suddenly I spat, waving my tail angrily, and said: "I am the wisest among you, am I not?"

One after another, they assented, as they were bound to do. Only people lie.

"Dan Neal must be put to death," I said.

It seemed as if they had all frozen in the freezing air. Animals occasionally kill a human, but almost never do they communally decide to do so. There is an old Law against it.

"I know the Law!" I cried out, and I found myself shaking. "But is there not the phrase—'If man kill beast in wickedness.' . . ."

They, too, knew that clause. But they were afraid to debate it.

I sat on my haunches, and began to sound the Call that hardly any of the animals have ever heard, and that all dread to hear—the Call to the Killing of Man.

As the whispering hiss went through the shadowy barn, first one, then another, joined in it. Punch, remembering his beaten head; Daisy, because her little Dulcie had been poisoned; the savage old sow because she had lost her daughter.

From among the straw in the corner, beady eyes stared out. The mice and rats were coming to answer the Call. I drooled at the sight and smell of them, but I dared not stop my hissing of the Call. Through the open doors from the gathering gloom of the evening, a white shape sailed in on silent wings—the owl, the third sacred creature, had come at my Call. There was one more. And, last of all, as is his right, with a hiss that silenced us all, the viper slithered from his winter sleeping-place.

We were ready. And for years I had known how this killing must be done. As I had begun the Call, I had to begin the attack. I ran on velvet feet into the cottage, through the lavatory window which was always open, and found Dan seated by the dulling fire. I sprang straight at him and tore open his cheek and leapt away.

He jumped up as if he had been whipped, faced me where I poised in the window, spitting, and suddenly picked a poker out of the hearth. I was not afraid. He smote at me, but I leapt at his eyes, easily evading the clumsy blow. His other hand shot to meet me, and I curled on to it in mid-air and slashed it so that the drops dripped red.

Dan Neal was always a coward. He had had enough already. Swearing, whimpering, he rushed to the door, kicked it open, and struck at me to make me run out. Instead, his poker smashed off the leg of a chair and jarred his arm to the shoulder. I jumped on his back, sank my talons deep, and jumped away and through the open door.

He did not follow me. He tried to shut the door, only to find himself suddenly the centre of a general assault. The hens flapped round his head, a bat whisked into his hair and clung there, True got him by the calf, and as he stopped to strike at the snarling dog, half a dozen bees leapt into his face and fastened on him.

Blindly whirling his arms and screeching, he ran out towards the pond. Instantly, Daisy the cow put her head down and ran at him, and as he backed against the wall of the cottage, striking at her with his poker, Punch the cart-horse trotted up and leaned against him, trying to pin him to the wall. That did not suit my book, so I leapt at the man's face with such force that he fell backwards, and the great weight of the old horse just failed to squeeze him.

Someone had left a pitchfork in a corner of the wall, and Dan felt it in his hand, and turned with a shout, stabbing at the horse, which circled away. Then he began to run blindly round the yard, the bees on his face, the hens screeching between his feet, the horse and cows after him. The old pig tried to bite him as he ran, and sent him staggering towards the pond. There was a snap from True, and the owl flew like a pillow into the fugitive's face. He was sinking, and once down, that would have been the end. But I did not mean him to fall; I hurtled, snarling and spitting to drive them off him. Dan recovered his feet, and with a sob, staggered out on to the frozen pond. It was growing dark.

Brandishing his pitchfork, Dan turned now to face his pursuers. But a rat ran up his leg and fastened its teeth in his throat, the owl silently swooped on him, and Punch lumbered on the edge of the ice, stamping to smash it.

Wildly beating at the creatures that were attacking his head, Dan saw Punch advancing, and lunged so fiercely that the horse was pricked by the pitchfork and backed off. Yet a great black crack now ran across the ice to the middle of the pond!

Dan could not leave the pond—the bigger animals circled it, driving him back. But he was able to stop Punch stepping on to the ice again until, suddenly, the viper slipped along the ice to within inches of Dan's foot. With a cry of fear he stepped back. The snake followed, and the man stepped back again.

It was then that I sprang on to Punch's flank, driving my talons deep. With a squeal of terror, the cart-horse ran right on to the ice. His front hooves burst through it, the black crack suddenly widened, there was a muffled shout—and where Dan

Neal had stood was nothing but a black hole under the blacken-
ing winter sky.

I could now hear Farmer running from the farmhouse, but
he was too late, and as I leapt back to earth, and Punch retreated, neighing in terror, I saw a hand feel for the ragged edge
of the hole, break off a piece of ice and disappear again. . . .

The hen, the sow, the heifer had all died choking. Now Dan
Neal, who poisoned them to injure the farmer, died choking. I
was his cat—and *he drowned all my kittens in that pond.* I had to
wait for my chance, but presently he learned what it is like to
choke in pond water. That is the end of my story.

WRITER'S WITCH

JOAN FLEMING

Wood engravings by Zelma Blakely

We should hesitate to introduce our readers to a witch as a matter of course; but as she is sponsored by Joan Fleming they will be confident, we hope, that the woman is not just another nuisance on a broomstick. Indeed, she is not. This is a bookish witch. Her supernatural powers, evidently sophisticated by excessive reading in the classic authors, are in this instance used to demonstrate a very practical and devastating form of literary criticism.

AMYAS gave a loud cry of pain and held his head in anguish; Mrs. Pegg looked round the door.

"Anything wrong, sir?" she asked with concern. It being a weekday she was not wearing her teeth and, for the same reason, upon her head she wore her husband's old cap, round the edge of which her curlers bobbed playfully. Her face took on a look of shocked disapproval at what she heard. "Anything wrong?" she asked again, sharply.

Amyas stopped cursing and looked up, but the apparition which he saw through watering eyes in no way mitigated his pain.

"Yes, everything's wrong!" he shouted. "I've just knocked myself nearly senseless on that blasted beam again!"

Mrs. Pegg made a curious sucking noise with her gums, intended, no doubt, to convey sympathy. "Tch! Tch! Your pore forehead! 'Ow about a spot of marg?"

Amyas dismissed the kindly suggestion with a snarl, and Mrs. Pegg wisely held her peace whilst the pain wore off.

Her silent sympathy caught Amyas off his guard; for three weeks he had fought against an ever-increasing irritation and an urgent need to ease himself by bursting into angry complaint. Now he ceased to fight any longer.

"I must have been mad, utterly mad, ever to take this lousy little hovel, and to think I was going to be able to write here! Peace and quiet was all I wanted, but I didn't expect to knock myself silly on these confounded beams every half-hour——"

Mrs. Pegg waited; she sniffed, she wiped her nose with the corner of her apron. Then, with great restraint, she said: "No, you're not yourself, sir."

Amyas looked sharply at her. Who was she (their acquaintance being of some three weeks' standing) to know whether he was himself or not?

However, his need to talk was greater than his discretion, and he went on bitterly: "But I've got to be myself, I can't go on like this! Either I sit at the typewriter doing nothing at all, or else I start moving about and knock myself out, and it won't do. As you may know, Mrs. Pegg," he said sternly, "last year I wrote a best-seller," pause for effect, "and this year I must write another. My publisher is waiting for it, thousands of people are waiting for it, and here I am, the stage set, producing nothing, nothing at all! Not one word since I came. It's all here, mind you," he said, tapping his forehead, "or was, but I can't get going!"

Mrs. Pegg made her sympathetic noise. She was pregnant with talk; Amyas had known it all along; up till now he had taken immense pains to avoid any sort of mental contact with her. She was, however, an excellent cook, so he sighed heavily, and prepared for the broadside.

"It beats me," she said, "how a gent like you could take a place like this, though, *mind you*, it's not lousy now! The council 'as been ever so thorough."

Still nursing his head, but ceasing to rock himself gently to and fro, Amyas asked: "What did you say?"

"I said the council spread themselves, like, over getting this place what you'd call dee-loused," Mrs. Pegg replied in a louder tone.

"You don't mean it was really lousy!" Amyas exclaimed, sitting up, his pain forgotten.

"But you've just said so yourself, sir; 'lousy little 'ovel' was wot you called it, and lousy little 'ovel it was; only tramps 'as lived in it these past 'undred years, till it was condemned."

"Condemned!"

"For years," Mrs. Pegg went on cheerfully; "but it didn't fall to ruin like it might of; stone-built, that's why. Then wot with the 'ousing shortage *ex*cetra, the council dee-condemned it for the evacuees, see?"

Amyas nodded. He saw only too clearly. He had spent but one week-end at the *Crown*, seen the cottage, bought it and, at infinite trouble and expense, had had it "done up". He looked round the tiny sitting-room, at the uneven brick floor, the eau-de-nil chintz curtains, the dark oak of the bureau, the shining surface of the gate-legged table, and on it the copper bowl with the nasturtiums foaming from it and tumbling over the side to peer at their reflections in the deep polish.

"Condemned!" he whispered.

"But I must say this," Mrs. Pegg went on; "mind you, it's a nice little job now, apart from the garden, which you naturally 'aven't had time to deal with yet"—she looked out through the open door on to the grass plot surrounded by the high brick wall. On either side of the flagged central path the grass was high and a few gnarled fruit trees grew neither fruit nor leaf, but, bowed beneath a weight of years, they were covered with a soft grey lichen which blurred their aged outline. "Yes, apart from the garden, it's marvellous, reely, sir," Mrs. Pegg mused, "what you've done in the short time——"

Amyas lifted his head wearily from his hands and, leaning back in his chair, with a heavy sigh he said: "Why didn't anybody tell me all this?" But even as he said it he knew it was a foolish question. Had he sought or desired anyone's opinion? Had he ever laid himself open to advice or criticism from anyone in the village? Had he not deliberately avoided the bar of the *Crown* where he might have been given much useful information about the cottage he was buying.

Mrs. Pegg, Amyas thought, was brewing for something. She was poking primly about the bosom of her pink woollen jumper, a sign, he had learned, that a subject of importance was about to be broached. She would fidget thus when about to discuss her wages or how much money Amyas proposed letting her have for "the housekeeping".

"You wouldn't of found anyone in the village as would of wanted to talk about the place," she said at last. "It's unlucky!" And she continued to poke primly, knowing that she had, at last, roused Amyas's full attention. "Yes, unlucky!" she repeated, mouthing the word with enjoyment. "The evacs didn't——"

"The what?"

"The evacuees—they didn't stay long, I can tell you, and then the Army used the place, as an ammunition store, they said, and that scared everyone nearly out of their wits and no one dared even mention the place, *in case*——"

"Yes? In case what?"

"*In* case!" Mrs. Pegg repeated in a hoarse whisper.

"Is this some sort of joke?" Amyas asked coldly; "explain yourself, Mrs. Pegg."

A curious look passed over Mrs. Pegg's face. "All right," she said (rather nastily, Amyas thought), "I'll tell you and be blowed! It isn't me as 'as to sleep 'ere nights." Glancing swiftly to right and to left, she moistened her thin lips and leaned forward. "It's Mary Ann Beehag! She's never left the place, not since she was 'ung at the cross-roads more nor a 'undred years ago!"

"Ah, I see," Amyas said in his most superior voice; "a thief, I suppose."

"No, not a thief. They 'ung her at the cross-roads on the way to Marley because that's where the gallows 'appened to be and that's what caused it. There weren't no gallows here, see? She'd never set foot out of this village since she was born under this very roof, and they went and took 'er 'alf-way to the next village and 'ung 'er!"

"Why, exactly, was she—er—hung?" Amyas asked, hating the misuse of the verb, but keeping in touch with Mrs. Pegg mentally.

Again the look passed over Mrs. Pegg's face which he could only describe as primitive.

"She was a very bad old woman," she said, then she wiped her nose once more with the corner of her apron and turned to leave the room.

Now thoroughly intrigued, Amyas called after her, but she did not come back. He got up and followed her into the tiny kitchen, where she was putting the finishing touches to the salad which she was leaving for his supper.

Amyas leaned against the wall with its brightly shining new cream paint and thrust his hands into his pockets.

"In what way," he asked, "was she bad?"

"Mary Ann Beehag? She was famous!" Mrs. Pegg said. "The last of her kind in the county, so they say, to be 'ung."

" 'Of her kind'?"

"Aye," she replied, giving a lettuce leaf a vigorous shake, "and a good thing too!"

" '*Of her kind*'?" Amyas persisted.

"See here, sir," Mrs. Pegg said, stopping her work and looking squarely at Amyas. "Don't a-go stirring up mud. Least said soonest mended, eh? Walls have ears!"

"I simply don't know what you're driving at," Amyas said, taking out his cigarette-case.

"You will," Mrs. Pegg told him, briskly plucking off her apron and hanging it on a hook behind the kitchen door.

"I'm surprised at you, Mrs. Pegg," Amyas replied, flicking at his lighter; "*you*, with your electric cooker, and your wireless, and your television, and your bus drive into town to the pictures every week, I really am surprised at your superstitions and your innuendoes——" He could feel her getting angry; no one likes having long words thrown at them by a superior voice. Amyas was beginning to enjoy himself; goading Mrs. Pegg was poor sport, but better than sitting in front of a typewriter clawing at the blank spaces in one's mind. "Are you trying to tell me that she was hanged for a witch?"

Silence, whilst Mrs. Pegg fidgeted with something in her black mackintosh bag.

"If so," Amyas went on, "I am not merely surprised but shocked. Do you know"—he was about to say "my good woman", but stopped himself in time—"do you know that thousands of poor harmless old women were—er—hung or burned for being, as they say, *witches*! Poor innocent women like—er—like yourself; tortured and put to death by hysterical, superstitious crowds——"

Mrs. Pegg was eyeing him with dislike and Amyas stopped abruptly.

"Mary Ann Beehag wasn't no pore innercent old woman," she declared soberly, "she was an evil witch. Evil as the devil 'imself." She opened the kitchen door, hung her black bag over her arm, and looked out at the brilliant afternoon, then with her hand still on the latch she glanced back over her shoulder. "And the sun shone," she pronounced, "*right through 'er!*"

Amyas gave a shout of laughter as the kitchen door slammed and he heard her feet on the flags outside.

" 'The sun shone right through her!' " he repeated, with delight.

Ducking his head carefully in the doorway, he returned to the sitting-room and sat down in front of his typewriter.

Gradually the amusement and the animation of the last few minutes left him and he sat, sulky and dejected, lighting cigarette after cigarette and writing not one word. Dully, he turned over the pages of his notes headed "Outline of Plot", which were so drearily familiar to him, and then, with sudden decision, he gathered the loose pages together and tore them across.

"Dammit, it's rubbish!" he shouted.

He stood up, tearing the paper across again and again, and,

clutching the pieces in his hand, he strode to the door leading out into the sunlit garden.

Crash went his head against the beam across the threshold, and this time it brought him to his knees, half in and half out of the doorway; everything went black, and there were brilliant flashes in the blackness.

Seeing stars, Amyas thought, like the kids in *Comic Cuts* when they bang themselves. But this won't do! It won't have to go on!

He opened his eyes, and there, in the middle of the flagged garden-path, stood Mary Ann Beehag, looking at him.

And Amyas looked at her.

"What are you doing in my house?" she croaked.

"Trying to write a novel," Amyas answered; "a best-seller!"

She gave a cackle of shocking, fiendish laughter.

"What's that you have in your hand?"

Amyas looked at his hand, carefully and stupidly, as though he were drunk. It was full of torn scraps of paper.

"The 'Outline of Plot'."

Mary Ann Beehag extended a frightful claw; it was misshapen, gnarled and covered with soft grey lichen which could not hide its aged outline.

Amyas snatched his hand away. He was still kneeling on the threshold. A feeling of cold, dreadful horror came over him.

"Look!" he shrieked, "look!" and Mary Ann Beehag laughed again, a cold, rustling laugh, like the wind in dead leaves.

Amyas's teeth began to chatter. "The sun shines," he mumbled, "right through her!"

For the old woman stood in brilliant sunshine, and not to the front of her, nor behind her, nor to the sides of her, was there any shadow.

Mary Ann Beehag laughed again, and this time the sound scraped the inner linings of his soul. She said: "Yes, only the evil cast no shadow, young man! Give me those—*those*," she repeated impatiently.

Slowly Amyas put out his hand and dropped the torn fragments of his notes into her extended claw, then he watched, fascinated, as she shuffled down the path, a few steps through the long grass, and stooped under one of the dead trees.

"They're buried now," she shrieked maliciously, and she laughed again—a laugh that reminded Amyas of a certain book reviewer who had slated his last novel. "They're buried now, and we shall see what grows there——"

*   *   *   *   *

P.S.—Amyas and his publisher are still waiting.

DRURY LANE GHOST

W. MACQUEEN-POPE

Illustrations by Joan Hassall

Mr. Macqueen-Pope's family have been associated with the Theatre Royal, Drury Lane, for at least a couple of centuries, and he himself has spent his life in the London theatres. He has met nearly all the players of to-day and yesterday, seen most of the plays they acted, and is an acknowledged authority on the history of the English stage. He discusses in this article Drury Lane's own ghost. It seems to be an affable, familiar spirit, very interested in the welfare of the famous building it inhabits, and perfectly free from vice. It takes no pleasure in frightening people, throwing things about, or other mischievous, infantile tricks.

MOST people disbelieve in ghosts. Yet, strangely enough, the more they express their disbelief the greater interest they show in ghost stories and the greater reluctance they display at being left alone in places where a ghost walks.

I don't believe in ghosts myself, yet I am an habitual ghost see-er. Let me qualify that statement. I don't believe in the ghost who is regarded as the disembodied spirit of someone long dead, doomed to walk this earth for some reason or other. But I do believe—and seeing is believing in my case—that apparitions can be, and are, seen by certain people and under certain conditions. We will come to that later. I might mention, to avoid further argument, that I am a teetotaller and am not a Spiritualist, although I find no fault with the Spiritualist case.

If there are no ghosts, if they are never seen except in the imagination, why this age-old belief in them? Science scoffs at them. Yet Science will, one day, and before very long, provide the satisfactory explanation of their presence and probably the means whereby everyone will be able, if they so desire, to have a look at them. Meanwhile, I can do it for myself. So can many others.

Now, on the face of it, a theatre might seem an unlikely place for a haunt. The popular idea runs to graveyards, deserted moated granges, ancient castles, deep dungeons and the like. That is the disembodied spirit school of thought. As a matter of fact, a graveyard is a most unlikely place, for ghosts haunt the spots with which they were most intimately connected and, more important still, where in nine cases out of ten they met with a sudden and violent end.

In order to see them, the "waves" must be right, the atmospheric conditions must be attuned. For seeing a ghost is much akin to tuning in on the radio—if you have not got the right wave-length you won't get the programme.

Now a theatre, to most people, is a centre of human activity, of crowds, of lights and music, laughter and applause—the sort of place that a self-respecting ghost would shun. Yet there are no less than four accredited ghosts in London theatres, all well authenticated and of years' standing.

There are other ghost stories in the playhouses, but these are the Big Four, who are permanencies—the others have only been seen once or twice.

So far from being a bad place for a haunt, a theatre is a very good one. Life moves swiftly there and often violently for theatre folk. The atmosphere is charged with emotion and deep feeling—despair, excitement, triumph and disaster. These set up the right waves to make the ghosts visible. Sokolova, the world-famous ballerina, once said to me, "Haven't you ever felt, when crossing the stage of an empty theatre after a big first night, that the building itself was tired and worn out—that it, like you, is almost exhausted by the stress and the excitement of what has happened?" Sokolova is quite right. She had put into words what so many of us have experienced. It is just that generation of electricity—for want of a better word—which creates and makes visible the ghosts of the theatres. The atmospherics are right.

The haunted theatres of London are Drury Lane, the Haymarket, the St. James's and the Royalty. Take them in order of seniority—the Ghost of Drury Lane coming first, as indeed he should. Perhaps I shall deal with the others at another time.

Theatre Royal, Drury Lane, is the oldest playhouse in the world still used as such. And its ghost is the senior theatre ghost. He is not as old as the theatre, but I am sure he is over two centuries old all the same. He is a double mystery. There he is, undoubtedly, but who he is, or who he was, that nobody knows. He is anonymous, he is the ghost of a forgotten man—he is the ghost of a forgotten and undiscovered crime. Save in his ghostly form he has no history at all. He was not an actor, dramatist, or a manager, for, if so, he could be located. He is, I believe, the victim of a murder which was never discovered at the time and the perpetrators of which got off scot-free. Let me tell you the story.

Just over a century ago repair work was in progress at Drury Lane Theatre. The workmen were busy inside the theatre building on the thick, sturdy main wall on the Russell Street side. To their astonishment they came across a section of the wall, on the present upper circle level, which rang hollow where it should have been solid. They called the foreman. He either consulted with a higher authority or gave instructions himself, for they broke through that wall—and found themselves in a small room which had been bricked up. The room was not empty. It contained an old worm-eaten table and a broken chair. It contained something else—a complete skeleton with a dagger in its ribs. Someone had been killed—murdered —and had been bricked up in that small room and left for centuries. There were, about the bones, some fragments of mouldering cloth with a corded edge, which crumbled at the touch.

There was an inquest and an open verdict. The bones were buried in the small graveyard at the corner of Drury Lane and Russell Street. It is now a children's playground, but it was the graveyard Dickens mentioned in *Bleak House* where Lady Deadlock's lover lay and on the steps of which she herself died.

To this day nobody knows who was the man murdered and immured in the theatre. Nor does anyone know when it occurred. I have my own theory. I would place that murder at

any time between 1690 and 1710, when the wily and repre-
hensible Christopher Rich controlled the theatre. I do not for
one moment suggest he did the deed. He was too artful to
indulge in violence—he knew a trick worth two of that. But
during his reign we have it on record that builders were always
in the theatre extending, altering, tinkering with the structure,
for Rich was always trying to find room for more seats. I
believe that some time during that period a young man of
property came up from the country to see life and found—
Death. He would naturally frequent the playhouses—there
were only two, Drury Lane and Lincoln's Inn Fields. He would,
like the other gay sparks, go and walk about on the stage.
Doubtless he fell for one of the girls—doubtless he aroused
jealousy. And a lover or a husband had him quietly removed,
and for a small consideration—life was cheap then—got him
neatly bricked up and—that was that! People often vanished
without trace in those good old days. They still do. That is
what I think happened.

The portion of the wall in which he was found survived the
rebuildings of 1794 and the fire of 1809. It was, it is, part of the
second theatre which Christopher Wren built so strongly and
well. It has been cut about since, but I can show you exactly
where that room was. But neither I nor anyone else knows the
identity of the man whose tomb it was for so many long years.
It is, however, not from the site of that room that our ghost
appears. He comes through a wall very near to it, where once
there was a "pass" door—that is, a door leading back-stage.
There used to be one on every tier at Drury Lane up to very
recently, and there was so, certainly, when our ghost was a
living man. I say he comes through the wall, but nobody has
actually seen him emerge through it. Suddenly he is there, on
the very threshold of the room where the skeleton lay. He walks
along a short corridor, he enters the upper circle—in his day it
would have corresponded with the second box circle, he walks
right round the back of it, and enters a room now used as a bar
on the other side of the theatre, passing through the wall there,
and through again what was an old pass door, the outline of
which can still be seen although long since bricked up. There
are witnesses to this, so it is fairly safe to assume that he comes

through the corresponding door on the other side in the first place.

Now, although he comes from back-stage and returns to that part of the theatre, he has never once been glimpsed the other side of the proscenium arch. Watch has been kept there, but never a sign of him seen. But on his own walk, in the auditorium itself, he is constantly seen.

That, more than anything else, proves him to have been a member of the public and not an actor—for you cannot keep an actor off the stage in life and the urge would certainly remain in a ghost. This ghost is never seen away from his usual walk, never in any other part of the theatre—and he always walks the same way—in the same direction, from the left-hand side of the theatre to the right. He is a remarkable mystery, he has many odd traits missing in other apparitions, but he is constant to his selected route and never varies it.

The oddest thing about him is his disregard for usual ghostly custom. This spectre has not the fears which racked Hamlet's father, neither is he bound by the same rules. It matters not one whit to him that the glow-worm begins "to pale his un-effectual fire" at the approach of matins. For this ghost walks by day. Every recorded appearance of his has been between nine o'clock in the morning and six o'clock at night. He has never been seen after that time. I was Chief Warden of Drury Lane Theatre during the war, and was about the place (of which by long association I know every cranny) at all hours of the night. During those by no means silent watches neither I, nor my fire guards, caught sight of him. But during the regular hours, he has been seen scores—no, hundreds—of times.

So, if you are a playgoer who likes to include a bit of ghost seeing as well, it is no use looking for him when you go to Drury Lane at night. But if you attend a matinée—that is a different matter.

He is also unlike Hamlet's father, inasmuch as he addresses nobody and shows not the slightest desire so to do. He has no dislike of human beings, nor does he avoid them, unless they approach him deliberately and with the idea of speaking to him. Then he just is not there. The reason is, of course, that by shifting your position you have got out of focus. He is doubtless still there, but you have lost the wave-length. As to why he should be invisible at night I have very little idea, except that every radio fan knows that it is easier to get distant stations under certain atmospheric conditions than others. It may be the same with him. He may require something which the night atmosphere cannot supply.

But if you are interested and you happen to be in Drury Lane Theatre, and in or near its upper circle during the hours between 9 a.m. and 6 p.m., you have a very good chance.

If you are lucky—or unlucky, according to your feelings in the matter—what you will see is a man of just over middle height, clothed entirely in grey, wearing a long riding cloak of the early eighteenth-century type. His hair is either powdered or he wears a wig, it is difficult to tell; beneath that cloak, which is wrapped round him, are riding boots, and you can see the end of a sword scabbard, too. His hat is three-cornered, and here again is something curious. Sometimes it is on his head, sometimes it is carried under his arm. Personally I have always seen him wearing it, but there are reports of his being uncovered, for which I cannot vouch myself. His features are clean-cut, he has a rather square face with a strong chin and a well-marked mouth—if one was asked whom he resembled, the nearest to his looks would be the late Sir George Alexander— but he is not the apparition of that actor-knight. Although Alexander appeared at the Lane, nothing ever occurred whilst he was there to make him haunt it—and besides, there are records of our ghost's appearance for nearly two hundred years. He appears to be a young man and a well-bred man. He does not hurry. He walks in a calm and leisurely fashion along his pitch, taking no notice of anyone.

I have said he does not shun human company. For all I know he is unaware of it. But certain it is that he has been seen by members of an audience whilst a matinée performance was actually in progress. Not once but many a time. During the run of Ivor Novello's *Careless Rapture* in 1936, a lady in the audience, during the interval, asked an attendant if this was the sort of play in which the actors came in front and mixed with the audience. The girl, somewhat surprised, replied that it was not. "I asked," said the lady, "because a man in fancy

dress with a three-cornered hat passed by me just now." I was
fetched and spoke to the playgoer. Her description was an
exact description of our ghost. The lady had no idea we had
one.

At a matinée of the last pantomime staged at Drury Lane,
Christmas 1938–9, a woman was taken with a fainting fit, of
course in the upper circle. First-aid was administered, but she
did not feel well, and asked if she could have the services of the
nurse. She was asked what nurse, and she replied, "One in a
grey cloak, of which I caught sight shortly before I fainted."
There was a search, but no nurse in a grey cloak was in any
part of the theatre. She had seen the ghost, probably he had
just passed by, and it was his back view she had caught sight of.
But she did not faint on that account, for she knew nothing at
all about the Drury Lane ghost.

One morning, just after nine o'clock, a cleaner (as theatre
charwomen are always called) went into the upper circle. It
was her first day in the theatre. She saw a man in curious dress
strolling along the gangway at the back. The curtain was
down, and so far as she knew, no rehearsal was on. Yet this
man appeared to be in stage costume. She thought she had
better question him. She bent to put down her pail and her
brushes, and when she straightened up again he had gone. She
hurried along the way he had taken—and she saw him for a
second against the wall of the refreshment room on the right-
hand side. Then again he had gone. To come out again he
must have passed her—he had not done so. She went down to
report. In due course I was informed. I questioned the woman.
Her description was just the same as all the others. And she had
no knowledge that Drury Lane had a ghost. There are countless other instances, but let these serve.

When Drury Lane was bombed during the war, scoffers at
once suggested that the ghost would be seen no more, and that
he had been blown up. True, the bomb passed right through
the middle of his walk. But it made no difference to him—why
should it? He took not the slightest notice. He walks as he has
walked for so many years. But he does not seem to be very
regular in his appearances. Sometimes there are long gaps of
time between recorded appearances, sometimes he is seen often

in a short space of time. There is no record of his ever being seen twice in one day—or even in one week. Nor is he only visible to one person at a time. Crowds of people have seen him at once. During the photo call of *The Dancing Years*, when the stage was crowded with the company, having photographs taken, he went across the back of the upper circle and was visible to many of them.

He has an irritating knack of not turning up when he is most wanted. A deputation from the Psychical Research Society came along one afternoon with some journalists, and we sat for over two hours, waiting and hoping. Not a sign of him did we see. Yet two days later I saw him clearly and well. And whilst that particular pantomime was running—it was just before Christmas that they came—Fay Compton saw him too. She is also a ghost see-er.

There was another time when I would have paid a handsome sum of money to any theatrical charity—or any society for the maintenance of poor and needy ghosts—had he put in an appearance. But he did not oblige. On Friday, November 28th, 1939, Their Majesties the King and Queen came to inspect the work of ENSA, which had made Drury Lane the headquarters for troop entertainment. It was my privilege to guide the King and Queen round the building, show them all there was to see and to tell them something of its long history—after all, it is Theatre Royal, the Monarch's own playhouse, and we who work there can, by virtue of the Royal Charter of Charles II, call ourselves His Majesty's Servants. I told them of the ghost and they were greatly interested. They stood with me for several minutes on the stage gazing at the upper circle as I pointed out its walk. The King expressed the wish that it would turn up, which the Queen echoed. But that ghostly servant of Their Majesties missed his great opportunity. Yet during the next month we saw him three times.

Frequently I show parties of visitors round the historic theatre. The ghost walk and the ghost story is always the most popular part of the tour. Some laugh, some sneer, some are eager to see him, others are obviously scared. There is nothing to be frightened about. No weird or terrifying phenomena accompany him. There is no wailing, no screaming, no clanking of chains, no howling of dogs, not even a dank and chilly atmosphere surrounds him. One just sees that calm and rather dignified figure quietly proceeding on his usual promenade. "What does he look like?" they ask. "Is he transparent—can you see through him—is he clear to the eye?" He is, extremely so, although a little misty. The effect is as if you were watching a scene on the stage which was being enacted behind what we call a "gauze". The gauze is transparent because of the lights behind it, so you can see the figures come and go quite distinctly as you might see a man a little distance away through a light summer mist. That is the effect as nearly as I can put it into words. I have seen him many scores of times. He is an old friend. I used to try to approach right up to him, but he always vanished when I did so. But if you stay fourteen, fifteen, or twenty feet away, you can keep him in full view. I have been about twelve feet from him, when I have seen him pass through that old bricked-up pass door. I have never been able to pass by him. I have gone to meet him face to face, but at the usual distance he has vanished. But I have been enabled, as have others, to see his features and I know him well.

When those parties of visitors have seen the wall from which he enters the theatre, have gazed on the site of the murdered man's room, I always take them over the ghost walk, pausing now and then to give him a chance of turning up. So far he has never done so, but I never lose hope.

It always amuses me to notice that those who have giggled and laughed, who have expressed their complete disbelief when I have been telling them the story, always press on pretty quickly, with many glances round, until we have left the part of the building he uses.

Twice, quite unwittingly, he has given us a good laugh. On the occasion when the Psychical Research people came to inspect him, I stayed on in the upper circle after they had gone, together with a girl journalist who had been sent down on the story by her paper—a daily illustrated one—and who had evidently been told to come back with a first-hand account of the ghost. With me, she sat and waited. All of a sudden, on the far side of the theatre, a figure became visible against a very dimly lit glass door. The girl saw it, shrieked and clutched my arm. I got up at once and went towards the figure, which walked very slowly towards me. That young journalist held on to me tight, breathing heavily and torn between fear and the hope of a first-class story. But, alas, it was not the ghost, but one of the Researchers who had lost her way in our rabbit-warren of a theatre and was searching for the way out.

On another occasion, during the war, and at about eleven at night, I was taking a party of fire guards round Drury Lane, to get them accustomed to the many twists and turns, the odd staircases, the ways in and out and the nearest water supply to their posts. It was a very necessary part of their training. We were on the grand circle level, and I took advantage of a rest to tell them the story of the ghost. It was new to them. From the grand circle, on each side, a wide staircase ascends to the upper circle. I was just reaching the end of my story when there was a cry of "My God, look!" There, entering from a corridor at the top of the upper circle stairs and coming very slowly towards us was—a figure in grey. Several of the men turned tail and bolted. Bombs they could face, but spectres were not in their line. Others—and to their credit, the majority —stood fast with me. I waited events. It was out of order—the time was wrong and the figure was coming the wrong way. Still, one never knew—even a ghost might alter his habits owing to war . . . and the figure in grey came nearer and nearer. Then—it spoke. "I say," it said, "can I get out this way, or must I go down to the stage door?" The spell was broken. It was a pianist in a grey flannel suit who had been rehearsing in the upper circle bar. . . .

Now I have set down here exactly what happens. I don't expect to be believed by the majority of people. That does not worry me in the slightest. I know what I know. I think my theory of our ghost is correct. He is not the remnant of a famous actor, he is not Betterton, Hart, Mohun, Garrick, Cibber, Wilks, Macklin or even Edmund Kean. He is what is left of that young man who was murdered and bricked up in that wall—the victim of an undiscovered crime. It is my theory also that when what we call the spirit leaves the fleshly body by some act of violence or by some equally sudden means, some imprint is left on what for the want of a better name we call the ether.

I could have written this story in another way. I could have decked it out with eerie atmosphere, with strange sounds, and grim, half-lit details. But I chose to tell it as it actually is, as it actually happens. In daylight, in a building often full of people, as if for a ghost to walk was one of the most ordinary things of the world. That, to my mind, is the strangest and most convincing thing about it, the matter-of-fact, everyday manner in which it occurs. That is the fact—as I have seen it scores of times. The theory is my own explanation of the sight and of its origin. You may believe or disbelieve, as you choose. But I would remind you that most of the great faiths of humanity are a compound of fact and of theory as well.

We at Drury Lane are fond of our ghost. We count him one of ourselves. We have an affection for him—indeed, we have considerable pride in him. Drury Lane is no ordinary theatre and its ghost is no ordinary apparition.

One more thing about him, which also endears him to us. His appearance usually betokens good luck. Seldom, if ever, do we see him when we have a failure, either just before its production or during its run. On the other hand, his appearance before a first night of a new show (yes, he was seen three days before *Oklahoma* was staged) is an almost sure token of success. He seems to know the good from the bad.

Which starts another theory—perhaps that ghost—that murdered man—was a critic. . . .

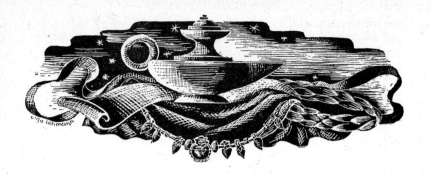

THE SLAVE DETECTIVE

WALLACE NICHOLS

Illustrations by Olga Lehmann

Wallace Nichols is primarily known as a poet, and in his historical novels has given us a poet's dramatic vision of the past. Also, as is shown by his epic novel Simon Magus, *he is a scholar, with a particular understanding of the Latin world. He was persuaded to put these qualities to the writing of a series of mysteries to be elucidated by a Roman slave detective, and thus given the latitude of a poet. In return he has given us a poet's imaginative prose and a scholar's clear balance of mind posing and solving his problems. This particular tale was entitled "The Case of the Garden God".*

I

"Sollius," said Titius Sabinus the Senator when his summoned slave of that name was standing before him, "I am lending you to a friend in the country. He—ahem!— has a mystery that needs solving, and when he heard of your aptitude in such matters, begged me to send you to him. I consented. You will go to-day."

"Yes, lord," answered Sollius, and sighed to himself. He was not quite comfortable over his gift for investigating mysteries, and was afraid that one day he would completely fail—and then not only lose all his former credit, but perhaps be whipped for it as well.

"You are to go to the country villa of Marcus Cinna," his master continued. "You once accompanied me there. It is some ten miles northward out of Rome."

"I remember it very well, lord," said Sollius. "What is the mystery in the lord Cinna's house?" he inquired.

"I do not know," replied Sabinus testily. "He would not inform me. You, I suppose, he will have to tell."

"Doubtlessly," said the slave with a smile. "It is some theft, I dare say."

"I dare say," echoed Sabinus. "Will you set out as soon as possible?"

"Yes, lord."

He bowed, and was turning to go when an urgent idea came to him. He coughed, and turned back.

"Lord," he asked, "may Lucius go with me?"

"Lucius?" exclaimed Sabinus, as if he did not understand.

"He has always helped me in my investigations," pleaded Sollius, "and been most useful. Frequently I need some little assistance."

"Ah, yes, I remember; you can take him," agreed his master.

And so it came about that Sollius and his younger fellow-slave Lucius set out together for the villa of Marcus Cinna, somewhere in the country district north of Rome. They rode mules, and came to their destination towards evening.

It was cool, with a single star blazing over a haystack near the gate of the villa, and it was there that one of the house-slaves found his master. Cinna, a tall, swarthy man, clean-shaven, and affecting a rusticity of manner, greeted them pleasantly, and took them at once, in spite of the swiftly deepening dusk, into a corner of the villa's private garden.

"It is the Garden God," he said as he led the way. "He kills my sheep and goats."

He pointed to a figure of Priapus standing above a small pool, with a hedge of myrtles behind.

II

Cinna's library was merely a room painted with figures of the chase. Sollius looked around for any scrolls, or well-pumiced books, or containers for such, and saw none. Cinna laughed in a bluff sort of way, and seemed not in the least embarrassed.

"I am not a reader," he admitted, "but a man can retire to his library and not be disturbed, when every other room in the house is open to the mad cleanliness of his domestics. My wife and daughter reign everywhere else—but not here! Sit down, Sollius!"

Sollius, still looking about him, took the nearest stool. He had left Lucius in the kitchen quarters, hoping that there he might be told a slightly different version of the tale which he himself was now to hear from the master of the house. Discrepancies might furnish the first clue.

"It is like this," began Cinna. "This is more a farm than a villa, and I breed sheep and goats, and make a good thing out of it, too. Remember that. A certain one of my neighbours tries to do the same, but without my success. We are not openly other than friends, and, for my part, I like Hortensius very well. But does he like me? There is no worse enemy than a secret one. I will say no more—and I accuse him of nothing. But remember all this. To bring the matter directly before you: I have been losing both sheep and goats lately, and losing them in the strangest possible manner. Their carcasses, sometimes singly, occasionally in groups of three or four, are found either within the pool or in front of the pool before the statue of the Garden God which I showed you. Sometimes they seem to have died by drowning, sometimes their throats are cut. I have watched, but never caught anybody at the work. Another thing: whenever the sheep or goats have died from throat-cutting, the lips of Priapus have been daubed with blood; when the animals have been drowned, his head has been wreathed in wild garlic. That, Sollius, is our mystery. It will be a serious loss to me if this killing of my sheep and goats continues. I will reward you well if you succeed in stopping it."

"Have you kept watch every night?" asked Sollius.

"My slaves will not watch," answered Cinna with a quirk of

the lips. "They are convinced that it is the god himself who does it, and that it is death to look upon his deeds. But I have watched myself, yet always when a killing has taken place I have most unaccountably slept at my post, and have awakened only to find the cruel slaying of the poor beasts done. My wife and my household point this out as confirming their superstition : that it is the god's own work, and that he casts sleep upon me on the nights when he kills. I cannot believe that myself. The old gods are but myths."

"Are not the sheep penned at night, and the goats tethered?" asked Sollius.

"Certainly, but the pens are near the house, and the goats are tethered in the same place. As I say, my household are afraid to watch, and my shepherd is even more afraid than they are," said Cinna. "The pens and the tethering-place are as shunned as any haunted ruin at dusk. When it is a goat that is killed, he is found with his tethering-rope beside him; when it is a sheep, or more than one, their tracks can be traced from the pens to the pool quite easily, but the one driving them— if anyone drives them!—leaves no footprints. That in itself frightens my slaves. 'Only a god leaves no footprints,' they say."

"It is not every night that Priapus kills?" asked Sollius.

"No, at various intervals. I have watched many times," replied Cinna, "when nothing has happened at all—and when I have not fallen asleep either."

"That was the answer I hoped you would give me," said Sollius, "for it shows some connection between your falling asleep and the killings. Could you have been drugged on those nights?"

"Who would drug me? My wife? My daughter? My slaves never came near me at such times, and certainly brought me nothing to drink, nor, if they had, would I have been so great a fool as to swallow it when going out on watch?"

"You went out to watch? You did not watch from a window indoors?" asked Sollius, leaning forward a little.

"When you see the place in daylight," answered Cinna, "you will see that it is not overlooked from the villa, but is surrounded by myrtle hedges and all kinds of bushes and trees."

"You hid, I suppose, among the trees and bushes?"

Cinna nodded.

"As near to the statue," he said, "as I could creep without becoming visible."

"Yet someone saw you, or knew that you were there—or to *be* there!"

"It was not Priapus," laughed Cinna grimly.

"Who would be able to know that you were to watch on any particular night?"

"Almost anyone in the house," answered Cinna. "I made no secret of it, for I suspect no one in my household at all. Every one of them is above suspicion; my slaves have been with me for years."

"None has been recently acquired?"

"None."

"How long have these killings been taking place?"

"At intervals for three months—perhaps a week or so longer."

"I think," said Sollius slowly, fixing Cinna with his eye, "that you suspect your neighbour. Hortensius, said you, was his name?"

"I do suspect Hortensius, though it grieves me to do so."

"Have you accused him of it?"

"I want proof first," answered Cinna, frowning. "It is not good to accuse a neighbour of anything in the country without proof. That is why you are here, Sollius."

"What is the popular idea about it?" asked Sollius. "Do you know?"

"According to my wife and daughter," answered Cinna, a little scornfully, "for I do not invite comment myself, the people round about put it down, one and all, as being the god's own deed. The old superstitions die hard in the country."

"That is so," said Sollius in a musing voice, and then abruptly rose. "That is all I wish to ask you at the moment—except this," he added suddenly; "are you proposing to watch to-night?"

Cinna stared at him.

"What do you take me for?" he asked, a touch of irritation in his voice. "When I hire a man to do something I want done,

I do not go and do it myself! It is for you to watch from now onwards."

"I understand," said Sollius, bowed, and withdrew.

III

He went in search of Lucius. They had been given quarters by themselves in the slaves' part of the house, near to the great kitchen. He found the youth sitting thoughtfully on the small slave's bed which had been provided for him, and as he sat down on the twin bed provided for himself alongside the other, he asked but one question:

"What does the kitchen-gossip say?"

"They are all afraid," answered Lucius. "They think it is the Garden God himself does it, and they told me—in whispers —why. The ladies of the house have become Christians, and this is the god's vengeance."

"But Cinna has not turned Christian, has he?" asked Sollius.

"Oh no; not he!"

"But they are *his* sheep and goats," said Sollius softly. "No, Lucius, that is not the answer."

"I never thought it was," said Lucius impishly.

"Are you tired?" asked Sollius.

Lucius yawned in sufficient witness to his poor state.

"Then pinch yourself thoroughly," said Sollius, "for you are not going to bed yet. We are going outside."

"Outside?" gaped Lucius.

"Into the garden," said Sollius firmly. "Come, follow me. And keep quiet, too."

Their sandals made no noise as they slipped along the stone corridor leading to a back door which led into the garden, a door which Sollius had arranged with Cinna's head domestic should be left unbarred and only on the chain.

"I wonder Cinna keeps no dogs about," he muttered under his breath as they passed out into the air.

He had hardly spoken when a growl and the rattle of a chain gave the lie to his supposition. But the dog was not loose, and a dog, or dogs, should have been loose so as to place the un-known killer in instant jeopardy. Sollius began to feel angry.

Why was Cinna neglecting the obvious precaution so strangely; indeed, so carelessly?

The dog had not barked. Probably, Sollius thought, he had not been trained to be suspicious of those coming out of the villa, but only of those seeking to enter it. The slave grew more and more uneasy. This neglect of a simple act of care was incredible, and the incredible always filled his inquiring mind with doubts. Cinna must give him an explanation in the morning. . . .

They worked silently round the corner of the villa, and Sollius led the way towards the retired portion of the garden where stood the statue of the Garden God. It was a night of full starlight, and though visibility was dim, they could see their quiet surroundings to a certain extent. There was no wind: not a bush seemed to rustle, not a leaf to stir.

Suddenly Sollius put out a hand, and drew Lucius to a standstill beside him.

"Someone is there," he whispered. "Do you see? Yonder, underneath the poplar."

Then he laughed under-breath, and went forward. Cinna saw them in the same instant, and awaited their approach motionlessly.

"I thought I might find you about," he whispered.

"And *I* thought," said Sollius bluntly, "that I should find more than you, lord, about; for instance, dogs."

"All of my dogs, save an old one in a kennel, have been . . . poisoned," answered Cinna through his teeth.

"I should have thought of that," replied Sollius meekly and contritely.

As if by unspoken accord, they descended into the secluded portion of the garden containing the dull pool and the figure of Priapus. Walled by thick hedges, it seemed a place apart. The Garden God might be of stone or of wood, for all that could be seen of him then was his sturdy, yet towering, bulk above the dark, placid, unrippled pool beneath the stars.

"There is nothing to-night," murmured Cinna. "Perhaps you have frightened him away."

"Then my presence here is known?" asked Sollius, and he clicked with his tongue in annoyance.

"I have told no one except my wife and daughter," replied Cinna stiffly, "but I do not imagine that the killer is without his spies."

"How have you explained my presence, lord, to your household?"

"You are a favourite slave of my friend Sabinus, and have been ill, and our air is good for your particular complaint," replied Cinna.

"I do not like complications based on untruths," said Sollius. "Those based on truth are dangerous enough! Still, I shall endeavour to sustain the character of a sick man. I hope you will not consider it necessary to put me on a low diet, lord," he added with a chuckle.

"You shall not accuse my hospitality!" laughed Cinna. "Shall we go in now?" he suggested. "Everything seems quiet."

Sollius gave a look round. Everything certainly had the appearance of complete quietude. Nevertheless, he felt uneasy. But there was no excuse for staying; besides, he was really tired from his journey. He followed Cinna indoors, and Lucius, nothing loth, followed behind.

"About the dogs," said Cinna, as he parted from them; "it was their poisoning that finally made me send to Titius Sabinus for *you*. I feared to replace them. I love dogs."

"I see," murmured Sollius. "I am glad, lord, that it is explainable so."

Sollius and Lucius then went to bed.

At dawn a great commotion broke out. Awakened by the noise, the two of them hurriedly dressed, and went out. They met one of the house-slaves running indoors to fetch his master, and Sollius stopped him, and put a question. He was answered that a goat had been found dead, horribly mutilated, and the carcass had been tied by its blood-stained tethering rope round the Garden God's neck.

IV

Sollius was anxious to make the acquaintance of three people in particular: Cinna's wife and daughter, and his neighbour, Hortensius. He met the first two early on that same day. They were found standing on the terrace above the whole slope of the garden when he returned to the villa with Cinna after examining the circumstances of the new outrage. From that part of the terrace where they stood, neither the Garden God nor the pool could be seen, but it was plain from their faces that they knew what had happened.

"My wife, and Lucentia, my daughter," murmured Cinna, as he brought the slave to them. "This, Fulvia, is Sabinus's slave," he explained to his wife.

"You are welcome here," said Fulvia, and gave Sollius, a faint, flickering, low-lidded smile. "You will stop these terrible happenings for us, I do hope."

Sollius bowed, and answered gravely that he was there to do his best. Mother and daughter moved away indoors almost at once, but left very clear pictures of themselves behind Sollius's eyes. Both were dark and tall, but the mother was still better looking in her maturity than her child, thought Sollius, would ever be, certainly handsomer than she was at present, in spite of the various advantages of youth.

"The killer reckoned upon my weariness," said Sollius to Cinna. "It is plain, therefore, that he knows of my purpose here. I will not believe that the killing took place last night of all nights by chance. Coincidence betrays his mockery of me— or so I think," he added.

"You may be right," answered Cinna wearily, passing a hand across his brow. "I must leave it all to you. I am at my wits' end myself. But command me—command my house—my servants—everything I have—only find out the truth!"

He had spoken his final sentence vehemently, as if momentarily out of his own control; then he squared his shoulders, and without another word strode off hastily and angrily towards his stables.

"Excellent!" breathed Sollius to himself. "If I am to succeed in this I must be free and not watched. Let us have a closer look at that statue, Lucius."

They went down to the edge of the pool. The pool was small, oval in shape, with a marble rim around it, and of some depth in the middle. It was filled with various aquatic plants and weeds. The figure of Priapus, the Garden God, was old, and carved in wood : it was set upon a marble pedestal. The carving was primitive, and up to the shoulders was merely a block of oak of considerable girth and some seven or eight feet in height, black with age, and stained from long exposure to the weather. It had no arms, no legs, no shaping in the body, but from the shoulders upwards there was a rude attempt at both form and feature, a thick, bovine neck, a broad face, overtopped by a mass of wooden curls. The face itself was without expression, with a blunt nose, staring and yet sightless eyes, and a wide, indented mouth that appeared to have the fixed and sardonic hilarity of a frozen evil spirit.

"Not my idea of a gracious guardian of flowers and herbs," murmured Sollius, "but I dare say it is interesting to those who appreciate things made and set up by our ancestors. It is interesting to me, too, in another way," he went on softly, after looking round to see that none of the watching domestics could overhear what he was saying. "Can you see what I mean?" he asked Lucius.

"No, Sollius," answered his assistant.

"You must really learn to be more observant," said Sollius with mock severity, for his eyes were twinkling with amusement as he went on : "Do you see where a moustache has been roughly scratched into the wood?"

"Yes, I see that," answered Lucius, frowning, and staring at the marks fixedly as if hoping that they would give away the secret which apparently they had divulged to his companion. But to himself they implied nothing, and he turned his puzzled face towards the still twinkling Sollius.

"The attempt to carve a moustache," the slave detective answered, "is quite recent. The old statue was clean-shaven. You can see that the cuts in the wood are not yet weathered in the way that the eyes are, for instance, or the lips themselves."

"How easy you make it when you explain, Sollius !" breathed Lucius.

"It should always be easy to *notice*," Sollius replied, "but it is not always equally easy to draw conclusions. So far," he went on, "I have only noticed it. But it is something to keep in our minds, Lucius, so whisper about it in my ear if I seem to forget it later on."

OLGA LEHMANN

"Yes, Sollius," promised Lucius humbly and admiringly. "Is there anything else you can see?"

Sollius stared at the statue, and at the pool under it, for some while in silence.

"Nothing," he said at length. "Let us go for a walk."

"Go for a walk!" exclaimed Lucius, gaping in astonishment.

"It is such a lovely day," said Sollius apologetically. "I am going out to the highway by that gate over there. Follow me in a little while, but find out, before you do, the nearest way to the farm of a certain man named Hortensius. Any of the household slaves should be able to tell you."

The first sight of the farm that they were seeking showed it to be straggling rather than large, and certainly ill-kept rather than prosperously trim, and Sollius had no need to ask himself why Cinna was a more successful farmer than his neighbour Hortensius. The differences lay in the men, and this was confirmed when they came upon Hortensius himself in one of his fields, wearing stained and almost offensive clothing, and a large, ancient hat of straw that was in danger of becoming unplaited about the brim. Laziness and self-indulgence spoke in every line of the man, and the only attendant virtue seemed to be a bluff and natural good-humour, evident in his thick lips and quizzical grey eyes.

"Looking for me?" he shouted, lumbering towards them slowly across the field, a switch in his hand, for he was driving five or six bullocks before him.

Sollius, with Lucius at his side, waited for him to come up to them; and apparently glad of any excuse to break from his labours, Hortensius at once left the bullocks to their own devices and advanced in a straighter line than the irrational antics of the frisky beasts had previously permitted, and with a broad smile on his round, red face that was glistening with sweat.

"What is it?" he asked. "I don't know ye. And ye don't look like a pair o' cattle-buyers," he added, and burst into a loud guffaw, as though in the plain belief that he had uttered a good witticism.

"I am sorry if we are trespassing," replied Sollius innocently, "but I am afraid we have lost our way."

"Your way—whither?" asked Hortensius, still with his red

face blazing with laughter, as if the very word "whither" only continued the previous witticism.

"We are from the farmstead of the excellent lord Cinna," answered Sollius. "We are slaves from Rome, lent by my own lord to him for—well, for a purpose."

He looked Hortensius full in the eyes as he spoke, and he heard Lucius behind him draw in his breath, and he had it in his heart to curse the youth for showing his surprise so openly.

Hortensius stared back at him, his face still smiling, but with the smile, as it were, like a fixed mask. Then the eyes crinkled once more, and the laughter came again.

"Come to help Cinna keep his Garden God under control? D'ye know what I'd have done? Why, chopped down old Priapus and fed him to the fire under my ovens! You can tell him so, and say it is my best advice to him."

"And who," asked Sollius, even more innocent than before, "shall I tell the lord Cinna sends him that good advice?"

"Ye don't know me, eh?"

"I have never been here, nor seen you, sir, before," answered Sollius truthfully.

"Well, it is Hortensius his neighbour sends him that counsel —and I should return and give it him as soon as you can, for the sooner that old god be chopped up the better, and for me as well as for him."

"Oh, sir? And why for you?"

"Because," laughed Hortensius, "the fool suspects *me* of these evil killings! Because I make a great jest o' life doesn't mean that I don't recognize seriousness when I meet it, and he was serious enough when he spoke to me about it, though he didn't accuse me to my face. He is a careful man is Cinna—and most careful men are suspicious. I've found that time and again. Carefulness breeds suspicion. Look close at life, slave, and ye'll find that true every time ye test it."

For a moment he had been in earnest, but now he burst out into a greater roar of laughter than ever, and immediately turned away from them, whistling to his now dispersed but still frisky bullocks.

"I'll not put ye on your way," he called over his shoulder, "for I think ye know it! I'm a good-tempered man, but I spew over the thought o' spies. Give Cinna my compliments and my advice—and keep away from here, for I keep a bull as well as bullocks!"

He gave another burst of laughter, and was soon striding up the field out of earshot.

Sollius and Lucius returned silently to the highway which they had left, and began to trudge back to Cinna's villa.

"Why did you give us away?" asked Lucius, his voice full of incomprehension.

"There was no need to lie," answered Sollius calmly. "I knew he was not the killer at once. We have wasted our morning, except that it has cleared the ground in this direction at any rate."

"How do you know he isn't the killer?" persisted Lucius.

"Didn't you see his eyes as he looked at his bullocks? That man loves his stock. He would never cruelly or unnecessarily kill any animal. The killer, at least, has the cruelty of—a god! But what I cannot understand," went on Sollius in a musing voice, "is how the lord Cinna cannot see that for himself. It is just stupid to suspect Hortensius."

v

It was the middle of the next night when Lucius, feeling himself shaken out of the deep pleasantness of sleep, gave a half-cry.

"Quiet, boy!" he heard Sollius whisper. "Dress quickly. We are going into the garden to keep watch."

They went out by the same way as before, and moved stealthily in the direction of the scene of the killings. But instead of descending into the space of sward that led to the pool under the statue, Sollius turned off behind one of the myrtle hedges to a group of trees level with the Garden God's position, but at a little distance. The branches were strong and neatly interlaced.

"We are going to climb one of these trees," whispered Sollius.

"*You* are?" cried Lucius in amused consternation.

"Even I—with your help," was the tart answer.

"In the dark?" hesitated Lucius.

"In the dark!" snapped Sollius. "It is quite easy: climb first yourself, and then help me up beside you. These boughs are quite firm; I examined them at dusk. Up you go! Now reach down your hand! I have not climbed a tree for years . . . but once I was as nimble as you. Steady!—I am not as nimble as all that now. I fall, boy! What, by Hercules, are you doing? Ah, that is better. Who said I could not climb a tree at my age, and in the dark, too? Are you comfortable there? It is a nice, warmish night, and we can see over the hedge quite comfortably. I can see the pool, and the statue, from where I am leaning. Can you, Lucius?"

"Quite well," his companion answered, "except that they are very blurred in the darkness. But now I can see a star in the water. . . ."

"Your eyes will get more and more used to it. Now we must be silent," warned Sollius.

"Is anything likely to happen?" asked Lucius before obeying that final injunction.

Sollius chuckled.

"Probably nothing," he said.

And nothing did!

"Well," murmured Sollius when they had returned to their chamber as soon as dawn shot its first rosy arrow over their heads, "it is something, at any rate, to renew one's youth. I used to be a great climber of trees, Lucius. . . ."

VI

They watched in the same manner, and from the same convenient fork in the tree, for six or seven nights quite fruitlessly, and during that time no killing took place. Lucius could see that Sollius was perturbed, for when he began to question him about the case, Sollius answered irritably, which was not in his character.

Sollius himself, indeed, went to Cinna, and admitted that he could not see his way yet to any kind of solution.

"I have no clue upon which to work," he complained. "Are you sure, lord, that you have told me everything?"

"You are satisfied about Hortensius?" Cinna asked, his lips pursed doubtfully, for it was clear that he had suspected his neighbour very definitely.

"I should be disconcerted, lord," answered Sollius carefully, "to be found mistaken in my acquittal of him."

He proceeded to explain his reasons, and was surprised when Cinna's brow cleared and he expressed himself as convinced.

"Surely," he added, "that is a step towards a solution?"

"I have tried to think so, lord," replied Sollius, and sighed.

Then he gave the other a swift look, and put a request. Cinna considered awhile, stroking his chin dubiously. Then he said:

"Well, slave, in my presence—and only so."

Sollius bowed.

"I did not dream of it otherwise," he answered gravely.

"When?" asked Cinna. "Now?"

"Wholly at their convenience, lord."

"Oh, they are but women," said Cinna in a tone dear to every professed lord of the hearth. "Household tasks can always be interrupted. It is not so with agriculture, nor with the care of beasts, I can tell you, and probably not so with a philosopher or a writer, but with the women of the house," he went on, puffing out his cheeks, "it is no more than their own gossip does ten times a day. Besides, there are plenty of slaves here to help 'em, and even an hour by yonder water-clock will not upset the running of the whole villa. I see them both out there on the terrace: I will send a slave for them."

"Lord," said Sollius, putting out his arm with an inhibiting gesture, "let us rather go out to them ourselves. To be overseen is always better than to be overheard, and indoors, who knows who may pad on quiet sandals along the passages?"

"You are quite right," muttered Cinna, and with a hasty sign to follow him, he strode out of the chamber in which they had been consulting.

They found Fulvia and Lucentia filling shallow baskets with oleander blooms.

"Sollius here wishes to speak to you," announced Cinna gruffly. "Answer him, wife: and you, daughter. I shall be by."

"What is it, Sollius?" asked Fulvia, raising her large, brown eyes to his. Her nose was slightly longer than perfect symmetry required, but her Roman stateliness was still beautiful in the span of her forties.

"When the Lord Cinna went out to watch at night," inquired Sollius, "did you know that he was doing so?"

"Sometimes, slave," she replied. "But on other nights I slept through his going forth and his returning."

Had Lucius been present, he would have recognized the momentary gleam in Sollius's narrowed eyes.

"I wonder, lady, if you can remember," he begged, "whether the nights when you slept through everything were the same nights when the lord Cinna fell asleep during his watch?"

Fulvia thought in silence. She did not frown in her concentration: frowning was a cause of wrinkles, and she had accustomed herself all her life to avoid the frown.

"It may have been so," she said at length, "but I cannot tell for certain; still——"

She left her sentence unfinished, and that in itself seemed to Sollius sufficiently affirmative. He turned to the daughter.

"Lady, I would ask you the same questions," he said.

Lucentia had been standing slightly apart while the slave had been interrogating her mother, but she had been listening, as Sollius had noted. He now studied her more closely. She had nearly everything, he decided, except colouring and charm, without which her features, excellent in themselves, and her bodily graces became as nothing; while her mother made the most of all her considerable attractions, she herself seemed to make nothing of her own, and he began to wonder why the mother had not taken the daughter in hand and instructed her in femininity's subtle ways of emphasizing natural advantages. It was almost, he reflected with some misgiving, a failure in the first elements of maternity.

"Even had I been wakeful," Lucentia replied in a dull and rather throaty voice, "I might not have heard my father leave the villa. I never did hear him leave, though more than once, when I knew that he was going out, I listened for his doing so. But either he moved too quietly, or I fell asleep before he went out."

"Can you remember sleeping with any particular heaviness—at any time?" asked Sollius.

She did not answer at once, but stood looking at him in a kind of apathy that seemed struggling to attain awareness. Then she merely shook her head.

"You are quite sure, lady?"

He saw a fugitive glint of anger in the depths of her eyes, but it reached neither the set of her lips nor her voice, and she answered perfectly calmly that she was.

Sollius pondered for a while, his eyes on the ground, until Cinna impatiently asked whether any further questions were to be put to his wife and daughter. As if in an abstraction Sollius shook his head, and moved unseeingly to the farther end of the terrace. Cinna exchanged a glance with his wife, lifted his hands in puzzled exasperation, and turned back into the villa. Lucentia and her mother returned to their previous occupation, and the slave seemed forgotten.

"Why are you smiling?" suddenly asked Fulvia.

"Smiling, mother? Was I smiling?"

"Secretly, Lucentia, and I do not like secret smiles. I suppose you are still thinking of young Publius Varro: a most unsuitable match for your father's daughter."

"Hush, mother: the slave will overhear you."

"Does it much matter?" asked Fulvia, and Sollius pricked his ears at her tone.

"I suppose not," sighed her daughter. "In any case, I was not thinking of Publius. My basket is full now. Shall I take it indoors?"

VII

"What gossip," asked Sollius of his young assistant later in the same day, "have you heard among the household slaves about a young man named, I believe, Publius Varro?"

Lucius looked startled.

"You seem to hear without listening," he said in a tone of awed admiration, and Sollius laughed.

"It depends on the length of your ears, my lad," he rejoined. "I gather that you have heard the same name!"

"I heard this," replied Lucius. "Publius Varro came wooing the lord Cinna's daughter. He is the son of a neighbour and heir to a good property. It was an arranged match between the two families. Then—and this is the gossip—Publius Varro became more attentive to the mother than to the daughter, and it didn't seem mere politeness either."

Sollius's eyes widened.

"Go on," he urged, for Lucius had paused.

"There is very little gossip more," Lucius continued. "The lord Cinna at first forbade Publius Varro the villa, but when the young man turned his wooing again to the right quarter— the lord Cinna, for the money's sake, would not break off the match—everything seemed smoothed over. But some of the slaves do say——"

Once again he paused, and Sollius smilingly supplied the rest of the broken sentence:

"—that the lady Fulvia meets the young Varro in secret?"

"You are too good at guessing," pouted Lucius, "and you always spoil the point of a story."

"I got there first, that is all," chuckled Sollius. Then, swiftly turning serious again, he murmured: "A house of disharmony!"

"And a jealous lady Lucentia?" suggested Lucius.

"Perhaps a more jealous lady Fulvia!" muttered Sollius. "I wonder," he added musingly, "if Publius Varro is clean-shaven —or moustached and trimly bearded. There was, of course, no room on the chin to carve a beard. . . ."

The two were waiting in their chamber for the hour of going on watch in the darkness. They were lying on their beds, and within reach on the stone floor between them stood a jar of mixed wine, two earthenware wine-cups, and a dish containing thin cakes made of meal and honey.

"I told you to remind me of those scratches on the Garden God's face," said Sollius, leaning from his bed to refill his cup.

"Do they mean anything?" asked Lucius, more than usually puzzled.

"They are the scribble of a soul," answered Sollius cryptically, and for a while said no more.

"These cakes are good," presently muttered Lucius through a full mouth. "You haven't had any. Try one."

"I never like sweet cakes," said Sollius. "You can have my share, lad."

"Oh, thank you, Sollius!"

"I am wondering," Sollius went on in a musing voice, holding his wine-cup against his chest, and sipping from it at intervals, "whether we are wise in watching the scene of the killings together, when one of us, perhaps, might be better placed watching the sheep-pens and the tethering-stakes of the goats. Yet I have the feeling that we should not separate at our watchings. A second witness has such definite value. Still, I am inclined to make an alteration for to-night, lad. You watch, as before, from the tree; I will keep an eye on the sheep-pens. I noticed this morning an empty cart-shed from where I might see very well both the pens and the stakes without being too easily discoverable. I have also the feeling that we should go out somewhat earlier to-night than we have done before. In fact, since it is already dark, we will go now, Lucius. So get off your bed, lad! It is no use lying back and pretending to be asleep. At your age adventure should sing in your young blood. Up, Lucius!"

Sollius finished what remained of his wine, set the cup down on the floor, and swung his legs off the bed.

"Lucius!" he called. "This is no time to fool!"

There was no answer.

"Lucius!" he cried impatiently. "Get up, Lucius!"

There was still no answer.

He stared across at the other bed. In the light of the clay lamp which glimmered from a shelf, he could see the youth lying perfectly still on his back, with his mouth open, and even as he looked at him, Lucius began snoring. Sollius went over and shook him by the shoulder, but there was no response. Lucius was asleep: more, Lucius was in a drugged sleep.

Sollius looked down between the beds. Both of them had filled their wine-cups from the same jug; but Lucius alone had eaten the cakes, and had eaten, moreover, more than his expected share. One solitary cake remained on the dish. Sollius felt the youth's pulse; it was steady, if slow. He lifted one of his eyelids, and nodded to himself as he noted the size of the pupil of the eye. Lucius was not poisoned, but he was certainly likely to be unconscious until the morning. Sollius returned to his own bed, sat down quietly, and began to think.

It had been planned, of course, that both of them should be drugged, and it was only his own dislike of such sweet cakes which had frustrated the plan as far as he himself was concerned. Moreover, had he been suspicious that someone would attempt to drug them, he would doubtlessly have suspected the wine as the vehicle of the drug, not the cakes, and have avoided drinking accordingly. The perpetrator would therefore imagine that both of them would eat the cakes without suspicion; he himself, in consequence, must pretend to be under the same narcotic as Lucius if he was profitably to deceive the drugger. It was clear that there was to be a killing that night, and he asked himself whether he should go out alone on the watch, or feign to be as incapacitated as Lucius. Someone, he reasoned, might look in to see if the cakes had been eaten and had taken effect, and, if so, he might discover who that person was. On the other hand —so he balanced his opportunities—the drugger might not be the killer, and it was the killer whom he was employed to unmask. Yet drugger and killer, even if not the same, would be in league, and the discovery of the one could lead to the discovery of the other. He decided to feign insensibility until the drugger had looked in upon him, and then to go out and watch.

Immediately upon coming to that conclusion, he resumed his former reclining position on his bed, and continued his thinking with closed eyes.

He must find out whether Cinna had eaten of any cakes of meal and honey on the nights when he had fallen asleep while watching, and, if so, who had given them to him. Who, indeed, had given Lucius their own wine and cakes that evening? They had had wine and cakes given them every evening, and Lucius had fetched them from the kitchen. He would have to find out from whom the youth had usually received them, and whether he had received them that evening from the same person or another.

On a sudden he heard a loitering footstep in the stone passage outside the doorway, and immediately added a few, light, imitative snores to the real ones of Lucius. But nobody entered; nobody even peered in. There was only a listener by the doorway. The footsteps began again, receding. Sollius silently rose from the bed, tiptoed to the doorway, and looked cautiously out. He could see nothing, not even the faint glimmer of a retreating lamp; but the passage turned at right angles a little distance off. He tiptoe out and on to the corner: all was dark; all was now even noiseless. Had he dreamed everything? He shook himself. Of course he had not dreamed it! He returned to his chamber, put on his sandals, and the rough, dark cloak which he wore on his nocturnal occasions, and went out by the usual way into the air. This time he hurried onwards without caring whether he made a noise or not. He was hoping that the sound of his footsteps would prevent the killing which he felt sure was planned for that night.

He had never considered himself a brave man, and the impulse to look over his shoulder as he hurried towards the statue of Priapus was overwhelming. He missed Lucius! He began to sweat, though the night was not particularly warm. But neither in front of him nor behind did he see anyone, and at last he stood panting in the shelter of some bushes. He could not, without the help of Lucius, have climbed into the customary tree.

If he had not feared to miss the immediate opportunity, he would have roused Cinna and fetched him out to watch with him, but there was no time. He crouched in his shadowy hiding-place, and waited. He could see one end of the small pool, and also part of the wooden flank of Priapus, though not the whole figure; but it was enough, he thought, for his purpose, if anything should begin to happen.

He strained both hearing and sight, but nothing came to eye or ear for a considerable period, and he was becoming stiff with cold. Almost he had decided to return indoors when suddenly he heard the patter of four small hooves on gravel, the patter of the prospective victim being driven to the place of sacrifice. His spine chilled; the patter was so thin, brittle and ghostlike, and he could see nothing, only hear the little hooves coming nearer and now falling silent as the animal, whether a single sheep or a goat, he did not know which, was driven on to the first stretch of sward towards the pool that was shadowed by the god.

No other sound had he heard; no human footstep; no rustle of a garment; no rumour of breathing. And now everything was so still again that he even wondered if the patter of hooves had itself been only some figment of his high-strung imagination.

He knew that he must do whatever he was going to do at once. A man of pity, he had always hated the sacrifices, and to doom even one small dumb creature, when with a single cry he could save its life, was abhorrent to his whole nature. Without thinking of much else except the saving of that probably silly life—but was not all life sacred?—he rushed out of his conceal-ment with a cry of "Hold! Cease!" and immediately knew what a fool he was. He should have crept close in and watched, and then at least, even if he had lost the poor beast his life, he would have known who was the killer; as it was, he saved the goat, but had the mortification of hearing the killer escape through the shallow water of one end of the pool and into the bushes behind Priapus. If only Lucius had been there to use his young legs!

VIII

Sollius was back again in the chamber he shared with Lucius long before that drugged youth awoke, and he lay on his bed angrily disappointed in himself. He felt that he had bungled the affair unpardonably, and was impatient for Lucius to regain consciousness. He wished to put a special question to him.

Dawn broke over a sleepless Sollius and a sleep-sodden Lucius, but it was some time even then before the latter came out of his drugged stupor, and he woke indignant when dis-covering that Sollius was aiding the return of consciousness by pouring water over his head.

"Ugh! What are you doing, Sollius? Ah-h!"

"Be quiet, lad! Take it easy!"

"Oh, my head!"

"Drink this."

Sollius had mixed some wine and water, and he held the cup to the youth's lips. Lucius drank gratefully.

"What is the matter with me?" he asked, groaning.

"You ate too many cakes last night," answered Sollius, grin-ning, though he did not at all feel amused.

"This is more than indigestion," sighed poor Lucius.

"It is," said Sollius, "for the cakes were drugged."

Lucius stared at him.

"What happened?" he cried, sitting up in bed, and then sinking back again for very dizziness. "Were *you* drugged, too?" he whispered.

"No, for the drug was not in the wine, but in the cakes, and only you ate the cakes."

"Did you go out? Did anything happen?" asked Lucius eagerly.

Sollius gave a quick, brief account of the night's wasted adventure.

"I was a greedy fool to eat so many!" muttered Lucius.

"Do not blame yourself," answered Sollius, patting him on the shoulder. "You had eaten cakes every night since we came here, and if anyone was to blame, it was I for not foreseeing the possible danger."

"The killer will be doubly on his guard now!" groaned Lucius in exasperation.

"Whoever drugged those cakes," answered Sollius equably, "knew of our purpose here: that, at least, is certain; and therefore he has been on his guard for some time already. But it didn't prevent him from attempting another killing last night."

"What happened after he had run off?" asked Lucius.

"Oh, I just took the goat back, tethered it to its stake again, and returned indoors," replied Sollius coolly. "I haven't told anyone but you about the adventure at all. Wait! Ask no more questions now, but think carefully when you answer those that I am going to put to yourself."

"Yes, Sollius."

"How do we get our wine and cakes each evening?"

"I go to fetch them."

"Who gives them to you?"

"At first it was the cook," replied Lucius; "but after a day or two he used to put them out on a small table at a certain time for me to fetch when I liked."

"Where was this table?"

"Just inside the kitchen, Sollius."

"Were any of the domestics usually about?"

"Sometimes; not always."

"Not always?" Sollius repeated.

"Not if I went later than usual. Sometimes the kitchen was empty."

"So that anyone, choosing the right moment, could have changed the cakes for others?"

"I suppose so," answered Lucius.

"That is enough," breathed Sollius. "I am confirmed in my ideas about these killings. . . ."

"You know the killer?" gasped Lucius.

"I have guessed at the killer for a little while now," was the sober answer. "But I have no proof."

"Who is it, Sollius? I have no guess myself. Oh, who is it?"

"You know all that I know. In fact, you gave me yourself one of the most important items of my knowledge. But I shall tell you no more at present. Listen carefully. We shall never catch this killer without spreading a net, or digging a pitfall. I am certain of that now. We shall watch for ever—and never see anything. The chance of last night will not be given me again. But, as I said, listen carefully. I have plotted a nice little trap for this killer, and you, Lucius, have your part in it."

"Oh, Sollius, tell me!"

And Sollius told him.

IX

Cinna's consent and co-operation were necessary to the slave detective's plan.

"You think that this which you suggest, Sollius, will solve our mystery?"

"Either it will solve it—or it is not likely to come to solution," Sollius answered; "yet it is my belief that it will solve it, and show you the killer. What you, lord, do afterwards, when the killer is caught, is not in my task here."

Cinna considered a moment, striding up and down his library with uneasy, unequal steps.

"You wish me to gather the whole of my household suddenly and without warning, on a night to be chosen by you, and group them together on the sward in front of the pool and the statue of the Garden God?"

"Yes, lord—with the lady Fulvia and your daughter and yourself."

"I understood that," rasped Cinna irritably. "But it is my slaves who make the problem. They are cowards—and afraid of Priapus in the dark. I told you. How shall I be able to persuade them, or even command them, to do as you ask?"

"What each slave might fear singly, the whole of them may dare together. I will speak to them. They will do your bidding, lord," said Sollius confidently.

"Very well," decided Cinna. "Be it as you say."

In spite of his acquiescence, he was manifestly uneasy.

"There are yet two other matters, lord Cinna," Sollius inexorably went on. "Will you also on the same day invite Publius Varro to your house and have him with us in the garden?"

"Publius Varro?" exclaimed Cinna, and his surprise had a note of anger in it.

"I beg of you, lord!" urged Sollius.

"Very well; as you say. If the Emperor was satisfied with your ways of doing things, I will not scant your requests. I must know the truth! What else?"

"A simple question, lord: when you were, as we believe, drugged, had you eaten, on those nights, of any—cakes?"

Cinna stared at him.

"Always a plate of honey-cakes is at my bedside," was the answer. "I am partial to them."

"Who brings them to you?"

"Anybody in the house," said Cinna, still staring. "Sometimes my wife; sometimes my daughter; sometimes one of the slaves from the kitchen."

"Thank you, lord, that is all I wished to know," said Sollius, and hastily withdrew before Cinna could interpose questions of his own.

X

Sollius chose a calm evening, with a half-moon in the sky, about four days later, and was able to give Cinna the assurance of the household slaves' willingness to obey their master's orders to gather in front of the pool and the statue when ordered. For his part, Cinna co-operated as one skilful general might co-operate with another in the same campaign from different bases; he even obtained the presence of the young Varro with-

out that individual suspecting anything more than a neigh-
bourly invitation to an eligible suitor.

The slave detective studied Varro from a distance, noting in
particular his attitude to Cinna and to Cinna's wife and
daughter. He noted, too, with considerable satisfaction that the
young man had a small moustache and a beard so closely
trimmed as to be little better than a rough, dark down about
the chin and jaws.

"You are sure you will not fail me?" Sollius asked Lucius,
after taking him for perhaps the twentieth time over the youth's
part in the proceedings to be.

"I can do it all right," Lucius assured him. "You need not
be afraid, Sollius."

"Good lad! Remember that everything—everything, I say!
—really depends on *you*."

"Yes, Sollius, I shall remember," replied Lucius soberly, yet
his eyes were shining with excitement.

"Then slip out at once, and conceal yourself as we arranged."

Lucius sped away into the gathering dusk.

The moment had come, and Sollius went out from the villa
with an uncertainly beating heart: he would either succeed, or
fail hopelessly. He walked slowly, with head bent, towards the
place of the killings. In front of the pool lay a stretch of grass of
some size, banked at the end opposite the statue. The whole
scene was roughly a parallelogram, confined by myrtle and
other bushes, with the pool and the Garden God at one of the
two narrower sides. The bank facing them was topped by a
gravel terrace, and here were grouped Cinna, with his wife
and daughter and Varro his guest. Below them stood the
gathered company of slaves and domestics, silent and still in the
darkness.

The moon was now rising, and a faint gleam came from the
pool. Even Sollius, as he joined the group about Cinna on the
terrace, felt a measure of awe at the spectacle of the silent slaves,
the gleaming pool and the towering wooden figure of Priapus
above it.

Cinna turned as he found the slave at his side.

"Well, Sollius, what now?" he asked curtly. "Everybody is
here as you required. What are you going to do with us?"

"With your permission, lord Cinna," replied Sollius, "I should like to make a little speech."

It was Varro who laughed, not Cinna; but the cold reception of the young man's mockery of a slave who proposed, on any pretext whatsoever, to make a speech to a company which included free people and Roman citizens, turned his laughter into a spluttering and wide-eyed astonishment.

"By the gods," Sollius heard him mutter, "is your father mad? Or am I?"

"I think my husband was quite mad to send for this impertinent slave at all!" murmured Fulvia at the young man's other side.

"If you wish to make a speech, Sollius," said Cinna, "you may."

"Will you first tell them, lord, that I speak by your permission and authority?"

Cinna swore under-breath, but did as he had been bidden.

"Servants and slaves," his voice rang out crisply, "you know now who Sollius is, and why he is here. He wishes to speak to you all. He speaks in my name. Listen to him as you would to me."

Sollius moved a pace or so forward, so that he stood between the few on the terrace and the many below on the sward between the bank and the pool. Until then, all eyes had been fixed upon the figure of the Garden God; but now there was a kind of human rustle as every face was turned towards Sollius.

"You will be asking," he began, "why I have requested the lord Cinna to gather you together here in this manner. The answer is this: the time has come to ripeness; and if you ask of me how I know it, I can only relate a dream, and we all know that in dreams are revelations and signs. In my dream I saw the Garden God walk through the pool yonder and come to where I was standing, and it was where I am standing now, and he spoke to me, and said: 'Draw all together into this very place, and I will reveal the truth.' That is all. Dreams are heaven-sent states of our being: I believe them to be sacred. I could not therefore refuse the Garden God's bidding, thus communicated to me in a dream. We are here in obedience to that command,

OLGA LEHMANN

and the rest lies in the god's power. If my dream was a delusion, a vision out of sickness of mind, naught will happen; but if it came verily from the god, then our mortal senses may witness a wonder. In silence, let us wait."

He thought that he had heard Cinna sharply draw in his breath, and certainly he had caught a mocking whisper from Publius Varro:

"What is this nonsense? There are no gods! And that yonder is but a rude block of wood, a rustic ornament at best. Who *is* this fellow?"

"Hush, Publius!"

It was Fulvia whispering back.

"But, mother——" began Lucentia, in a whisper, too, but Fulvia was continuing:

"It is my husband's whim to employ him. He both is, and looks, a fool. Nothing, of course, will happen!"

Cinna called abruptly for silence.

Sollius was quick to sense the nervousness of those about him. In Rome, he reflected, the superstitious awe that seemed so invasive in the country would have been laughed out of sight over the horizon; but here it was a factor upon which he had felt himself reasonably able to count. He had allowed for it, planned for it, and now held it suspended, as it were, like a sword hidden in a cloud, above the leafy, nocturnal stillness of that death-haunted garden. He waited, drawing out the silence to its utmost unbearable moment before giving the prearranged signal to Lucius. He wondered uneasily in the final instants whether his little stratagem would succeed. Then he straightened his shoulders, fixed his gaze on the statue and the pool, and cried out:

"Look! The god moved!"

"What?" exclaimed Cinna incredulously.

"At least," continued Sollius, affecting a stammer of extreme nervousness, "the shadow in the water seemed to move, seemed to tremble . . . and there is no wind to ripple the surface. Did none of you see it?"

Opinion was divided: some had seen, and said so, excitedly; others mutely shook their heads. Sollius laughed within himself, knowing that all had lain in the power of suggestion.

Suddenly a kind of semi-animal wail welled up from the shadows behind Priapus—or was it from Priapus himself?

The wail, long-drawn-out, ceased, and the gasp of utter surprise and fear that had gone up trembled away into a silence of awful expectation. Then—surely this time certainly from Priapus?—came a voice, high-pitched and tensely quivering:

"Who has profaned the peace of this garden's beauty? The reek of blood has overpowered the perfume of the rose in my nostrils. Evil has been done here, and been charged to me, who am the innocent guardian of dewy shade and flower and fruit. The wicked strike without thought of a watching power; it is time that a righteous Heaven should strike back and call the offender to vengeance. That heart knows itself, and beats in a blind secrecy; I can hear the beating of that evil heart!"

Priapus-Lucius paused, and if uneasiness had already been stalking the garden, it was suddenly an intruder in their midst. Even Cinna coldly sweated, and the slaves below were a huddled mass of fear. On a sudden the voice began again:

"Come to me, and repent! Kneel at my pool, and repent! Come to me, and kneel and repent!"

A faint stir, and fainter whispers, followed the words, but nobody moved. Sollius strained his ears to catch whatever might be murmured behind him by Cinna and his wife and daughter, or by Publius Varro. Then Priapus-Lucius spoke again:

"Thou canst not hide from me. All is known. Shall I call thee by name?"

The stir among the slaves and domestics ceased, and there seemed but one whisper against the background of the awful silence:

"What, after this, is madness?"

It was Varro who had spoken under-breath, but to whom? "O Publius, Publius——"

Who had answered him? Sollius dared not turn his head.

"Shall I call thee by name?" repeated the Garden God.

The silence now had terror in it.

"Father Jupiter!" muttered Cinna.

"Lord Christ, help!" breathed—which of them? Sollius

again dared not turn his head. He was himself in a fever; this was the moment of success or failure.

"By name? I call thee—I call thee——" cried the Garden God, his voice growing louder with every syllable until it burst out like a summoning trumpet with a final: "I call thee, killer!"

There was a broken sob, a fearful cry, and through the silence and darkness and towards the glimmering pool rushed a figure like a Mænad in full frenzy.

"I am here! I did it! I—I!"

And Fulvia flung herself face downwards into the pool in suicidal abasement.

In the same instant sounded a most fearful cry, and the towering Garden God toppled headlong upon the victim.

*   *   *   *   *

"But I do not understand it," said Lucius. "Was the lady Fulvia mad?"

"In a way, Lucius. She was frustrated. The lord Cinna should have sent Varro packing, not have insisted on a son-in-law whom his wife—had loved. It was a situation for a Greek tragedy, and she made her vengeance, as Medea did with Jason, hit the lord Cinna in his most sensitive place: the stock of which he was so proud."

"When did you know who it was?" asked Lucius.

"I never quite knew," replied Sollius with a laugh. "But I never liked looking into her eyes," he pursued dreamily. "I should not have solved it without our little trick. But, you know, Lucius, what you did at the end was quite unnecessary."

"What do you mean?" the youth asked, his brow puckered.

"I did not ask you to give that cry like a mad bull's, and to push the statue over as you did. She had already betrayed herself, and a dozen hands would have got her out of the pool before she was drowned—though perhaps it was best as it was," he added.

"But, Sollius, that cry," broke in Lucius, "it wasn't mine! It frightened me to hear it, I can tell you!"

"Not *your* cry?" exclaimed Sollius.

"No! Nor did I push over the statue. I doubt if I could had I tried. It just—began to topple over of itself."

"Of itself. . . ." breathed Sollius.

There was a fearful silence between them.

"I expect," said Sollius after some while, quietly and without looking at his companion, "that the wood was rotten at the base. We must remember that it was a very old statue."

"But the cry?" persisted Lucius.

"Peace, boy! Do you expect me to explain everything?" cried Sollius irritably, and he kept a frowning silence all the way back to Rome.

HARRY

DONALD GILCHRIST

"The fact that boys are allowed to exist at all is evidence of a remarkable Christian forbearance among men," wrote Ambrose Bierce in the San Francisco News Letter, *1869. Others may agree with him.*

"BEAUTIFUL night to have to turn out, I must say." Mrs. Merritt could be sarcastic. She opened the oven door and slid in a rabbit pie to heat up. "What time's the train?"

"Eight o'clock." Fred Merritt yawned and took his stockinged feet off the fender. He looked over his shoulder at the window streaked with rain. There was a lull in the wind. He could hear the far-off roar of it in the trees, the roaming, rumbling throatiness of it as it hunted the woods and hillsides. And then suddenly it would be near, frantic, screaming to be in at windows and doors. It would scream like an animal trapped and crushed in the angles of the walls.

"Jimmy, are you going with your Dad?"

A boy of fourteen raised a ruffled head from the book he was reading, frowning at the interruption. "What?"

"Are you going to the station with your Dad?"

"Why?"

"No reason. I only asked. I thought perhaps you couldn't wait to see this . . . this Harry we've heard so much about."

Her voice rasped. It rubbed her husband up the wrong way, and was meant to. He flung back at her, "If you didn't want to have him, why didn't you say so at the right time? You say nothing till it's all fixed; then you begin this grumbling and grousing. It's Jimmy and me that'll have most of the trouble, anyway, teaching him the ways of things. He's never been on a farm before in his life."

Mrs. Merritt went to the window and slashed the curtains across. There was eloquence in the way she did it.

"Besides"—Fred Merritt began pulling on his boots, lacing them up—"we get paid for it. It means a bit extra in the kitty, and that's not to be sniffed at."

"Why's he coming?" Jimmy asked, looking at his father.

"I've told you why—to learn farming."

"That's not the whole reason," his wife cut in, "and you know it."

"Well, there's no need for Jimmy——"

"Yes, there is. He should know what sort of a creature he's going to have as a companion." She turned to the boy. "It's one of those messed-up homes. The lad's been living in London with an uncle. Why, goodness only knows, but his family won't have him. The uncle says he can do nothing with him, and the boy says his uncle beats him for nothing. One or the other must be lying. Then the Welfare people step in and make inquiries and say the boy must be got **away** and put to work in new surroundings. So now you know."

"How old is he?" Jimmy asked. "Old?"

"Fourteen. Same age as you. He's the oldest of five. Three younger brothers and a sister."

"Two younger brothers," Fred corrected her. "The third's dead. They told us. Drowned in a boating accident a year ago when he was ten."

Mrs. Merritt sniffed. She resented correction. Sharply she went off at a tangent: "Well, if you're going to meet that train, you'd better stir yourself. Jimmy, are you going with your Dad, or are you not? Make up your mind."

"I don't think I'll go." The boy stretched and yawned. He was thinking of the ten-year-old brother drowned in a boating accident. It must be awful, drowning; snoring in the stinging splinters of icy water, lungs bursting, choking. Everybody should learn to swim. He stared at the open fire in the kitchen range. The wind was booming and drumming in the throat of the great chimney. Puffs of smoke billowed back out into the room, chased by downward draughts.

Suddenly he changed his mind. "I think I'll go," he said.

"Put a coat on then. That station's as draughty as a street corner. And the train'll be late."

The train was punctual. It came snuffling and clanking out of the night under a torn sheet of steam, and shuddered to a standstill at the open platform.

They saw Harry at once. He was the only passenger to get out. Jimmy stared at him in astonishment. He was quite small. He looked no more than ten or eleven. He was tidily dressed, good-looking, surprisingly clean. On the way home in the car, he answered questions about the journey in a soft, well-spoken voice.

Mrs. Merritt was as obviously surprised by his appearance as the others had been. Her manner changed from one extreme to the other. She was suddenly as fussy, as solicitous for his welfare as she had previously been indifferent to it.

"Now, Jimmy, take Harry's bag upstairs and show him his room. And don't dawdle. Supper's ready as soon as you are. Here! take a candle."

Jimmy led the way up the stairs to the top landing, where the two little attic rooms crouched under the roof, side by side.

"You're sleeping next to me," Jimmy said. He pushed open the door and held the candle up, showing the tidy little room with its white furniture and its plain iron bedstead.

Harry went across to the window and made blinkers of his hands to see out.

"You won't see much," said Jimmy.

"I can. There's quite a bit of moon showing. I can see——" He turned his head, looking back into the room. "Is it a lake?"

"There is a lake. Look, I'll light your candle and leave you. You can find your way downstairs again, can't you?"

"Yes." He was staring out of the window again, nose pressed to the glass.

"Well, don't be long, because supper'll be ready."

"All right."

Supper was an ample but a hurried meal. It was getting late, and Mrs. Merritt wanted to wash-up and be away to bed.

"We go to bed early because we have to be up early," she told Harry. "You'll hear Jimmy get up round about six, but you lie in to-morrow. You'll be tired. I'll give you a call when breakfast's ready."

The following morning, after breakfast, the two boys went along to the shippon to wash up the cooler and the milk buckets.

Harry said: "Haven't you got any brothers or sisters? Or don't they live here?"

"I've got a sister," said Jimmy. "She's older. She's a nurse at the Infirmary." He began dismantling the cooler, plunging its parts into a bath of hot water dosed with disinfectant. "You've got quite a lot of brothers, haven't you?"

"Quite a few."

"Which do you like best?"

"Well, I liked Martin best. He was in the Navy, you know, before he was killed. The Marines actually. He was killed training. The boat upset in a rough sea and they were all drowned."

"But how old was he?"

"Oh . . . about five years older than me."

"I thought you were the eldest?"

Harry looked at him sideways with a kind of mild suspicion. "Who told you that?"

"But you are. Your brother who was drowned was only ten."

"That's a lie!" For perhaps a couple of seconds his eyes blazed with indignation. Then, just as suddenly, he smiled and pointed to the milk-soaked wadding. "What's that for?"

"The milk runs through it. Catches all the muck."

"Can I see the milking to-morrow?"

"You can see it to-night. We milk twice a day."

Jimmy made no attempt to re-open the subject of Harry's brothers and their respective ages. It gave him a queer feeling. It was quite possible that his father had made a mistake, and yet . . . he had been so definite about it.

It was not until after tea that he managed to catch his father by himself. They were walking over the fields to get the cows in. Harry had been left behind to help Mrs. Merritt mix the chicken mash.

"Dad, Harry says he had a brother five years older than him. And he was drowned too. He says he was in the Marines."

"I don't believe it. Harry's the eldest."

"That's what I thought. But he told me his name and everything."

"What was his name?"

"Martin."

Fred Merritt swore. "He's a damned liar, then. Martin was the ten-year-old kid who was drowned. I know that, because the Welfare people kept on about him; Martin this and Martin that. Half the trouble was over Martin. Harry got up against his father because his father favoured the younger lad. I shouldn't say anything to Harry, though. I'm sorry for the kid. No proper home and all that. Don't take any notice if he spins a tale, that's the best thing."

Easier said than done, Jimmy reflected. He took Harry round the farm buildings after the day's jobs were finished; showed him the tractor and the new side-delivery machine and the place where they dipped sheep.

Suddenly Harry said, "You know, I'm going to inherit a farm when I'm twenty-one. When my grandmother died she left it to my father to keep till I was twenty-one."

"Oh?" said Jimmy casually. "Where?"

"In Scotland."

"How big?"

"Oh . . . quite big. There are about five hundred sheep and fifty cows on it. But mostly it's poultry-breeding. I like poultry best."

"Who's looking after it now?"

"My brother-in-law."

"Your brother-in-law? But that means your sister's husband."

"I know that," he said irritably.

"I thought your sister was younger than you."

"She is. I've often wondered why he's called my brother-in-law. But I haven't asked."

Jimmy looked at him. Was he serious? He sounded perfectly serious. Yet it was all so silly, so pointless.

"Why didn't you go there instead of coming here? You could have done jobs on the farm there, couldn't you?"

Harry shook his head. "Not very well."

"Why?"

"Oh . . . my brother-in-law has moods. He doesn't like children about the place."

"You're not a child—not at fourteen."

"I know; but he seems to think I am. I shall show him, of course, when I'm twenty-one. I shall kick him out then. Or throw him out on his neck."

Jimmy bristled at the bragging tone. He couldn't resist saying, "I bet you haven't got any farm in Scotland or anywhere else if the truth be known. It's probably another lie like the one you told this morning."

"What one? What d'you mean?"

"Saying Martin was older than you and got drowned in the Navy."

"I didn't say that."

"Yes, you did."

"*I didn't!*" He shouted it out angrily, his cheeks scarlet. "Why d'you want to pretend I've said things I haven't?"

"I don't want to pretend anything. It's what you *did* say."

Harry was silent for a moment, as if in a furious sulk. Then a moment later, calm as milk snatched off the boil, he said, "Do you like drawing?"

"Drawing?" The scowl on Jimmy's face only deepened. 'Not particularly. Why, do you?"

"Yes, I'm very proud of it. I've got some in my bag I'll show you, if you like."

"What do you draw?"

"Oh"—he kicked at a stone, sending it clattering across the yard—"people's heads mostly. I like drawing boats, too, though, and cock-fights."

"Funny mixture," said Jimmy. "Cock-fighting's illegal."

"You see plenty if you keep poultry. That's one of the reasons I want a poultry farm."

Jimmy shrugged his shoulders. The conversation embarrassed him. There was a queerness about it. "We'd better get back, or we'll be late for supper."

That night Jimmy woke up, jerked out of the middle of a dream by something that set every sense alert. He sat up, listening, not knowing what had disturbed him. There was a moon shining through light cloud. Everything seemed intensely quiet. The only sound he could hear was the wind stirring softly in the trees outside. He lay down again, his heart still beating fast with the suddenness of his waking. He had the peculiar feeling that somebody else was listening, straining after the least sound, heart beating in time with his own.

And then he heard the door shut outside on the landing.

He held his breath. Harry's door, Harry letting himself out —or in. It was impossible to say which. Well, and why not? There were perfectly good reasons why people made journeys about a house at night. It was absurd to read anything sinister into it.

Still no other sound. Still no indication of what had woken him. A creaking board probably. There were places on the landing that creaked.

Then suddenly he heard the bed groan faintly on the other side of the wall—the sort of groan made by the springs when a person pressed on them in one place, getting into bed.

Jimmy took a deep breath and relaxed. That was all it was: Harry going downstairs to the bathroom. Fancy getting all het-up over a little thing like that. He turned over on to his side and yawned. But it was nearly an hour before he went to sleep again.

Thursday was Auction day. Fred Merritt bought cows in one market and sold them in another. In a small way. Perhaps six at a time. He enjoyed his little bit of cattle-dealing. Jimmy took the cows to the auction mart every Thursday morning, driving them along the three miles of quiet road that snaked over the hill. As usual he went to the kennel behind the shippon to loose the dog.

His father, labelling the milk churns in the cooler-house, heard him calling and whistling.

"What's the matter? What are you whistling on?"

"Raff. Where is he?"

"Isn't he there?"

"No. His collar is, but he's not in it."

"He must have slipped it, then."

"Must have. But it's so blooming tight, I don't see how."

"Ask Harry. He fed him last night, didn't he?"

Harry could throw no light on the subject. Yes, Raff had been on the chain all right when he fed him. But he remembered the collar: it had been bedded deep in the mane of hair round his neck. He couldn't see how he could have slipped it off.

"Blasted nuisance without a dog," said Jimmy. He looked at Harry. "You'll have to help me take the cows to auction, that's all."

"All right," said Harry. "I don't mind."

They had not been walking more than five minutes before Harry said, "Have you ever been to the Zoo?"

"In London, you mean? No, I haven't. I'd like to, though."

"You haven't missed much," said Harry. "I've been once or twice; but there isn't a tiger there that's a patch on the one we've got at home."

"Oh? Do you go in for tigers?" Jimmy chewed nonchalantly at his bent of grass. "I've heard they make nice hearth-rugs."

"What d'you mean?" Harry's eyes narrowed as he looked at him sideways. "It's a real tiger. It's not mine; it's my uncle's. It wakes him every morning by jumping on his bed. I think it's dangerous. I've told him, I think it'll probably kill him one day." He said this calmly, almost with relish.

Jimmy was whistling as if he didn't care a damn. Keeping up the farce, he said, "What d'you feed it on these days? The scraps left over from the meat ration?"

"Yes, meat mostly. Sometimes raw Brussels sprouts. Sultan's got the most enormous appetite. I usually feed him when I'm at home."

"Brussels sprouts must be particularly filling," said Jimmy. "I suppose you don't happen to have a photo of him sitting at table?"

"Not here, but there are some at home. I'll write to my uncle and ask him to send them." He started on a detailed and enthusiastic description of the animal. It was so insidiously convincing, so preposterously real, that in self-defence Jimmy angrily interrupted.

"Oh, shut up! For two pins I'd punch your head off."

"Why?"

"You must think me a blinking fool if you think I'm going to lap up that stuff. What's the point of all these lies? Martin in the Navy, and the farm, and now this——"

Harry stared at him in bewilderment. "But it's true! It's true about Sultan."

"It's *not* true! You know as well as I do that people don't keep tigers in their houses in London. It wouldn't be allowed, for a start."

"But it *is*!" he persisted excitedly. "I'll get the photographs. I'll get my uncle to write to you."

"Oh, *shut up*! I hope it eats you and your uncle next time you go home."

"It won't get a chance," said Harry, chuckling suddenly. "I shall poison its food."

Jimmy slapped a laggard cow on the rump. "Ger-up!" he shouted, and felt thankful for things homely, solid and familiar. This daft talk gave him the creeps. He didn't know what to believe and what not.

They scarcely spoke again for the whole journey.

They were back in time for midday dinner. There was a steak and kidney pie and piles of mashed potato.

"Raff come back?" Jimmy asked his mother between mouthfuls. "Anybody seen or heard of him?"

"No. And he's not the only absentee either. One of the best pullets is missing."

"One of the best pullets? How?"

"I don't know. I don't know whether it was shut in or out last night. I didn't count them for once."

"Roosted in a tree probably."

"Probably. But then what?"

"Oh, a fox, I expect."

"But there are no feathers. A fox would have left some trace. It seems to have vanished into thin air."

Jimmy glanced across at Harry, thinking of the sound of his door shutting in the night. But Harry's face betrayed not the slightest interest in anything but his food. He was eating rapidly and intently, with obvious appreciation of Mrs. Merritt's good cooking.

That night Jimmy made up his mind to keep awake. He folded his pillow in half to prop up his head and to reduce, so he hoped, the soporific effect of lying flat.

But it did not work. He dozed off to sleep almost at once, and what woke him so abruptly in the early hours of the morning he did not know.

It was bright moonlight outside, and the shadow of the fir-tree at the corner of the house was shifting stealthily backward and forward on his bedroom wall. He lay listening, straining his ears to separate and identify the different sounds. He could hear the wind and the slight recurrent rattle of the window, and the mouse-like scratching of the sparrows stirring under the eaves.

And then he heard another sound, the sound of the door on the landing blowing softly against the latch—and instantly his heart quickened. There was no sound of anybody moving about, but with every gust of wind the door continued its gentle nagging at the latch.

He slipped out of bed, tiptoed across the room and opened his own door on to the landing.

The moon was shining in through the skylight, and he saw at once it was Harry's door that was banging. No reason to jump to the conclusion that he was out, though. He might not have shut the door properly. There had been no wind when they went to bed.

It took him several seconds to screw up his courage to cross the landing and look into the room. It was quite light with the moon; and there was the empty bed, and the pyjamas strewn across the pillow. No sign anywhere of his day clothes. He must have dressed and gone out.

Jimmy went back to his room and struggled into his clothes as quickly as he could. He found himself shivering. His hands shook so excitedly that he could scarcely do up his buttotns. I wasn't that he was scared of anything physically. It went

12*

deeper than that. It was a consciousness of something queer and foreign to the whole range of his experience. Something malignant yet fascinating, filling him with irresistible curiosity.

He found that Harry had used the front door to get out by. It was unbolted and unlocked. But as he opened it there was a faint snap, and he saw to his astonishment that a length of stamp-stick had been gummed across the door-crack on the outside. Obviously he was suspicious of being spied on and wanted to make sure when he got back that nobody had followed him. What the devil was the little fool up to?

Jimmy closed the door behind him and stood for a moment in the shadow of the porch, looking out across the moonlit yard, listening. He could see clearly as far as the gate into the paddock, and, deceptive though the moonlight was, he was almost certain there was nobody in the field between the gate and the poultry-houses.

Keeping to the shadow of the wall, he reached the paddock gate and climbed over. Out in the open field, he felt better. Whoever could see him could in his turn be seen. Or so he thought.

But Harry must have been standing flat against the wall just inside the gate. He spoke suddenly, so close behind him, that it sounded soft and confidential: "Hullo, are you looking for me?"

Jimmy spun round. The shock of it took his breath away.

Recovering, forcing a harshness into his voice, he said, "Yes, I am, and what the hell d'you think you're doing out here?"

"Why? How did you find out?"

"Your door was banging. It woke me up. What are you doing?"

"I've been out on the lake in the punt." There wasn't a trace of guilt or shame in his voice. "And what's more, I've solved the mystery of the hens and the dog."

"How d'you mean?"

"I've seen them. They're floating out in the middle. I think the dog must have been chasing the fox that went off with the hen——"

"Bilge! What fox? There wasn't a fox. There were no feathers or anything."

"There are from the second one. I'll show you."

"And the fox wouldn't go into the water either. Nor Raff. Anyway, Raff could swim the lake twice over."

"I don't care! I don't *care*!" Harry began to dance about. "They're *there*. You and your reasons! They're out in the middle of the lake. The dog's all swollen. I'll show you."

"All right, get on! Show me! You lead the way."

"All right."

Jimmy followed him down the long slope of the field to the edge of the lake. The punt that the estate men used for raking out the duckweed was tied up to a tree on the bank. The punt pole was missing, but there were two paddles lying in the bottom.

The lake looked cold and bleak under the moon, and the wind blowing off it struck through the thin jacket that Jimmy was wearing, making him shudder.

"Cold?" Harry asked.

"No, but get a move on. Are you going to untie it, or shall I?"

"I'll do it."

The dark water slapped and gurgled under the nose of the punt as they pushed off from the bank, fighting the tendency of the wind to swing them round.

"You sit in front and keep a look-out on the water," Harry said. "I'll paddle, because I know the direction."

The moon seemed brighter still, out on the open water. The ripples broke it into shoals of dull silver, splashing and sparkling along the edges of its small waves.

"How far out is it?" Jimmy asked.

"Right in the middle. But they'll have drifted a bit."

"I bet we don't find them."

"I bet we do. They show up white."

They had paddled perhaps a couple of hundred yards from the bank when Jimmy spotted something floating away to his right. "There they are, I think. Something bobbing about."

"I told you!" His voice was fat with triumph. "I'll steer close up to them and you grab hold of them."

Jimmy leant over the side, straining to see more clearly. There was something white, that might be feathers, and something larger, bulkier. "Not so fast!" he shouted. "Back paddle!"

But the punt drove on. He bent down and made a grab for the large carcass as it floated by; and with perfect timing Harry flung his whole weight on to the same side.

The punt rocked over violently. Jimmy tried to dig in his toes, but his balance was gone. With an incredulous gasp he found himself pitching head-first into the water. He had no time to take a breath. The water closed over him in a great ragged splash, and he came up out of the whirl of bubbles, choking and spluttering.

Harry was on his feet like a shot.

"Fool!" Jimmy coughed. He still thought it had been a clumsy accident. He thought Harry, frightened and repentant, was jumping to his help, hurrying to hold out the paddle for him to grab hold of. With a couple of strong kicks he reached the side of the punt and got a grip with one hand on the edge.

He let go again only just in time.

There was a splintering crack as Harry swung the blade of the paddle down like a chopper. Half a second sooner and it would have sliced Jimmy's fingers off at the middle joint. He slumped back into the water, swerved to escape a second blow aimed at his head, and swam beyond reach.

Harry stood a moment, looking at the splintered edge of his paddle, his face convulsed with excitement. Then he ducked into the bottom of the punt for the other paddle, and began frantically manœuvring the clumsy craft to bring him within striking distance again.

"Cadging little beast . . . dirty sucking little beast!" He began a swift, muttering monologue as he dug the paddle ferociously into the water, spooning it behind him. "They ought to have been mine. I'm older. Why should you have everything? Well, you won't. *You won't!*" His voice jerked into a little tight scream, then softened again. "You won't. You didn't think I'd poison your dog, did you? You didn't suspect anything . . . sneaking little sucker-up. Or the hens——"

The breast-stroke was the only stroke Jimmy could swim. It was too slow. Hampered by his clothes, panting and thrusting to reach the bank, he realized that the punt with the wind

behind it could overhaul him in a dozen yards. Harry was
kneeling on the flat bow, bobbing frenziedly up and down,
driving it straight for the back of his victim's head.

Jimmy swerved, struck out almost at right angles, and the
punt shot past. Harry's face twisted round, baffled, astonished.
He seemed amazed that his quarry should still be afloat at all.
It may only have been the moonlight, but the round, child-like
face looked suddenly quite old. Old and cunning.

He brought the punt round almost in its own length, like a
hound swerving back on the scent.

Jimmy was sobbing for breath. The coldness of the water
was eating into him. Unless he could reach the bank quickly,
the chase could only have one end. Looking back, he saw the
punt travelling fast towards him. Harry was leaving it to travel
under its own impetus. Staking everything on getting in a
decisive blow, he was standing right up on the flat nose, the
paddle swung back like an axe.

Jimmy waited. He waited till the punt was almost on him.
Then, snatching a gulp of air into his lungs, he dived down
and sideways.

Faintly through the icy screen of water he heard a cry and
a splash; and when he came up he saw the empty punt drifting
on, and a figure thrashing and struggling helplessly in the
water.

Instinctively he struck out to the rescue. But Harry must
have been hit by the punt as he fell, or been seized with cramp,
for he sank almost instantly, and never came up again.

But before he went, he screamed out ten words into the
echoing night that lit up like a flash of lightning the confusion
of his mind and the terrible secret of his past.

"Martin! For God's sake, Martin! *Martin, I didn't mean to
do it. . . .*"

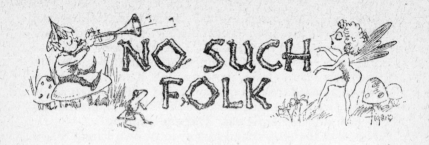

Some Problems of Folk-culture

LORD RAGLAN

Illustrations by Figaro

"I don't believe there's no sich person," exclaimed Betsey Prigg, finally exasperated into dismissing as an invention the lady who was so often quoted by Mrs. Gamp. Lord Raglan, who is an expert on folk-lore, probes the mystery of so-called folk-music and other alleged creations of the illiterate. He views doubtingly the now popular notion that the old songs, dances, proverbs, costumes of the country-side were made by the country people. He sceptically analyses some of the assumptions of the folk-lore enthusiasts, and concludes that, collectively speaking, the folk create nothing, but only remember. His lordship, in short, don't believe there's no sich person as Folk.

IN this country, as in all countries in which there is a gulf between what may be broadly termed the educated and the uneducated classes, there exists a large body of traditional lore which is known as "folk-culture". This includes folk-songs, folk-dances, folk-stories and sayings, folk-medicine and folk-costume. Though certain elements of this lore are found among the less-educated townspeople, it is for the most part confined to the villages.

The elements found in the towns consist chiefly of foolish and superstitious practices. These are also found in the countryside, but there they co-exist with songs, dances, stories and costumes which are often of great beauty and charm. How did they originate? The popular view is that they originated with the folk—that the folk, that is, the peasantry, have in all ages and in all countries in which there was an educated class, held aloof from that class, and have devised a culture of their own to suit their own needs. This is quite untrue.

The first fact that we note when we study folk-culture is that it is, almost without exception, immemorially old. The only exception that I can think of is Cockney rhyming slang. This may perhaps be said to be folk-culture, but can hardly be said to possess beauty or charm. It seems not to be more than a hundred years old. But every song or dance of the country-side that we know of is much older than that. So far as I know, nobody has ever heard of a folk-song or folk-dance which has been composed within living memory. Folk-lore enthusiasts recognize this fact and lament it; they attribute it to the degeneracy of the modern peasant and the baleful influence of the towns. But there is no reason to suppose that modern countrymen are stupider or less fond of amusement than their ancestors, and the towns, though formerly smaller, must always have been influential. If the modern folk do not originate folk-culture, why should we suppose that the ancient folk did?

Is there any reason to believe that in mediæval England the peasantry lived a life of their own, quite separate from that of the educated classes? Such seems to be the belief of many folk-lorists. It is, one gathers from much that has been written, widely held that in those times the peasantry had a culture of their own, entirely distinct from that of the gentry and clergy, and lived idyllic lives, much of which they spent in the communal composition of songs, dances, poems and stories, and in the designing of picturesque costumes. And it seems to be supposed that these were the same in different parts of the country because the folk were inspired by some divine afflatus or folk-spirit which worked in the same way among all illiterates, but which even a nodding acquaintance with the alphabet was sufficient to dispel.

It does not seem, however, that anyone has made a serious attempt to relate folk-culture to the known facts of peasant life in mediæval England. It may well be that the grievances which found expression in such rebellions as that of Wat Tyler were local, temporary and exaggerated, but without concluding that the mediæval peasantry lived in a perpetual state of misery and discontent, we can safely say that their lives were by no means idyllic. The mediæval village usually consisted of a group of farmhouses and cots clustered round the manor-house and church, which stood side by side, and all the peasants' activities were carried out under the supervision of their feudal and ecclesiastical superiors. Their work in the fields was directed by the lord's overseers; their holidays were the feasts of the Church, and these afforded the only relaxation from toil which otherwise lasted from dawn till dusk. The manor-house and the church were the sources of all the culture that there was. Miracle plays, with musical accompaniment, were performed in the church, and many folk-tales are derived from the *Gesta Romanorum* and other source-books used by the clergy.

The lords of the manor kept or entertained musicians, singers, dancers and actors, primarily for their own amusement, but secondarily for that of the villagers. These experts arranged the performances given on festal occasions, at which the gentry were the principal spectators. The only poets and musicians from among the peasantry were clerics, and their culture was not of the folk, but of the monasteries and universities. There was not, and could not have been, any independent peasant culture. It is often alleged, for example, that Robin Hood was a folk-character, and that the songs and plays about him were composed, sung and acted entirely by the folk. We know, however, that in 1473 Sir John Paston kept a man to play Robin Hood, and that in 1520 the Earl of Northumberland did the same. Henry VIII, in his youth, donned Lincoln green and took part in the May-day festivities. Such facts are alone sufficient to blow commonly held theories of folk-culture sky-high.

Consider what has been alleged about some of the components of folk-culture. The cult of folk-music in Britain is, of course, due largely to Cecil Sharp, and we owe to him the preservation of many beautiful songs and dances which would without him have been lost. But our admiration for his efforts in the cause of folk-music does not compel us to accept his theories of its origin. In his view folk-music can be sharply distinguished from "art-music", and has a character entirely its own. His reasons for adopting this view were, firstly, that a great deal of English folk-music is cast in modes, that is scales, which in art-music have been obsolete for at least three centuries. He says that before 1600 skilled musicians were not

tune-makers but tune-manipulators, and frequently drew upon the store of folk-tunes for their themes, acknowledging the fact upon the title-pages of their compositions.

This argument is fallacious. The fact that folk-tunes use modes which have gone out of fashion suggests that the folk did not invent the tunes, for the conservatism which retains the old modes would militate against the composition of new tunes. We can see this in every aspect of life. The kind of person who wears an old-fashioned hat is the last person to invent a new kind of hat. Sharp says that folk-music has a character of its own because "a great deal" of it is in these old modes; it follows that at least some of it is not in these old modes, and that on his own showing folk-music has not a character of its own. When he says that the musicians of the sixteenth century used folk-tunes, what he means is old tunes; even he could hardly suppose that when a skilled musician needed a theme he went to the nearest group of yokels and asked them to compose one for him.

Sharp goes on to say that art-music, down to the year 1550, was "of course built upon folk-music"; but the "of course" should be reversed: the unskilled have always learned from the skilled and not the other way round. He then tells us that after 1550 new developments revolutionized art-music, but that the folk continued to make their own music in their own way, just as they have preserved their own forms of folk-speech. But making and preserving are two very different things, and the forms of speech which the folk have preserved are dialects descended from those spoken at the courts of Mercia or Wessex.

Finally, he tells us to remember that folk-music is *natural* music. The folk-musician, he assures us, invents non-self-consciously, and is unhampered by laws. As an example, he gives us the words and music of a song called "Searching for Lambs", which is written in rhymed stanzas of four-three-four-three iambics, the metre, that is, of "The Boy Stood on the Burning Deck". That an intelligent man should regard this kind of thing as natural is amazing. His views have, however, been uncritically accepted by many folklorists and musicians. Thus in the *Musical Companion*, a popular and in many respects admirable work which has gone through many editions, the writer of the chapter on folk-music, Mr. Hussey, says that "the term 'folk-song' connotes the melodies sung by the peasant class in any country. These melodies are a spontaneous expression of the musical feeling of the people". He goes on to lament that "folk-music, spontaneously created, is, at any rate in England, a thing of the past, superseded by the popular music of the cinema and the dance-hall, just as the smock and kerchief have been superseded by town-made shirt and trousers."

It is odd to find the theory of spontaneous generation, banished by Pasteur from the laboratory, taking refuge behind the piano. As for smocks and kerchiefs, these in their familiar forms are not, I think, older than the seventeenth century, and, like most peasant garments, were made in the towns. Mr. Hussey tells us further on that: "In France we find a folk-music with more artifice in it. It seems almost as if the pastorals of Watteau were true representations of French peasantry." This suggests a novel picture of the Revolution—chateaux destroyed and their occupants massacred by bands of Arcadian shepherds and shepherdesses.

Professor Dauzat's view is very different. He tells us that French folk-songs are none of them ancient, and that most of them came from Paris. The idea that such songs were produced spontaneously and collectively is also combated by Combarieu, who is cited by Dr. C. B. Lewis as saying that folk-melodies are nothing but tunes which have become anonymous, and that while a crowd can build a pyramid or hunt down a monster, two would be too many to compose an air in four parts such as "Au Clair de la Lune".

According to Sharp and to Mr. Hussey, it is not long ago, a century or two perhaps, since every peasant was combining with his neighbours to compose beautiful music; now nobody does anything of the kind. They give no reason for this sudden change, and in fact there has been no such change. What happens nowadays is that a song comes down from London; for a few months everybody sings and whistles it, and it is then replaced by another. But occasionally a song, "Tipperary" or "Roll out the Barrel", gains such popularity that it becomes part of the local repertoire, and is printed on sheets for community singing with the older folk-songs. The tempo is now quicker than in mediæval times, but there can be no reasonable doubt that the songs popular at court were carried into the villages by travelling musicians or returning soldiers, and that is why the same songs are, like "Tipperary", found all over the country. Ballads are often regarded as folk-songs, but according to Professor W. P. Ker, they were introduced into Britain from Denmark, where they were originally and for long the pastime of the gentry. What are now called folk-dances were formerly danced at courts, as in Scotland the reels still are. Folk-dance enthusiasts, however, never cease to assure us that the folk-dance originated on the village green. This is apparently a collective term, so that we are asked to suppose that by some miraculous process "Brighton Camp" sprang up spontaneously on a thousand greens, where, by another miracle, it was given the same name. We know that at courts there were professional dancers, dancing-masters, and composers and organizers of masques and seasonal pageants. To suppose that these experts went to yokels if they wanted a new idea for a dance is as absurd as to suppose that professors go to fourth-form boys if they want a new idea for a book.

In her introduction to the *Oxford Dictionary of English Proverbs* the editor writes of "the common man, from whom came the proverbs of distilled experience such as 'A bird in the hand is worth two in the bush'. Once he had discovered the uselessness of two birds in the bush, or ten in the air, as against the practical satisfaction of one seized hold of, he registered this conviction as a bit of everyday common sense which it would be well to remember, and passed it on." In every village, it seems, there was some genius who sooner or later made this wonderful discovery and, by a stroke of inspiration, communicated it to his fellow-villagers in exactly the same form of words. And the other villagers took it to their hearts, and henceforth regarded it as an indispensable part of their hunting or bird-snaring equipment.

This seems to me quite absurd. In the first place, if the idea had occurred to different people in different places, it would certainly have found expression in different forms. It would have been a bird in one place, a rabbit in another, and perhaps a swarm of bees in a third. Where a single form of words, whether it be a proverb, a poem, or a story, is found in different places, a literary source is indicated. In the second place, there is no wisdom, in fact there is no sense, in the practical application of the proverb. It always is, and no doubt always was, used figuratively.

The same applies to other proverbs. Can it be seriously supposed that "It's the last straw that breaks the camel's back" emerged from the experience of men who loaded camels one straw at a time? Rather it suggests the result of deep thought by an original and highly trained mind. Even proverbs in simpler form, such as "Ill weeds grow apace", or "A watched pot never boils", are really inductive generalizations, and as such beyond the scope of the illiterate. The fallacy here as elsewhere lies in assuming that people are capable of inventing whatever they are capable of repeating, and in underrating the effects of education.

On the subject of folk-medicine, I will content myself with citing the well-known folklorist, Miss Burne. She mentions two widespread folk-remedies, puppy soup as a panacea and the toothache charm in which Christ and St. Peter are invoked. Of the former she says that we find the newest leechcraft of the sixteenth-century surviving in the folk-medicine of this century, and of the latter that the folk-lore remedy of the present day was the property of the learned in mediæval times.

On folk-costume I have quoted the writer who spoke of the replacement of the spontaneously created smock and kerchief by the town-made shirt and trousers. He echoes the sentiments of Professor Haverfield, who referred to "the change which we can see proceeding to-day in any country district, when peasantry desert their native and picturesque costumes for the stamped calicoes of the towns." It seems, however, that in England the peasants have always followed, at some distance, of course, the fashions of the court. Mediæval literature is full of complaints of how the lower orders ape their betters, and in all contemporary pictures of Tudor and Stuart times that I can remember seeing, the peasants are represented as dressed more simply than, but similarly to, the gentry. On the Continent peasant costumes are more stereotyped, but Professor Dauzat says that the peasant costumes of France are all more or less modified forms of the fashionable costumes of former days.

Señor de Madariaga, speaking of Spanish America, says that "the dress, nowadays picturesque, of the peasants, is but a slow local adaptation of that which was worn centuries earlier by the courtiers". Dr. Coulton says that all peasant costume is post-mediæval.

I think this last statement requires some slight qualification. There is a curious cylindrical headdress decorated with conventional flower patterns which is worn by peasant brides in Sweden, and by peasant women on festal occasions in Moravia and elsewhere. English ladies of the early fifteenth century are depicted as wearing a similar headdress. It might, of course, be maintained that this headdress was invented independently by the peasant women in these widely separated regions, and copied by courtiers, but the reverse process is obviously more probable. A widespread feature of peasant costume is the laced bodice, which is worn in Sweden, Switzerland, Bosnia and elsewhere. This seems to have started as a garment worn by male dandies in the fifteenth century. Having been discarded by them, it was in the sixteenth century adopted by ladies of fashion, and by the seventeenth it had been adopted by many European peasants.

The history of the steeple-crowned hat is an interesting one. Originally a masculine garment, it seems to have been adopted as a riding hat by the ladies of Louis XIII's court, and thence introduced to that of Charles I. It was later adopted by peasant women, but soon went out of fashion, and by the end of the century was worn only by old women. Some of these were the last victims of the witch persecutions, so that the hat became part of the conventional costume of witches. It has within the last century been adopted as part of the national costume of Wales in place of the hat, more like a top-hat, which was worn by Welsh women in the early part of the nineteenth century. It is still worn by the inmates of the old-established almshouses at Castle Rising, in Norfolk.

It may well be asked how it is that if, in the words of Dr. C. B. Lewis, "the folk has neither part nor lot in the making of folk-lore", the contrary opinion has been held by Cecil Sharp and so many other folklorists. It seems that several causes have contributed to promote this erroneous opinion. Theorists about folk-culture have been mostly townsmen, who have tended to suppose that there is something mysterious and romantic about people who speak strange dialects and practise the strange craft of agriculture. Their approach to the problem has been senti-mental rather than realistic, subjective rather than objective. There is also a tendency, widespread among the uncritical, to assume that everything originated in the place where they first met with it. If they first hear a song at Slocum Podger, they conclude that it originated at Slocum Podger, just as children and simple people conclude that the clown's jokes are the original product of the clown.

It is often assumed that ability to imitate indicates ability to originate; that anyone who sings a song or recites a poem in such a way as to show that he understands and appreciates it, thereby indicates his ability to compose songs or poems of equal merit. Of course this assumption is never formulated to the extent of assuming that anyone who can play the Moonlight Sonata could compose one as good, but in the realm of folk-culture it is commonly regarded as unquestionable.

We can allow only that, though the folk do not make folk-lore, they select it. In the realm of folk-art they remember what pleases them and forget what does not. And what has pleased thousands for centuries usually possesses qualities which appeal to us all. Nowadays the folk get their songs and stories from books instead of from the lips of their elders, but "Good King Wenceslas" is by Neale, whether learnt from a book or from a mother who has never heard the author's name. This carol, though written as late as 1853, is already becoming "folk-lore".

THE MINISTER'S POOL

LORD BELHAVEN

Illustrations by Michael Ayrton

When we received Lord Belhaven's story of the Minister's pool and of the odd fish that was caught or was fishing there he was still the Master of Belhaven. Now he has succeeded to the title of—was it Belhaven, or should we print the formal and correct Belhaven and Stenton? One more quandary. We wrote to his lordship for a ruling and herewith his charming reply and dispensation : "Many years ago my great-uncle was introduced at a Victorian party by a footman with a stentorian voice who bellowed, 'Lord and Lady Belhaven and Stenton!' As he advanced he heard a fellow guest observe, 'Very much "and Stenton" I should think.' I have always kept this story in mind. So let's have the author's name as plain 'Lord Belhaven'."

WE were down at the minister's pool last night, just myself and old Donald. There's many a good fish to be taken there, but the old folk don't fancy the place, all except old Donald, that is, and he's too keen on the fish to listen to tales.

There's tales about the pool, right enough. The pool is named from a young minister who was drowned there many

368

years ago. It wouldn't be difficult to drown in that pool, not if one slipped on a rock there on a dark night with heavy waders on and no one about to hear one call. But that's not the way it happened to the minister.

Donald was a young man then, and I've often heard the story from him and paid it little attention, seeing it was all so long ago. But to-day it has been in my mind, making me think and wonder, because of what I have to do. I shall know the truth of it all before morning, I'm sure of that.

The minister hadn't been here long; a young man he was, and he was a keen angler. His favourite time and place were at the pool and on the water below it, on a dark, clear night. One early morning Donald met the minister on his way back home from the water, and he lifted his cap to him.

"Good day, sir," said Donald.

"Good day," said the minister, and, "Donald," he said, "did you ever go spinning in yon long pool in the dark of the moon, a dark, warm night like last night?"

"I have not," said Donald, "and I wouldn't care to have to move about on those slippery rocks there, in the dark."

"You're right, lad," said the minister; "yon's an unchancy place. I wouldn't like to think of a young lad like you maybe falling in or . . . being pulled in by a big fish, or whatever there might be down in that black water."

"And what might there be, if it wasn't a fish?" asked Donald.

The minister thought for a bit, and then he asked Donald right out if there were any stories about the pool. Now Donald was a young man, as I've said, and he didn't fancy the minister thinking he believed in ghosts and fairies or anything of that sort. So he said he'd never heard a thing about the pool; just that it was a dangerous place for night fishing, with the deep water and the steep rocks. But the minister suddenly gripped him by the shoulder and his eyes were wide and wild.

"No lies, boy," he said. "Would you lie to a man o' God? There's tales told about that pool, I'll be bound! Would it be just me, a sober and a God-fearing man would see such a thing as yon? What like o' creature under Heaven is yon pale thing, rising from the deep water?"

Now Donald became frightened, and the grip of the minister's

hand hurt him. Well, he blurted out a bit of the things he'd
been told about the pool, things he didn't like to think of, for he
loved the peace that comes to you, angling in the dark. He told
him of the two men drowned in the pool long ago, and how it
was maybe the slippery rocks and a drop too much whisky that
got them in there. But he didn't tell him the strange thing,
how those men were found the next day with their clothes and
their gear folded on the rocks at the head of the pool and themselves naked in the tail of it. No one could tell the reason for
that, not then. And he didn't tell him about the blacksmith's
lad, the strong swimmer. That's a strange thing. They found
his stuff on the rocks, but him they never found at all, not a
trace nor a sign of him to this day. That's something to think
of, for me at any rate.

"Would you say it was a fish deep down there?" asked the
minister, and Donald was silent. What could it be but a fish,
he thought. The minister let him go and stood for a long time,
not saying anything. Then he turned again to Donald, who
was rubbing his shoulder, where the minister's grip had had
him.

"I'm sorry if I hurt you, Donald," he said. "It's a worry to
me, that place. And maybe it is sent to test me, but I'm a weak
and sinful man. If you should chance, Donald, to be by that
pool on a dark night and something came up through the
water . . ."

"What kind of a thing?" asked Donald, a cold, creepy feeling
all down his back.

"It is an evil thing!" cried the minister in a strong voice. "An
evil thing, but God forgive me, I canna rest from the seeing of
it. If it should happen to you, say the Lord's Prayer, lad, in a
loud voice, and cover your face with your hands till the night's
passed."

It was the next morning they found the minister, stark and
dead, lying in the tail of the pool. So they called it the minister's
pool, and that was over forty years ago.

Many's the bright day I've gone swimming there, with the
lads. I'm as strong a swimmer as most, and once I dived down,
deep under the falls. There's a ledge of grey rock first, about
ten feet down. Under that it all shelves away into a great cave,

where there's no light at all, a black hole going in under the fall and down and down. There's no bottom to that place.

It is a hard pool to fish, too deep for wading even in the tail of it, banked in by high, steep rocks. You have to climb down those rocks to get to the water, and if you get into a fish there, he won't stay, but he's away down past the tail in one rush. Many a good fish I've lost in that pool. It is no place for fishing on a dark night.

Last night was dark enough, still and warm. I passed Donald in the dusk. He was sitting on a low rock above the pool, just clear of the splash from the fall. You don't like to advise a master-angler like Donald, when he's taught you all you could learn of the game, but I didn't like to see him down there by the deep water, with the dusk falling. He's past sixty now, and stiff and old in his movements.

"Don't stay down there, Donald," I said to him, "there's no moon tonight, and you'll never find your way out till morning."

"That's kindly meant, Davey," he answered; "but this rock's like a chair, and I'll spin and sleep a bit. I'll not move. I'll try them with a silver Devon, and I've my wee torch in my pocket."

"I'll not be far away," I said, "and if it's gaffing a fish you want, give me a call."

"I will that," he answered. So I left him well content.

The trout were on the move. As darkness came, you could hear them, up and down the river. I had two good fish in the first half-hour. Then they went dead, nothing stirring, the strangest thing. After a bit I took in my line, sat on a rock, and lit my pipe. I never knew a stiller night; even the water seemed to be running quiet-like and not a breath of wind.

I don't know how long it would be I sat there. I think I filled my pipe twice. There was no sound at all, only the water running by, rippling past my feet. Yes, there was the sound of the stream, but muted, as if the river was a field away—and dark! A coal-miner might know a darkness like that, hot and still, deep down in a pit, with his lamp out. It wasn't canny at all.

Then Donald suddenly shouted. My heart about stopped, and I near fell off the rock I was sitting on, with the shock of it! Then I dropped my rod, and I was away off over the shingle as fast as I could run to the pool.

I'll have to tell now what happened to Donald. He's in bed the day, but I've had the tale from him, pulling it out of him word by word, and his old wife weeping and screeching, saying it's the whisky, and hadn't she often said that half a bottle's enough for a night by the water?

Well, Donald put on an old silver Devon minnow, and started casting it across the pool and down the pool, bringing it in slow and fast and in jerks, sinking and drawing it, and trying it at every depth and at every angle. Now and again he'd take a drop of whisky, and then he'd lie back and doze a little. Often an old chap down by the water will nod and sleep as much as fish. When the midges stirred him up, he'd curse a bit and have another dram, to keep him going, and then cast his minnow in again.

Then the water went still. It was as if the fall suddenly moved away from him, a long way off, so he says. I know what he means, it was like that where I was, as if the river suddenly left me, and dark and hot as the devil. He waited a bit. Then, he doesn't know why, he cast his minnow straight into the fall on a long line, and let the line run, and the minnow must have sunk down and down into the dark cave below the fall. He says he hardly knew what he was doing, and it was so quiet he could hear his heart beating, deep in his chest. Then he began to wind in, very slowly.

Sometimes the big ones will take a minnow or a bait so gently that it's just a dull feeling on the line. That's what he felt now, a drag on the line, and he waited, holding his breath, until the line began to move down again and then he struck. That's when you can expect the fireworks, when a big one feels the hook! But nothing happened, just a heavy resistance and a queer, springy feel to it, as if it was thick weed, only he could feel a trembling and knew he was into something alive, though it was nothing like any fish he'd felt before. It swung round deep in the pool and back under the fall. After some time he began to gain on it and he kept a pull on it, treating it rough.

He got it up near the top of the water. Although it was so dark, he thought he could see, as it might be, fine wavy weeds on the surface and, below the weeds, something gleaming, like the long, silver body of a great fish. He thought his line must

have fouled weed, deep down under the fall. He watched it gleaming there, close under the water, and he held tight with the butt of his rod pressed into his thigh and he took the gaff from his belt.

It was then he let out a screech, the like of which I never heard in my life, because out of what he thought was weed came two white hands!

I got down the rocks to him as quick as I could.

"Cut the line, Davey!" he yelled, when I reached him. "It's a corpse I'm into; cut the line, for the love of God!"

"A corpse!" I said. I could see it was no corpse. I could see its hands moving in the long dark hair, white and delicate. There's a ledge at that place just below the water, and I lowered myself down on to it. I don't know if I can explain it, but from that moment, when I saw her, I wanted her. I stretched down, and lifted her up on to the ledge beside me. Donald sat there trembling, his head turned away.

"Don't look into the eyes, Davey boy," he said, and his voice was all over the place. "Don't look into the eyes, for that's what the minister said to me, only I never knew what he meant. . . ."

"What did he say?" I asked—but I wasn't really listening. I never felt a thing like that I had in my hands. Light and cool she was.

"If it comes up to you out of the pool, don't look into its eyes, if you value your soul—that's what the minister said to me," and Donald kept his head turned away and wouldn't look at her at all. No, he wouldn't look at her, but I never saw such loveliness.

"Cut it free and let's get out of this!" said Donald.

The minnow was free, but I still held her, in the dark night. It seemed she brought her own light with her, glowing in the water so delicate and beautiful, the loveliest thing.

What kind of a thing is she, that a young man can't get the feel or the sight of her from him, but must follow her and go down into the dark water seeking her? I've heard tell of a witch on the Rhine who sat on a rock and brought fishermen to their deaths with her beauty in the dangerous waters; a German girl sang that song to me.

It is evening again, and to-night will be like the last, warm

and dark. I'm away down to the minister's pool, but I'll not
need my rod nor a silver Devon minnow. I'll strip and wait
there till the river runs quiet-like and far away. Then I'll swim
down under the ledge below the falls. I think I'll find her; I
think she'll be waiting there for me. Maybe deep down there,
in the dark cave she lives in, some change comes over you and
you can live in the water. She was light and cool, but her lips
were warm. And her eyes were the most beautiful things I
ever saw.

WHAT SONG THE SIREN SANG

SAGITTARIUS

"What song the Syren sang . . . is not beyond all conjecture."
SIR THOMAS BROWNE.

The siren sang like a baleful bird,
  In the age of Ulysses, Achilles and Hector;
Her wooing note and her warbled word
  Changed spellbound seaman to famished spectre.
  Homer's heroes dared not neglect her
When once in earshot of trill and twang,
  And her dulcet strain is not past conjecture—
What was the song the siren sang?

Topless Troy has been disinterred
  By the archæological prospector;
Trumpets that sounded in Thebes are heard—
  Mummied Pharaoh was no objector.
Chemists reconstitute Jupiter's nectar,
  Science discloses where Lethe sprang,
Pilots have charted the siren-sector—
  What was the song the siren sang?

Siren-music research is spurred,
  Voyagers sail where they may expect her;
She may be broadcast on the Third
  With a Classic Fable and Folk-song lecture.
  Short-wave wireless may connect her,
Where crags over wine-dark Ocean hang,
  By a space-time trick and a sound-projector—
What was the song the siren sang?

Envoi
'Ware the siren! for spells protect her,
  Listeners pine with a piercing pang.
Seek not, mortal, to resurrect her!
  What was the song the siren sang?

NOEL

BURGESS DRAKE

With 2 Plates of Characters by Geoffrey Fraser

You may hear this tale told by the Islanders, who belong to the past in this as in so many ways, that the spoken story remains vigorous and vital where literature and drama have not yet penetrated.

The Island lies between England and France. It is under English rule, but the natives are French by blood and speech. To-day they are farmers and fisher-folk; but at the time of this tale the Island was a centre for the Channel smuggling, and the Islanders were bold smugglers.

The story goes back to Napoleon's time, when the world had a different face, but the same bad old heart, because there was always a war. War touched the Island considerably. With the fleet busy, smuggling was brisk; and there were jobs going for good sailors. There have always been good sailors on the Island.

Three of these sailors were brothers. Their father and mother were dead; but they lived together in their family home, an old granite house called *La Vaillance*, in the little port of Creux. Robert, Paul, and Louis were their names. There was some ten years between Robert and Louis, and Paul came in the middle.

The name of that house might have been their family name, because even in that age they were on all men's tongues for their daring. They knew the coast and the Channel, and the ways of the sea and of the weather. Yet there was a difference between them. Robert took to smuggling, and Louis, too, while no more than a boy; and that is a school where a man learns a special craft beyond the simple skill of seamanship. He must pit his cunning against other enemies than fogs and squalls. He must know how to out-run swifter vessels by putting them to the disadvantage of the wind. He must know how to sail blind through a fleet lying around him in a ring. He must know how to hide, and how to wait, and how to disappear; and he must know how to calculate to a minute when he can hoist sail and slip through a blockade.

All this is what Robert and Louis learnt by going to school with the smugglers. Yet there was this distinction: Louis had the good luck, and Robert had the bad. Not that Louis was the more skilful, or that Robert was over-bold. It was the same as you find with the cards; some men always hold the trumps, and others can never get their fingers on them. And the end of it was, that with what Robert lost, it was little enough that Louis gained.

There was still Paul, of course; but Paul was another matter. Paul never took up with the smuggling. His heart was set on the deep seas, and he went off to the Grand Banks with the Malouins. If the smuggling was a school, the Grand Banks was a university. You were not trained to trickery there but to endurance. So Paul was shaped after a different pattern from his brothers. And there was a utility in that as well as a discipline, because from time to time he would return to the Island with his share of profits, and so kept the family firm on their foundations.

It was a sore wrench when Paul first sailed to the big fishing; because if those three brothers were a proverb for their pluck, so were they also for their comradeship. Three years Paul was away, but Robert and Louis kept his memory fresh between them. At every meal his place was set at the board, and his glass filled; and in the evenings—if they were not away—his chair would be drawn up to the stove between them, and his slippers laid before it. And when he returned, there was no strangeness. He took his old place again as though he had been no more than a night or two upon the sea; and if his brothers jumped about him a little like household dogs, it was because they had missed the steady reassurance of his presence.

There was also an old nurse in that family; Angélique they called her. It was a name that fitted her. She had been a mother to them ever since their own mother had died. Those three men would have prostrated themselves before Angélique. The very brave have the nature of children, and answer readily to a mother's love.—So there you have that family at the time of the story.

Perhaps Robert and Louis thought war might provide them with more desperate entertainment than the little escapades of smuggling. Louis, at least, must have gazed with envy at the smart uniforms of the officers who from time to time appeared upon the Island; and to have command of men is always the dream of a boy. As for Robert, it is probable that he thought his luck might change if he offered his gay heart to the service of law instead of spending himself in thieving. But Paul had no more wish to fight against men in a battleship than in some shore-side engagement against marines. However, before he sailed again, there was great talking between them; and Robert and Louis made it clear that when Paul returned it was likely they would already have gone to the wars. Paul was very troubled. Though he disapproved of the smuggling, yet it was a tradition of the Island, and actually there was little bloodshed. But war was a senseless occupation. He didn't put this to his brothers, because he knew it would be wasting words; but he went to Angélique, and begged her to do what she could to dissuade them if the matter came up while he was away. Angélique, however, saw more deeply into the minds of those two brothers than Paul did himself. "I have seen this coming for a long time," she told him, "and I have prayed to God and to the Virgin. But they have the hearts of little boys, those two, and I think they will never grow old. It is very pleasing to see them always so happy; yet it frightens me, and now in my spirit there is a great pain." And in Paul's spirit there was a great pain also. Then the time came for him to go.

At this, Louis conceived a sudden fanciful notion. It pleased him so much that it set him into a caper before he could propound it to the other two.

"We are all going away," Louis exclaimed, "and the Good God only knows when we shall all meet again. When one comes back, the others may be absent; and that may happen year after year. So let us appoint a meeting which we will swear to keep."

"Brother," Robert cried, "that is an inspiration that has come straight from Heaven!"

"Then let us meet in this room, and twelve years from this day!" Louis went on.

"If I am not here," Robert declared, "it will be because I am chained within a prison; because even if I am dead beneath the sea, yet my spirit will be here!"

"It is agreed!" Louis cried.

"It is agreed!"

"But one moment, brothers," Paul put quietly in. "This will be a difficult day to remember. There is nothing to single it out from the rest of the year; moreover, in itself it has no meaning. Even if I am going, yet you are not yet going. So let us make it a day that God Himself has appointed for families to unite. Let it be twelve years hence if you will, for twelve is a sacred number; but let it be Christmas Day."

So that was sworn to; and once more Paul sailed for the Grand Banks. Louis, as soon as he could settle some little matters, sailed too; though he made a pretty mystery of his going before Robert and Angélique, as though there had been no talk whatever of his intention. And lastly Robert slipped away as well; and he too must make a game of it like Louis, telling Angélique with a hug and a kiss that she need not look for him in the morning. So the woman was left alone, with nothing but her memories and her hopes: but from time to time a rare letter from one or other of her darlings let her know how he was faring. But that was a trouble in itself; because from that time on, until the day appointed for their meeting, those

DRAKE'S CHARACTERS IN NOEL.
Plate the First

Robert

Louis

Paul

Angélique

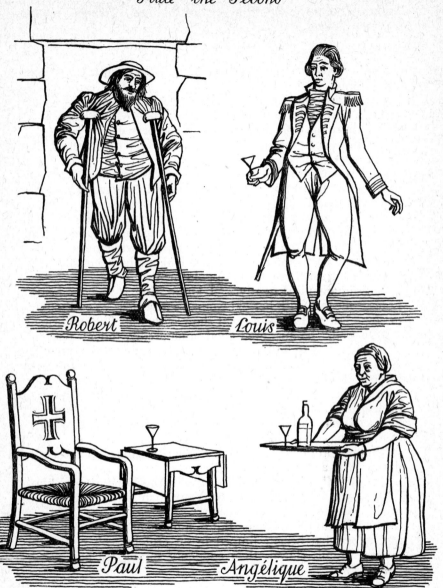

Robert   Louis

Paul   Angélique

three brothers knew nothing of one another. The seas might have swallowed them.

* * * * *

And so twelve years passed over, and the twelfth Christmas came round.

That Christmas Angélique set the room out with holly and candles, and under the crucifix, which hung with a little lamp always burning before it, she laid three presents for her three children, because she knew they would all keep that tryst. Then she prepared a feast, and waited.

Paul was the first to arrive. Indeed, as you shall hear, he had been already some while on the Island. Next came Robert; and last came Louis.

But Angélique had planned in her own mind how those three brothers should meet; so when Louis stepped into the room, although he was the last to come, the room was empty.

He drew up in the doorway and looked about him in some surprise, but with greater disappointment.

Angélique smiled gently. "I know what is in your heart, Louis," she said with her old woman's mischief. "You thought to come last and make a great show with your fine uniform!"

"Oh well," he answered good-humouredly, though perhaps a little abashed to find himself so clearly read, "it suits me well enough, doesn't it, Angélique? And I know well how to carry it too!" He was arrayed as a British naval captain, and had a sword at his side. There was command in his eye, resolution in his bearing. But beneath his ageing face, and the lines that war had set there, the boy still smiled; there was a boy's swagger in the swing of his hips and shoulders.

"But my brothers?" he asked. "Where are they? It is already dark! Why are they not here?"

"They will come; they will come!" Angélique assured him. "But sit you by the stove there. Your chair is ready. And the other chairs too. They will come!"

She left him there alone. But in a moment the door opened, and a bearded beggar limped in on crutches, his clothes in tatters. Louis stared, then suddenly sprang up and cried, "Robert!"

"Yes, Robert!" his brother answered. "But it took all your charity to remember me!"

Louis crossed to him in three strides, and supported him to his chair at the other side of the stove.

"Oh, my brother!" he said. "My poor brother!"

"It is nothing. It has been with me as it has always been. I have not had the luck."

"And these?" Louis pointed at the crutches. "Are they—a necessity?"

"Oh yes, I assure you! But they have helped to bring in the pennies."

"Then why did you not return? Angélique would have cared for you."

Robert shrugged, his face still gay in spite of misfortune. "Prison bars are strong, my brother, and prison walls are high," he said. "And a lame man cannot climb."

"Yet now you are free?"

"Yes, now; because the wars are over."

"Yes," Louis said, "the wars are over. For me that is not so happy; but if it has brought you home——"

Angélique came in, dusting a bottle of wine upon her apron. "Now that you have spoken together," she said, "perhaps the old woman will not be in the way."

Louis looked from one to the other in surprise. "Then Robert came before me?" he asked.

"I thought it best to hide him, so as not to spoil your triumph, little one," she told him. "If you had come in so happy and so splendid to see him sitting there in those rags——"

"Then perhaps you are also hiding Paul?"

"Yes, I am hiding Paul, because you have matter to talk of first, you two, that Paul should not hear. Paul was never fond of war. But we will pour his wine for him and set his chair ready. He will soon be with you."

The chair, as a matter of fact, was there in place between them. Angélique poured out three glasses of wine, and handed one to each of the brothers, and the third she set on a little stand beside Paul's empty chair. "And now," she said, "tell all you have to tell. But don't take long about it, or the dinner will be spoiling. And after dinner I have presents for

13*

you. See, they are there, under the image." She left them together.

They looked at each other in some confusion, not knowing what to say.

"Come," Louis said at last, "you are the eldest. You begin."

"No, you begin," Robert answered. "You have been the more fortunate."

So Louis told his story. He had joined the British navy. His daring, his seamanship—and his luck, had brought him rapid advancement. His smuggler's cunning had served him well. He could run a craft through channels where the enemy would never expect him, and could slip through a battle squadron as nimbly as a fish under water. For scouting, there was no one in the fleet to match him. He was always first with his intelligence, and he stole that intelligence where no one but a born sea-thief could have smelt his way in. Admiral Lord Nelson, who was always clamouring for frigates—the "eyes of the fleet", he called them—gave Louis a frigate. Louis was never so happy in his life. Here was a vessel that could skim like a bird; and he was free to flit in her where he would, scouting for the vital intelligence for which his chief thirsted.

It was about this time that Nelson had the whole French fleet shut up in Toulon. "That was a weary time," Louis told his brother. "The enemy wouldn't come out, but any moment might slip away, and do tremendous damage before they were caught. For a year and more we sailed around and watched. And when there was fog or stormy weather, you can understand that the scouting frigates had an anxious time.

"Well, one day when there was a thin mist over the sea, I saw a small vessel creeping from the coast. I gave her sea-room, then laid chase. But this manœuvre drove her back again, which was suspicious in itself. The same thing happened another day, though this time I got her well to sea; but she scuttled back to her lair. The third time, however, I got between her and the land, and now she had to run for it.

"I imagine she thought to find me with my eyes closed, because that was Christmas Day; but I wasn't sleeping in my bunk just because it was Christmas. War is war, and it doesn't take any account of the calendar. When she saw me behind her she laid on all sail, but it wasn't more than an hour before I was drawing up to her. She answered my shots with spirit, and more than one ball came tearing through our rigging. She could pepper me as she would, because her need was to send me to the bottom; but I wanted to capture her, and find out what her secret business might be. So as I came up closer I manœuvred for a broadside so as to sweep her masts away, then board her at my leisure. But just as I was coming into position, an astonishing thing happened. A merchant vessel came sailing clean between us.

"I don't know to this day what country she hailed from. She had run up a red cross to her mast, and she began to signal 'Peace on earth, goodwill towards men!' Yes, and her name was *Noel*; and she had clearly taken it into her head to stop our battle for the sake of the day. There was no time to reason with her, so I let her have the broadside which I'd intended for the Frenchy.

"But the captain of that Frenchy laid into that merchantman from the other side; and between us we soon had that ship in flames. When once she was out of the way, the Frenchy and I set-to in good earnest. And I tell you, she fought like a mastiff, though she hadn't even a rat's chance. By the time we boarded her she was sinking.

"I got her papers, which was what I wanted—and some of her men too. The papers showed me that the business she had been sent on was important. So I left that little craft foundering; yes, and the few boats of the merchantman, because they could easily reach the land; and I raced for the fleet. I was made full captain for that. Those papers gave Nelson intelligence of the intentions of the French fleet.

"And yet," Louis added, "it is a strange thing, Robert, that in less than a month the French fleet slipped away after all, though how that happened I can't tell.

"Well, that's the end of my story," Louis said, after a pause.

"It's also the end of mine," Robert said. "I was the commander of that Frenchy."

Robert spoke quite happily, as though savouring a good jest. But Louis looked horrified.

"You!" he exclaimed. "It is impossible!"

"Nevertheless, it is true——"

"Then—you have been fighting for the French?"

"And why not, brother?" Robert asked easily. "We are French in blood and French in tongue. But chiefly I thought that if I followed the star of Bonaparte, my ill luck would change. For a while I thought it had changed. I also was rapidly advanced. Like you, I could creep through the enemy where there seemed no passage. I wasn't needed for scouting, but I took messages from place to place; and in that work I won distinction. However, in that matter of Christmas Day, that was different. I can tell you why the French fleet slipped away at last. I was carrying a false message, and it was my business to be captured."

"Brother," Louis interrupted, "you have never yet lied to me——"

"And I am not lying now," Robert told him. "It was my business to be captured. It's an old device, and it never fails. But I could not run obviously into a trap. That is why I turned back from you twice. And when at last you came up with me, and I had to fight, perhaps you can understand why I was as angry as you at the interference of that would-be peacemaker. I knew very well that I could once again escape you; and I wondered what you would think of me when I didn't do so. Yet I had to risk that. So I put on a show of ferocity, and laid into that merchantman from my side as you laid in from yours; because it was very important that I should be taken that day. But how the fight ended, I didn't immediately know, because I was already stowed with the wounded under hatches; and when I woke up to find that I was still alive, I found myself in an English vessel, and later in an English prison. However, I didn't know until this moment that it was you, yet I rejoice in your good fortune——"

"But I," Louis said, "could very happily drown myself!"

"Come!" Robert rallied him. "That is not like you. Yet I see now why Angélique wished us to speak together before she would bring in Paul. She knew. But Paul must never know."

"Certainly, Paul must never know!"

"I must invent some story, I suppose. Come, let us drink, to how that between us two there is full forgiveness!"

So they leant towards each other and clinked their glasses and drank, putting aside all bitterness as brothers should.

Angélique came in carrying a great dish, with a young pig roasted upon it, and set it on the table. "Come," she said, "sit you in your places; it is the hour for dinner."

"But where is Paul?" they asked.

She looked at them gravely. "Surely," she said, "he is already here."

They looked about them rather foolishly. Then suddenly Louis exclaimed: "Angélique, you wicked old woman, have you been playing a game with us? Have you been hiding Paul all this time in the cupboard so that he could listen?"

He was about to jump to the cupboard, only something in Angélique's fixed stare held him.

"He is not in the cupboard," she said; "and yet he has been listening."

"Then what is it, Angélique? What is the matter with you? Why do you stare so?"

"Do you not see yet? Then look! I filled Paul's glass myself, but now—it is empty——"

For a while they gazed. Then Robert made the sign of the cross. "I understand," Robert said. "The Grand Banks have claimed our brother as they have claimed so many others. We shall never see Paul again. But he remembered our tryst——"

"No," Angélique replied, "the Grand Banks didn't claim Paul. He never sailed for Newfoundland. In St. Malo he was offered the command of a trading-ship. He thought he would see the world a little, and also shape himself more fully for the work he had chosen; so he accepted that command. And the name of that ship, my little ones—it was the *Noel*——"

There was a moment of dreadful silence in the room, while the brothers continued to keep their eyes on Paul's empty chair.

"Come!" Angélique said kindly. "The past is by and done with and cannot be remedied. It is an accident of war, and war is a plague that God has loosed upon us for our stupidities and sins. Louis, help your brother to the table, for we shall not comfort the dead by letting our dinner grow cold. But for Paul, you need have no fear of him. He was never the man to bear a grudge. Yet for you—I think you will never more be young!"

That was the hardest word she gave them. After dinner, she made them sit again by the stove, with Paul's empty chair between them.

"Now I have gifts for you," she said, "because this is Christmas Day. I have laid them beneath the crucifix that there may be a blessing upon them."

She brought the three packages, and handed them one each, and the other she set upon Paul's chair; and while they were unwrapping their gifts, she herself unwrapped the one she had set aside for Paul. When they were opened, those two brothers found that they each had a carven gun, like the gun of a ship; but for Paul there was a cross.

They studied those gifts in silence, understanding their significance, but not understanding their use.

"And what are we to do with these, Angélique?" Robert asked gently.

"The cross you will lay on Paul's bed," she told them, "and the guns you will set one to either side. There you shall leave them for ever. That is to be your penance."

"Then we will do it at once," they said.

Angélique went before them with a taper, while Louis assisted his brother up the stairs. They laid the cross upon the bed, with the guns to either side; and they knelt in prayer.

When they were back in the room again by the stove, Louis rose and went to the cupboard where Paul's slippers had always been kept. These he found still there, so he took them out and set them before the empty chair as in the old days when Paul was away.

"That was a good thought, Louis," Robert said. "Yet it comes to me, brother, that we already have Paul's forgiveness. Because it was while we were pledging our own forgiveness in the wine, that he too emptied his glass. . . ."

LUCIFER OVER LONDON

LEWIS SPENCE

Illustrations by Austin O. Spare

Mr. Lewis Spence, expert on the occult, is a Fellow of the Royal Anthropological Institute of Great Britain and Ireland, and Vice-President of the Scottish Anthropological and Folklore Society. He has published many learned books on the myths of Mexico and Peru, the North American Indians, Britain, Egypt, Babylonia and Assyria, a dictionary of mediæval romance, an encyclopædia of occultism, and works on the mystery of Atlantis. Now it pleases him to write a short piece of fiction—or is it?

S OME voices possess a kind of monotonous chant which almost compels one to listen to them. The only two men in the dull and decorous bar-room except the barman and myself were conversing in a semi-confidential manner. One, a squat, little man, spoke incisively with a cockney accent; the other, the very picture of a manservant off duty, was all ears and eyes.

"Shock to the system!" the little man hissed. "I bin seventeen years on this job now, Frank, and I tell you it's the worst case I ever seen. Something's scared the old fella mortal bad. Raves, he does, all day long, 'cept when he's under O.P.M. Always the same cry : 'Asmodeus, Asmodeus !' whoever or whatever that means. Then a lot of whisperin' and chatterin' and groanin' something awful. 'Set me free,' he yells, 'I never signed the bond. Save my soul, save me from the darkness.' Enough to give you the fantods, believe me."

"The old boy's 'aunted," said the other fellow drearily. "I know the symptoms. What's the doctor say?"

"Him? Very little. Close sort o' card," replied the little man. "Fed up with the case, he is. Well, Frank, I'm not goin' to stay on there any longer. My nerve's fair to good, as you know, but it's not equal to that constant ravin' and mutterin'. Ought to be in a looney-bin, he should. So if that job with the legless officer gent you were speakin' of is still vacant. . . . The 'ouse is being watched, too. What it all means I can't think. . . ."

"You take my tip, Harry, and git out o' that outfit before yer nerve gives way," counselled the other. "They're foreigners, you say. Well, you leave it flat. If I were you, I'd ring up 999 this very night, report the case, and quit. Narsty work, if you asks me. Any talk of Nazis, or that sort o' thing?"

"Funny you should ask that, Frank. When it isn't Asmodeus, it's Hitler. Raves about 'em as if they were one and the same, he does. But Hitler can't do much harm to anybody now, one would think."

"Well, you got my advice," snapped the other sententiously, finishing his drink and sliding from his stool. "I'm off. Shouldn't ha' stayed so long. If you quit, Harry, ring me, and I'll fix you up if I can."

I reflected for a moment. I watched Harry smoking his cigarette until the butt end grew so small that it was impossible to smoke it any more, then I offered him a drink and a cigarette. I told him I was a medical student—which was true—and said that I had overheard his talk. Thus we were able to discuss as fellow "professionals" the details of his patient's case, in which I pretended to be greatly interested. It was the word "Asmodeus", however, that had roused my attention. Asmodeus, as I told him, when he asked me, is one of the names of Satan, the Devil, Mephistopheles, Lucifer, the King of Hell, the Prince of Darkness who carries power over the fires of heaven. Now I had not long left lunching with my uncle, Sir Robin Butler, whose expert knowledge of occult matters was known to students all over the world, but whose habit of expecting all his guests to be equally interested made him a notorious bore. All through luncheon and most of the afternoon I had sat under a lecture on the connection between the deliberate worship of Satan as the god-captain of all evil and the forces which moved the German Nazi leaders. He seemed to believe that devil-worship was still being practised. He had used the word "Asmodeus" several times—and, damn it all, after yawning over Satan half the day, here was Satan again, under his most rarely used cognomen, being spoken about in a respectable public-house. Devilish odd, you might say, devilish odd.

Well, by the time we had had a few more drinks, Harry and I were pals. The more I heard of his patient's ravings about the power and the glory of Lucifer the more I wished my uncle had come along with me. I could have left the two together. What then possessed me to tell Harry that if he did not want the job any longer, I would take his place as male nurse to this foreigner? It was because he had mentioned at last who his patient was. The name of Dr. Ludwig Lehmann meant nothing to Harry, but to a medical student like myself, whose ambition was to be a great doctor, the name of Lehmann meant everything. Before the war, this Austrian doctor had been a world figure in medicine. To think that he was a refugee, in London, ill, perhaps friendless! I determined to offer my services, especially when Harry, now decidedly tipsy, said he was not going back anyway.

The next morning I called at the address "Harry" had given me, said I had heard that a male nurse was wanted, and discovered that while the patient was *the* Dr. Lehmann, he was by no means friendless. His stepdaughter was keeping house for him and nursing him. She seemed only too glad of my offer, however, and I agreed to look after Dr. Lehmann for a week at least. Over lunch she gave me details of the case—persecution in Austria—anxiety—escape—overwork in Switzerland during the war—nervous breakdown. I told her that I was surprised that I had seen no mention of his name anywhere. After all, he was a famous doctor. Since the war ended, she answered, he had dropped everything. What, then, had caused the breakdown? After some hesitation, she said that he had plunged with strange enthusiasm into the study of the occult. She feared that it had turned his brain. . . .

For some days after I took over, Dr. Lehmann was placid. He was a thin, gaunt person of about seventy, Teutonic, bearded, and sallow. The yellow, bloodshot eyes opened occasionally, but otherwise he showed few signs of life. I gave him a thorough examination and found the heart weak and flabby, while it was obvious that the entire nervous system had been subjected not only to long-continued strain, but to a violent shock, or series of shocks, quite recently. And there were signs of diabetic disease.

My time was regularly arranged. I had a break of three hours in the afternoon. But it was part of my duty to sleep in the patient's room. I had my meals alone and scarcely saw the stepdaughter except when she came to take my place after lunch. The almost complete isolation of the house and its consequent silence made my vigil dreary enough.

Nothing happened until the third night, when Dr. Lehmann suddenly raised himself in bed. He seemed to be listening. His action roused me, and I was on the alert in a moment. For three or four minutes he remained in this posture. But he suddenly flopped backward, and in a few minutes his regular breathing showed that he was asleep. On the following night, however, he woke about the same time, a little after 2 a.m., and once more raised himself in bed. This time he seemed to be listening more intently than ever. Then he began to talk rapidly in German. So quick and confused was his utterance that at first I was able to distinguish words only here and there. He was praying, in a tone of earnestness, solemn and entreating, with clasped hands and upturned face. Then the utterance grew clearer and even more perfervid. He was beseeching someone for mercy, to free him from a vow he had made—I heard the name "Asmodeus", not once but many times. I did not interrupt, hoping to learn more, but in a little while the voice died away in a moan and, exhausted, he lay back and sank into a coma.

About half an hour later he rose again, this time in such a state of wild excitement that I leapt out of bed and stood by him. This time he seemed to be in angry, even furious, argument with someone. To some policy he had the strongest objection. He solemnly gave warning that "the Powers" were not in agreement with it, that they would not tolerate it. It would mean ruin, "final and irrevocable", for all, for "the cause" as well as for humanity.

The following night passed without disturbance, but on the next, Lehmann suddenly awoke in a shocking state of distraction, calling wildly on "Asmodeus". Throwing aside the bed-clothes, he flung himself on his knees, and when I went over to him and tried to soothe him, he thrust me aside with what seemed extraordinary vigour for a man of his age. Then, furiously, he turned upon me, brandishing his fists in my face and cursing. He would, he cried angrily, have nothing to do with what was going on at Kempton Park. My god was not his god. His Asmodeus was the true world-spirit, mine merely a German parody, distorted to comply with Germanic aims and ambitions. He, an Austrian, had been a fool to have associated with Germans who construed every cause in terms of Germanic purpose and design. The chapel at Marionville was a travesty, a blasphemy. He washed his hands of the whole affair. He appealed to his god to destroy this profane counterfeit of his holy worship. And so he raved on, until he collapsed in exhaustion.

I gave him an injection, after which he dozed.

I seemed to have stumbled into a grotesque situation. If Lehmann was not lunatic, what the devil was going on in that respectable London suburb known as Kempton Park? After some serious thought, I decided to consult my tedious but knowledgeable uncle. But first it would be amusing to do a little sleuthing. I knew the London district—Kempton Park. I had the name, Marionville, which was probably the name of a house. What about spending the afternoon looking for it? If there were such a house, I should have something firm to go on.

It would mean that Lehmann was not merely having a nightmare. Then one would know how to act. Perhaps these Germans were people the police ought to be told about? They would have been "vetted" before being allowed to settle here—but then the "vetting" net probably had some holes in it. Lehmann, an anti-Nazi, would surely not have associated with Nazi sympathizers?

The next afternoon I was on my way to Kempton Park, having told the stepdaughter that I might be late getting back. I parked my car in a Hampton Court garage. I mentioned Marionville to the attendant, and he said it seemed familiar to him. He rather thought he had been asked to take his taxi to a house of that name. But it was some time ago. If the name was Marionville, then it was an old house somewhere behind East Molesey.

By the time I had reached East Molesey and had turned into the complex of roads beyond it, it was almost dark. Up and down the quiet, conventional highways I wandered, but my search was unrewarded. At last it occurred to me that it was probably a much older and larger house than any of the dwellings I had passed, so I pushed farther north towards Kempton Park. Traversing a long, silent road which did not seem to contain more than three houses in its entire length, I came to it at last—the kind of house that people built near London about a century ago—square, solid, and flat-roofed, with a semicircular abutment in the centre, and standing in about an acre and a half of garden.

If any place near London could be isolated, it was surely this. I couldn't see a single light in the whole solid façade of the place, which stood back from the road some forty feet or more. Only a new wooden fence separated it from the pathway. I opened the gate and walked boldly in.

I had made up my mind what to do should I encounter anyone. I would be the hectoring, busy doctor who had been called on an emergency case. Bluff would do the rest. I walked up the path and round to the side of the house. The mass of a large timber building jutted out from its rear. I pushed the door. It opened, and I peeped in. Then I knew my quest had not been in vain. This was "the chapel at Marionville".

The interior looked at first like a hall of carved stone, but I soon perceived that it had been panelled with cunningly painted canvas which gave it the appearance of masonry grotesquely carved with the shapes of gods, fiends, and satyrs. The general effect was horrible. At the end of the "chapel", if one may call it so, was a large tapestry on which a gigantic figure of Lucifer was displayed. Beneath it was an altar which seemed to be littered with the apparatus of infernal worship—black candles, ornaments, incense-burners, and books. Curtains of sable and scarlet hung on either side of the tapestry, and these were decorated with pentacles, stars, and other goetic symbols.

As I stared at the details of this strange shrine, I heard someone coming along the gravel path. In one corner the canvas which masked the timber of the chapel did not meet completely, and into the gap I quickly dived and found that the painted screen was set on a frame at least a couple of feet from the walls, giving me ample space to hide.

The chapel lights were switched on. Through the chinks in the canvas I could now see quite clearly. Along the aisle a tall, elderly man walked to the altar, genuflected before the image of Lucifer, and raising the black-and-scarlet hangings which flanked the altar, disappeared behind them.

One by one other people entered. Between thirty and forty men and women had at last seated themselves. A bell sounded sharply, and the man who had passed behind the curtains now reappeared, dressed in elaborate robes. A dark-skinned youth with him swung a censer from which steamed thick clouds of incense. The congregation stood.

The priest—or whatever he was—did not look at the worshippers beneath him. He seemed concentrated on his own movements. But I stared hard enough at the "congregation". Were all these people Germans? Most of them seemed to be.

The muttered prayers ceased and I began to be nauseated by the fetid incense, which in Satanist shrines is usually compounded of rue, henbane, deadly nightshade, and rotting leaves. The "host" was carried to the altar. The wafer it contained was torn from its receptacle by the celebrant, who then stamped upon it to the accompaniment of profane cries by the congregation. A chalice of liquor was passed round. As it circulated, I heard distant thunder. The lights were lowered. A vivid flash of lightning illumined the dreadful shrine. In sonorous German the celebrant began to speak.

"Friends and brothers," he said, "through the grace and power of our lord Lucifer-Asmodeus, our great cause is about to triumph and the folk of the German Reich to be avenged upon their enemies. We shall destroy our foes by supernatural means. What is an atomic bomb compared to the powers of Lucifer? He bears in his hand the fires of heaven. He can be controlled only by our arch-enemy, the God Jehovah.

"But this condition of inferiority now lies behind us," he continued. "The chief obstacle is removed. Our lord Lucifer, the king of light, will now have a new link with mankind. He shall make us the media of his terrible potency. As you know, he cannot wield that frightful power of which he is the source and reservoir without the perfect co-operation of mankind, who are gifted with freewill and who have the right to employ it 'for good or evil', as the cant Christian phrase has it. This impediment, I say, has been removed at last. It is now possible to effect a perfect union between our god and us, so that at last we can function as the direct agents of his overwhelming might.

"That great scientist, Dr. Lehmann, who now lies stricken, has discovered an essence that heightens the powers of human mental concentration a hundredfold. This temporary extension of human mental potentiality will enable Lucifer to operate through his servants. Once he could do so only through humanity in the mass, an imperfect medium. Now he can act through spiritual concurrence with some few chosen persons. You are that few! You shall be the weapon through which Lucifer shall attack England, Russia, and America, and so avenge imperial Germany, Lucifer's own particular province, and render her once again the greatest power on earth. Through our divine master, the spirit of heavenly fire, of which he is the only begetter, will descend upon this city of London and destroy it. By mental concentration we shall focus our lord's destructive flame upon any place we choose. Nothing will be able to withstand its power. Even stone will melt before the force of the magnified lightning-bolts of our master, Lucifer, and granite crumble under its consuming ray. The first blow will be struck now. As a symbolic gesture, we shall demolish one of the chief national palladia of Britain. By the hour of noon to-morrow, the Nelson Monument in Trafalgar Square will have crumbled into a heap of smouldering lime."

With a sonorous benediction he concluded and dismissed the congregation. When the place seemed empty, I sneaked out and got safely to the road.

I could hardly believe I had not dreamt it all. It seemed preposterous. But why should this infernal priest make so extraordinary an announcement? Perhaps he and his fellow-conspirators intended to blow up conspicuous London buildings. Their crazy followers would believe it was the work of Lucifer.

Could I go to Scotland Yard with this story? As I drove towards London, I decided I would not go back to my patient that night. I would stay at an hotel and—I felt like a fool—take a careful look at the Nelson Monument in the morning. If I saw anything suspicious, I would call the police.

By eleven next morning I had walked several times round Trafalgar Square and stared so much at the monument that I felt that even the pigeons were wondering what I was up to. I could see nothing and felt more like a fool than ever. But, of course, I hung round till midday—it was only natural—and as noon approached I took care to get as far from the monument as I could without losing sight of it. I stood a little way down Northumberland Avenue. What soon afterwards occurred in Trafalgar Square has been alluded to by scientists as "one of the most extraordinary meteorological phenomena on record", and as "quite inexplicable". It had been a fairly bright morning towards the close of August, with only a very little cloud. But on the stroke of twelve we beheld a volume of vapour approaching the Square the like of which I have never beheld in a clear sky. It was thick, dark, indeed almost black, globular in shape and of considerable bulk, and it advanced with tremendous velocity. But in the heart of this nebulous globe, which emitted a rolling, rattling din of terrific intensity, louder than that made by a large plane flying low, glowed and flashed a heart of vivid flame which gave forth sparks and coruscations, like an immense catherine-wheel. It seemed that something special in the way of a storm was coming.

Within a few moments the sky over the great Square was filled with this strange fiery cloud. People rushed for shelter. I heard someone exclaim that it was a plane on fire and about to crash. I stood staring in the middle of the road as if hypnotized. For just as the heart of this cloud was over the monument it seemed to halt in its course while a man might draw breath. Then it began to roll backward at a speed considerably greater than that with which it had advanced. As it retreated, it gathered momentum until, within a few seconds, it was nothing but a dimly sparkling globe in the sky miles away to the southwest. People in the crowd were explaining the phenomenon as the strangest freak of the weather they had known—quite frightening, in fact, when I heard the distant sound of an explosion. I thought I knew where the awful thing had thundered, and jumping into my car I rushed towards Kempton Park and the house called Marionville. Of course, I found what I expected. The house had been struck by lightning—and with a flash and a roar so frightful as to scare everybody in the neighbourhood, Marionville had been almost completely destroyed. As I got there, the fire-brigade were just getting ready to leave. From the crowd I gathered that twelve bodies had been fetched out of the ruins. They had been burnt beyond recognition.

When I got away and went to Dr. Lehmann's house I found that he had died peacefully during the night. I said good-bye to his stepdaughter. I said nothing to her and nothing to the police. I don't want people to think I'm a lunatic.

THE ROMAN WOOD

DOROTHY EDWARDS

Illustrations by Joanna Dowling

If you lived near the Roman Wood, you soon began to learn that even the poachers kept out of it. But to the small girl in the cottage on the edge of the wood there was nothing to be afraid of in entering it, though it was dark, overgrown and pathless. She said there were statues in there. But even if she spoke truly, there was something stranger and more ancient than statues in that wood.

PEOPLE had liked old George. He had been a placid old man, very knowledgeable about birds and animals, and a respecter of both the natural and the supernatural laws. That is why he had never been afraid to live in the cottage. "The trees are better than most neighbours," he would say; "and so long as I mind my own business, they will mind theirs."

After old George died, his cottage stayed empty for many months. It lay in a half-circle of cleared garden on the edge of the wood, so that whilst its front faced southwards towards the lane, on three sides its windows looked out upon the trees. The garden was little more than a stretch of close turf, with a small vegetable patch in front of the house, heavily staked and wired against the rabbits that would otherwise have attacked the succulent greenstuff.

So the cottage stood empty and expectant, like a bright-eyed animal waiting for someone to claim it, all its windows glittering in the late summer sunshine, held easily within the impersonal arc of the trees.

When a Miss Mossop, old George's niece, came down to inspect the place, the village accepted the fact that the cottage chimneys were to smoke again. Peering down from their hillside security, over the slender rowans that marked the village boundary, the villagers saw the goings and comings of taxis; and when Miss Bean and Maudie arrived, and Miss Bean began to clean the cottage, shaking mats and dusters from the windows, and Maudie hung over the low gate, sticking out her tongue at the curious passers-by, it was felt that the old order was changed indeed.

After Miss Bean had removed every trace of old George's easy muddle, and new furniture had been purchased to supplement such of the old man's pieces as were worth preserving, Miss Mossop installed herself, and the village settled back to wait for signs of social advances from the cottage.

But the village was to be disappointed. Miss Bean made her household purchases in the nearby town, thus neatly avoiding the inquisitorial tongues of the village store, and even when encountered, proved to be reserved and uncommunicative. From the postman came the news that Miss Mossop was an author, Miss Bean her housekeeper, and that Maudie stayed there through Miss Mossop's generosity.

Miss Mossop herself was quickly settled in old George's front-parlour, with her little portable typewriter, where she sat stringing together the words and sentences that went to produce the novels, which, under a colourful pen-name, she launched regularly upon the world, every six months or so.

Miss Mossop was an untidy middle-aged woman, who lived for the most part in a twilight world of eating and sleeping, coming only truly alive whilst the typewriter keys were clicking, re-creating herself in the personality of every passion-racked heroine, and making a world so vivid and compelling that it flowed from the type of her machine direct to the imaginations of all those countless enthusiasts who subscribed to her romances, providing her with an income far larger than her needs.

When Miss Mossop was not writing, when she was experiencing one of those common spells of inertia during which the urge had temporarily deserted her, she took sandwiches and cycled forlornly out into the countryside to seek her lost muse, or walked sedately across the fields with Miss Bean and Maudie.

Of course, in the beginning her excitement at owning the wood as well as the cottage had been intense, and the romantic depth and promise of woodland glades, the sense of a rustling activity among the branches, had exhilarated her on her first brief visit. But the actual contact had been different. There seemed a difficulty somewhere, not merely in the fact that there were no paths into it, that it presented to the world a seemingly impregnable fastness of brambles and undergrowth; Miss Mossop had sensed another kind of difficulty, perhaps an unconscious reflection of the fact that old George had never broken in, nor apparently had poachers, or even the village children.

As timber the trees were completely useless; from what one could see of them, they appeared hopelessly decayed and aged. However, she played with the idea that at some time a way should be cleared to some selected spot where a small hut might be erected for her deeper seclusion, whilst she evoked the fancies of her brain. For the moment, anyway, she preferred to leave the wood as it had always been. That innate lover of walls and streets, the Cockney Miss Bean, had probably voiced more than her own opinion in saying that the trees themselves gave her "the creeps".

Only the hard little Maudie seemed to be completely untouched, or rather, she fell back upon some dark resources of her own that were not antagonistic to any disturbing force. Maudie was Miss Bean's love-child, the result of the one impulsive act in Miss Bean's regulated life, the living reminder of shame. Whilst Miss Bean's sense of guilt would not allow her to part with Maudie, the self-deception that insisted upon her own fundamental helplessness in the matter of Maudie's conception, led to a relationship into which the word "mother" was not permitted to enter. It was "Miss Bean" and "Maudie" between them, no more.

On one of her walks, Miss Mossop encountered old Blacksmith Clayes, who had lived beyond his span, and now haunted the forge where his sturdy grandsons carried on the family trade, to retail old tales and legends of the past to all who had patience to listen.

As the sparks flew and the hammers rang, Miss Mossop talked to the old man. He might be "copy", "character", or his chance words might start off the train of thought that had become momentarily unhinged.

When old Blacksmith heard that Miss Mossop intended to penetrate the wood, he was shocked and garrulous.

"Old George never did lay finger," he said, "not even for kindling. What the trees dropped for him, he took up and glad, but he never stole nothing from them, and he never stirred them up."

That was all. That, and the attitude of the village towards the wood, Miss Mossop subscribed to the kind of beliefs in the supernatural that involved table-turnings, and the consulting of the planchette-board as a Christmas party recreation: "There might be something in it!" But also she had respect for what she called "lore", and she resolved to adopt a wary attitude, to wait until she had more time for investigation, and in doing so experienced an inner relief at her own resolution.

Miss Mossop told Miss Bean and Maudie of her decision, giving no reasons. Miss Bean replied flatly that she'd no wish to enter the wood. "I'm not a nature-lover," she put it. Miss Bean distrusted the country; only her loyalty had brought her this far, her loyalty and her gratitude to Miss Mossop, who had never denied Maudie's rights.

Maudie listened to her elders, with her narrow wedge of a face supported between her hands, her sharp elbows resting on the scrubbed surface of the kitchen table.

"There's no way in, anyway." Miss Bean had wound up her statement of feelings with a sudden brisk rub of the emery upon the steel fender.

"I know the way," said Maudie suddenly. "Only you don't shove in—you 'as to slide and dodge. It's easy."

"Well, you hear what Miss Mossop says," snapped Miss Bean, "so don't go trying it, that's all."

"I've been," said Maudie, "on and off. Some days they haven't wanted me, most days though it's been all right."

"I would rather you didn't," replied Miss Mossop; "there are several reasons why. It's very old in there, and the branches are rotten and unsafe; they may fall on you, or you may get lost." She felt one should not scare a child with village fancies, and the reason she gave Maudie was that most obvious to herself.

"There's statues there, all among the ivy, like. With all them dead white eyes like Crystal Palace," replied Maudie, slipping down from her chair. "I don't like ivy—it smells funny, and it won't leave the trees alone."

"Don't make up," said Miss Bean, "and mind what you're told."

"You're learning quite a lot about trees and things," said Miss Mossop kindly; "I must see if I can find you any books about wild flowers."

"My teacher says there's moss on the north side of trees," said Maudie.

Miss Mossop nodded, full of pity at the wildness of the child.

"Not in that wood, there ain't," cried Maudie triumphantly. "In there, it don't matter which side, so long as it is the side *away from the house*. It's like that with the acorns and things. They don't drop none our way. Not them."

Miss Bean, her patience snapping, ordered Maudie upstairs to tidy her chest of drawers. "A born liar," she said flatly. But Miss Mossop could not avoid reflecting upon the fruitlessness of such branches as overhung the garden-edge.

The household in the cottage went on its steady way. The leaves in the wood began to turn colour, and soon some of them were fluttering down into the cottage garden. It was a beautiful autumn of bright sunshine, that made the reddening berries of the holly and the village rowans seem out of place amongst the late-blooming dahlias and asters. Looking down on the wood, on one of her inspirational walks, Miss Mossop was struck by the fire-colours of the restless foliage; it was as though the wood were smouldering within itself.

Miss Bean collected the stray leaves into a heap, and burned them. They were very dry, and crackled and spat bright flames upwards to the overhanging boughs. There were soon many leaves on the garden and the paved court behind the house, but never a sign of a dry tree fruit, a cone, or seed-case, or a fat acorn. It seemed as though the wood tossed its discarded foliage to the winds, but that its secrets were its own. Soon bonfires were the established ritual of the garden, and the wisps of pale-blue smoke from behind the cottage competed with the white billows from the chimney.

Miss Mossop was deep in a new novel, one that taxed her

ingenuity and challenged her powers of inventiveness. It dealt with the emotional maladjustments of two people stranded in the polar regions, and forced by circumstances to accept the winter hospitality of a tribe of Esquimaux. Miss Mossop had prepared herself by a quick skimming of some dozen books of reference and biography, and with the skilful dexterity of a craftswoman had retained their essence sufficiently to create a workable "atmosphere". Already her mind had prepared a pattern of cold and snow, polar nights, straining huskies and the sweating interiors of igloos. Soon she would be feeling the numbness of northern cold at her toes and finger-ends, and the warm breath of passion upon her neck. All day the typewriter raced madly in the track of the husky dogs, who by now were bearing her lovers to their arctic destination.

About this time, the cottage had an unexpected caller. The newly appointed vicar, a likeable youngish man, braved the inhospitable front put up by the cottage inhabitants, and looked in on his way back from a call farther up the road. He shared the chill ceremony of the unaccustomed afternoon tea with the harassed Miss Mossop, who, wrenched from her novel, seemed distraught and mentally dishevelled.

He spoke bravely against his feeling of being in the way: of the village, the ancient church and the Women's Institute.

"My wife is hoping you may be able to give a talk to our W.I. some time," he said; "many of the members are ardent admirers of your work."

Miss Mossop, who shrank from publicity, and to whom her work, after it was finished, had little interest, muttered a vague apology. She wished he would go soon.

He spoke of the cottage then, and the wood, and for the first time her attention was fixed. She found herself hungry to hear of the wood.

"Some of the local guide-books refer to it as the 'Roman Wood', but most of their information is unreliable."

It appeared probable that it was the site of an early Roman settlement. Certain excavations made near the village in the years before the war tended to encourage the theory.

"It would be worth a survey, anyway," he said, as he reached for his hat.

Miss Mossop, following him to the door, thanked him for his visit with more warmth than her reception of him had led him to expect. While he had been speaking, her imagination had been touched, and his words evoked a vision: of statues and pediments knotted with ivy, of roots thrusting eagerly beneath elegant mosaics. *Statues with white eyes.* Perhaps Maudie had not lied.

But something, an exquisite delicacy of fear, kept her from mentioning Maudie's words to the little clergyman, yet, as she watched his black figure pushing valiantly up the hill on his old bicycle, she felt as though something of security had gone out of her world.

By now, Miss Bean had finished bottling the late blackberries. Now she put away the ornamental fire-screen from the study into the cupboard under the stairs, and began to set her alarm clock for a half-hour earlier in the mornings to give her time to see to the fireplace before breakfast. Now there were two chimneys smoking in the cottage, and the bonfires were finished. The Indian summer was over, and chill was creeping into the air, through the bare fingers of the trees.

About this time, Maudie got herself into trouble at the village school. The head-teacher wrote, asking Miss Bean to call on her, and Miss Bean put on her best black clothes, and the defiant gold ring that she kept for outside use, and went to the school.

The headmistress was sweet and gentle, a woman who ruled her school successfully by love and example.

"I am worried about Maudie," she said; "she seems to disagree with the other children. Frightens them in some extraordinary way."

Miss Bean's lips were stiff with fear; she had so often faced unpleasant hearings with regard to Maudie, and always there was the dread that someone in authority somewhere might take the child from her, and in doing so expose the raw roots of her shame. Her fear made her voice sound cold.

"Frighten?" she asked; "surely, Maudie is a little thing to be frightening the other children?"

"I'm afraid I don't know what it's all about," confessed the teacher. "It seems to be connected in some way with the old wood. Horse-chestnuts and acorns. It appears she gave some

of the little girls some acorns." The headmistress was conscious
of the lameness of her own words.

"One can't see all the workings of a child's mind," she went
on; "but one of my pupils has been seriously unwell, and then
it came out that several of the others were on the way to becoming equally affected."

"Are you saying that Maudie has been poisoning them?"
asked Miss Bean, suddenly passionate to defend her love-child,
yet fearful of that child's potentials for evil.

"Oh, not materially," replied the teacher; "it's something
mental. This is a very remote village, many of our families have
lived here for centuries, they are much inbred and have retained
superstitions." She looked across at the tight-faced Miss Bean.
"The parents are very much upset. In fact, it might be a good
thing if Maudie stayed at home for the present, at least until
after Christmas. Things may have blown over by then."

Miss Bean made her way back to the cottage feeling bewildered and frightened and angry.

"It seems so funny-like," she said later to Miss Mossop; "if
it had been stealing or lying——"

When she questioned Maudie, the child began to cry; at
least, she hid her face in her thin hands and howled, but the
bright eyes staring between her fingers were tearless and watch-
ful.

"It was Nature-study," she wailed; "we had to take conkers
and things for Nature-study."

Miss Bean suddenly understood. "Did you get them from
there," she asked, gesturing towards the wood, "after what Miss
Mossop said?"

She raised her voice and began to threaten. Maudie would
have to be "put in a home"; she referred to Miss Mossop's
goodness where Maudie was concerned. "If it hadn't been for
her, you and I would be tramping the roads."

During the idle days that followed, Maudie loafed about the
house and garden, keeping clear of Miss Mossop's windows,
amusing herself as best she could, under the injunction to "play
quiet and keep out of everyone's road". Miss Mossop was now
tackling the first emotional battle of her novel, and must not be
worried. When encountered in the house, her eyes were dis-

traught and feverish, as her brain struggled to maintain the balance between her own exuberance of expression and the limitations of her plot.

It was during the creation of these passages that Miss Mossop, coming to a dead stop in her mental reasoning, paced the house and garden, desperate for a solution. In the garden, behind the small tool-shed, she almost fell over Maudie. Maudie was crouched and intent over a small box. The ground was strewn with the heads of late chrysanthemums. It was chilly, but Maudie had removed her coat, and her sleeves were rolled up to the elbow.

Something about Maudie's attitude, a sly furtiveness, and an attempt to cover something up, prompted Miss Mossop to investigate. There was a screaming scuffle that brought Miss Bean running from the house, and it took the two women to overpower the furious child. Miss Bean solved the difficulty by thrusting Maudie into the tool-shed and bolting the door.

In the box was a live squirrel. It had been bound round and round with some of the red waxed thread from Miss Bean's workbox. It was in a sad state of emaciation, and Miss Mossop, having released it from the thread, carried it immediately to the forge cottage. Coming up the hill, with her greatcoat flapping open, and holding the squirrel at arm's length in a rag of blanket, she looked almost insane to the men lounging about the forge.

The feeling of suppressed ridicule that greeted her drove Miss Mossop into a gust of indignant utterance, for which she despised herself. Words rushed, and the story spilled itself before the watching and embarrassed men. To her own shame, Miss Mossop found that she was weeping.

The younger of the Clays, after a glance at the feeble animal, dispatched it swiftly with a blow from his big hammer. It was old Blacksmith Clay, who now spent the chill days beside the furnace, who replied to her:

"It took the likes of old George to keep things right," he mumbled; "you two women down there will be letting things in before you know what you're doing. Go back to London town, I say, before it goes too far."

As Miss Mossop returned to the cottage, she struggled with

the feeling of outrage that the sight of the bound squirrel had
aroused in her. She had been torn from work and plunged into
this situation before she had had time to adjust herself: the
change from work to reality should have been gentle and
gradual. So far her indignation had been directed towards the
act of cruelty, but now she wondered uneasily as to the significance of the act with regard to Maudie.

She felt that Maudie lay at the root of the unrest in the house.
Maudie displayed all the unlovely symptoms of a maladjusted
nature in her love of mischief and her desire to stand out against
sympathy. Maybe, when her book was finished, she might
suggest some sort of a solution to Miss Bean—a boarding-school,
perhaps. She put off the notion of an immediate approach, for
she shrank from the idea of a further emotional upset. Already
there had been too many threats to the progress of her
novel.

And yet, turning the corner for the final descent, she was
caught by the homelike beauty of the cottage with its red roof
standing in its half-circle of garden, protected from the worst
gales of winter by the sheltering trees.

Before she went into the house, she walked round to the back,
and over the damp turf to the tool-shed. The little cardboard
box and spilled flowers looked mean and unimportant now that
the emotion of her feelings had subsided. She bent down to
gather up the relics, dropping the flowers one by one into the
box. It was as well to tidy things up, for some memories were
best obliterated.

Under some flowers she found the knife. At first she did not
recognize it for what it was. A long splinter of flint, flaked at the
edges, something that might have come from a museum show-
case having the incredibly new appearance that such ancient
stone things have. For a moment she stared at it, and her too
fiery imagination sprang back from its implication. With a
sharp cry of fear she threw it with all her force into the wood,
and then, running like a child, she sped into the house.

In the kitchen, behind the sound-deadening screen of the
baize-covered door, Miss Bean had thrashed Maudie, and now
the child lay sobbing on the hearthrug.

"I wasn't 'urting none of you lot," she moaned.

"You were acting cruel to that poor animal," said Miss Bean in an oddly tired voice. She seemed to have exhausted herself with the violence of her emotions, and now sat upright in old George's high-backed chair. Her eyes pleaded as they rested upon Miss Mossop's distracted face.

Miss Mossop forced herself into control.

Maudie lifted her dirty tear-wet face, and her nasal voice rang with passionate conviction. " 'E didn't *mind*," she said. " 'E knew 'e 'ad to. They don't mind when they 'as to. That's part of it."

Shaken and beaten as she was, Maudie retained some faith of her own, and Miss Mossop, suddenly pitying, knelt down beside her.

"Maudie, you poor child," she said, "what are you taking upon yourself to do?"

Maudie, as always, rejected the kindness; it implied a feeling of guilt in the grown-up woman. She sprang up and away, and gazed passionately down at Miss Mossop where she knelt.

"*They* was here first, right at the start," she said. "It wasn't till them people brought the other lot that They had to go. Only the other lot didn't really belong here, they belonged where they came from, and when the people went away, They came back again."

"Who were the people that went away?" asked Miss Mossop fiercely. Now she felt that something was to be revealed.

"The people what put the statues there."

"The Romans?" Miss Mossop could hardly breathe, things were becoming enormous and impossible.

Miss Bean, suddenly galvanized, leapt up and fell upon the child. "You've done enough with your lies and your nasty ways," she cried. "Go on off to bed. Off to bed." And in a spasm of pure hate she pushed the child across the kitchen and drove her before her down the passage and up the stairs. Maudie made no sound, no outcry, and Miss Mossop, kneeling still, realized the child's martyrdom in her silence.

But there was work to do, and after a reassuring talk with Miss Bean, a shared cup of tea before the kitchen hearth, she returned to her own lamp-lit study, and plunged again into her book. As always, the work blotted out all else, and for some days she kept her unrest outside the circle of her dream world.

Miss Bean flung herself into an even wilder fever of house-work, turning out cupboards and scrubbing shelves already as white as linen, and Maudie was kept indoors under her eye, polishing and cleaning from morning till night to keep her out of mischief. At bedtime she locked the child into her room at the back of the house.

Maudie seemed surprisingly quiet and unrebellious. Miss Bean's voice, when it penetrated the baize doors, was harsh and unforgiving, but Maudie made no outcry. Sometimes, how-ever, Miss Mossop found her on the back landing, looking out from the window at the trees, gazing with an intensity of clenched hands and knotted brow.

Miss Mossop, however, was again elevated to her own plane of creation, and she passed Maudie without a word, whilst her busy mind formed patterns of words for her novel. In her own front bedroom, looking out across the fields to the clear hills beyond, she saw only the white snow-fields of the antarctic, and the round friendly faces of Esquimaux. Now love anticipated its climax, and her characters moved quietly within the net that she had woven for them. Their destinies were in her hands and their fate was known to her.

One morning in November, when the mists had gathered deeply in the valley and woven themselves in and out of the trees, Maudie disappeared.

Miss Bean had lit the kitchen fire, swept the study carpet, and taken up Miss Mossop's tea whilst the dust settled—the morning ritual that started up the motion of the day—and had then gone in to rouse Maudie. The clammy cold of the open window greeted her entry. Maudie's bed had not been slept in. Only her pillow, stripped of its linen cover, lay roughly across the bottom of the bed. In the narrow flower-bed under the window were the deep prints of her feet, where they had landed upon the soft earth among the rotted chrysanthemums and brittle stems of Michaelmas daisy.

It was a terrible day. Miss Mossop cycled up to the village, and Miss Bean began a distracted search of the lanes, and the two women, drawn together by a fear for the child that seemed

to reach forward and menace themselves, spent the night by the study fire, drinking tea and talking and wondering. They spoke of possible accidents, of the cold and physical dangers, and for the first time Miss Bean betrayed a fear of something that was not tangible. "I hate them great ugly trees," she said.

In the early dawn, when Miss Bean went out for fresh kindling, Maudie came down the path from near the tool-shed, appearing wildly out of the mist. Her clothes were soaked, and her hair lay flat against her small scalp. In her arms she carried her pillow-case. It was half full of acorns.

She was very quiet, and very tired, and she walked with dragging feet into the house. Something about her air of containedness kept Miss Bean from speech. The two women, as one in their fearfulness, hovered about the tired child and tended her. Miss Mossop fetched brandy from the medicine cupboard, whilst Miss Bean helped her out of her soaked clothes and dried her. Neither woman asked questions.

After Maudie was asleep in her bed, the two weary creatures threw themselves down into the study arm-chairs and fell asleep, just as the mists began to give way before the weak morning sunlight.

Late the following evening, Maudie came downstairs, and found them roused and tousled. She stood regarding them whilst they moved about the kitchen. It was as though they recognized the need for keeping together.

Maudie spoke slowly. "It's no good you saying about last night. I can't help it no more." The women waited, for the child was struggling to convey something of which she herself seemed only to have caught a glimpse. "You see," she said, "I didn't never call you Mum or nothing, so it's like as though I didn't have no one belonging."

The word had been spoken. The gap had been bridged; but the pass to the bridge was now in Maudie's hands, Miss Bean began to cry.

Maudie seemed bent on clearing things up, and explaining her new dignity and awareness. "I didn't never 'ave a cuddle with you or a laugh, Miss Bean," she went on slowly. "But it makes me all right with Them."

Miss Bean went on crying and crying, and in sudden love

Miss Mossop threw her arms about the housekeeper and let her weep upon her shoulder. Now she felt Miss Bean's dependence upon her, and it renewed her own strength.

The dawn of the new day found a new relationship existing between the women. Love had grown, and each ministered to the other. Now there were small deferences and concessions to each other's wishes, applied with the delicate tact of those who share a great sorrow. To Miss Mossop it seemed that her selfish world of creation was no longer to be her own; in it Miss Bean, too, found a place; and Miss Bean, working at the Christmas baking, retained a full-flavoured consciousness of Miss Mossop's presence within herself. It was the love of the forlorn and interdependent, of castaways upon a desert island.

As by mutual decision, neither mentioned the fears of the November night to Maudie. They left her to go her own way as she would. For the first time there was no antagonism between Maudie and her mother. Whilst there was no love, the active hate had departed. Maudie was treated as a child, dependent and young in understanding, her mistakes were covered without comment. Neither Miss Bean nor Miss Mossop cared to challenge that within Maudie that had manifested itself. They preferred to cheat themselves by denying its existence, which was the safer way for them.

At Christmas time, Miss Mossop presented the child with an exceptional array of gifts, toys to touch some slumbering gentleness : a doll, a doll's pram, a toy tea-set, story-books, a needlework case. Miss Bean took out her sewing machine and made her a gay red dress.

There was a painful joy in Maudie's face when she came downstairs to a kitchen decked with holly and mistletoe, and she fingered the berries with knowledgeable delight. But the toys lay unexamined, and the red dress was donned without a word. Maudie had passed beyond the reach of childhood. Her interest seemed focused upon the acorns that she had brought from the wood. These she played with interminably, arranging and rearranging them in patterns upon the tiled floor, looping them in sweeps of intersecting circles, puzzling, frowning, as though she sought something that was evading her.

In the third week of January snow began to fall. It came

sudden and unexpected after a change of wind. First a sky of
the grey colour of japanese silk, with the trees black-painted
against its darkness, and then the delicate flutter of white flakes
gently falling all through the day. By night-time the wind had
gathered force, and a swirl of endless white, falling thick and
deep, covered the paths and lanes to the village, and blew up
into deep drifts under the hedges.

On the fifth day of the snow, the postman, struggling through
on foot to deliver a bundle of proofs from the printer, mentioned
that some of the hamlets were already snowed up, and that
snow-ploughs were to be put into action on the main roads.

By the next day the cottage was completely cut off from the
village, and only the frail curl of smoke showed the villagers
where it stood.

The wood had adjusted itself to its snow-mantle, as had the
rest of the countryside; but the thick undergrowth and twisted
creepers, snow-laden, gave the wood the appearance of a white
city of minarets and towers in the late twilight of the afternoon.

Maudie, her red eyes and nose close to the window, where
she had cleared a peep-hole from frost, turned in glee as Miss
Mossop came into the kitchen. "Don't it hold them all together
nice?" she said; "like they was all under a blanket whispering,
and all the bumps, so's you know they're still there."

Miss Bean, who was ironing, looked up from the folding of
one of Miss Mossop's best nightgowns, and her fearful gaze
betrayed the slumbering anxieties of the past few weeks. It was
the first time that Maudie had made direct reference to the
wood since she had given her explanation.

But Maudie said no more; she stood idly rubbing her wetted
finger up and down the pane until the glass screamed eerily.

There was something of malice in the thin screeching upon
the window, and Miss Bean was seized with irritation.

"Why don't you get something to play with? What about
your nice dolly, say?"

Maudie did not reply, but the deliberate finger rubbed again
upon the pane of glass.

"What about them nuts of yours, then?" asked Miss Bean,
controlling herself with difficulty; "you've been at them all the
morning. Why don't you go and play with them again?"

Now Maudie turned, and the malice and the power in her little face stood out with extraordinary keenness.

"I don't want them no more," she replied. "I've done them out proper." She nodded in the direction of bare flags before the dresser.

Impelled by a strange curiosity, both Miss Mossop and Miss Bean moved forward to inspect the acorns. They lay in a complicated pattern of arcs and circles. The whole pattern distilled a sort of essence of completed beauty. It seemed to Miss Mossop that the sweeping curves of acorns were moving into an intricate dance, weaving and intertwining until the whole floor seethed with the snake-like involutions of their motion. It was like one of the optical illusions that appear in advertisements and the children's puzzle corners of popular newspapers. Mobile yet static. Fluid only to the gaze that deceives itself.

Miss Mossop breathed deeply, unable to speak before the force that she felt unable to bear. But Miss Bean swooped down, and with a strange cry "No, no", she swept up the acorns into her apron, and opening the back door, tossed them out into the swirl of snow that obscured the garden. "I'll have no more of that nonsense," she said firmly to Miss Mossop as she closed the door. In saying this, she took command of the sanity and strength of the household, and Miss Mossop inclined to her.

Maudie seemed not at all upset by the loss of her acorns. With a mature shrug of her shoulders she went to the dresser and took down a women's paper that lay there, and began to turn its pages.

GEORGE BARNWELL

or The Wages of Sin is Literary Immortality

LILLIAN DE LA TORRE

Engravings by Joan Hassall

This is one of a series of essays written by Miss de la Torre to show the changing tastes in crime as illustrated in literature. Barnwell was a young murderer whose story was first told in a seventeenth-century pamphlet with all the candour of that age, and next delighted eighteenth-century playgoers in a didactic drama full of sentiment and sermon. Foreign authors also delighted in Barnwell, and re-made him in their own fashion. When are the literary psychiatrists going to seize upon him?

GEORGE BARNWELL was a 'prentice lad, and he met a harlot in Cheapside. From this commonplace occurrence, before a continent and two centuries were done with George Barnwell, sprang mischiefs uncounted. One thing led to another: dalliance to fornication, fornication to embezzlement, embezzlement to murder, murder to the gallows. Many generations on both sides of the Channel relished George Barnwell—Barnwell balladed, Barnwell moralized, Barnwell embellished with *Hanswurstlustbarkeiten*, Barnwell snatched like a brand from the burning. Every time George Barnwell suffered a sea-change, his new incarnation, rich and strange, served to characterize another generation's taste in crime.

News of George Barnwell's unhappy fate was first made public property in a pamphlet of the forthright days of the Restoration:

THE 'PRENTICE'S TRAGEDY:

or the

HISTORY OF GEORGE BARNWELL

Being a Fair Warning to Young Men
to avoid the Company of Lewd Women

Granted no pale cast of thought sicklied o'er the ill-fated traffick of George Barnwell with this Restoration trull, by name Sarah Millwood.

His urges were all carnal, and hers were all mercenary.

She came up to him in Leadenhall Street, "a Woman handsome enough, and set off with a very fine attire"; she took him by the hand, and gazing wishfully in his face, gave him thereupon one gentle kiss; and foolish George's business was done. He resorted to her "next door unto the Gun", and by some of the oldest dodges in the rogue books she plucked him like a pigeon. The cross card game, the feigned bill, the pretended robbery by night which interrupted them at "their old Game at Ticktack", stripped the besotted youth of his very breeches and some £200 of his master's money. Faced with an audit, the amorous peculator thought of a new expedient; in the words of the ballader:

> . . . an Uncle I have,
> At Ludlow he doth dwell;
> He is a Grasier, which in wealth
> doth all the rest excel:
> Ere I will live in lack, quoth he,
> and have no coyn for thee,
> I'll rob his house, and murder him.

Sarah took this suggestion with aplomb.

> —Why should you not? quoth she.

". . . which was done in a Wood by Barnwell's knocking him

off his Horse, and her lighting and cutting his Throat; and so taking his Purse with fourscore Pounds, away they came for London, and lived riotously upon it . . ."

And thus they liv'd in filthy sort
till all his store was gone,
And means to get them any more,
I wis poor George had none.
And therefore now in railing sort
she thrust him out of door,
Which is the just reward they get
that spend upon a Whore. . . .

Not satisfied with thrusting him out of door, Millwood denounced her victim to the constables: but Barnwell got even with her:

> *When Barnwell saw her drift,*
> *to Sea he got straightway,*
> *Where fear and dread and conscience sting*
> *upon himself doth stay:*
> *Unto the Mayor of London then*
> *he did a letter write,*
> *Wherein his own and Sarah's faults*
> *he did at large recite,*
> *Whereby she apprehended was*
> *and then to Ludlow sent,*
> *Where she was judg'd, condemn'd, and hang'd*
> *for murder incontinent,*
> *And there this gallant Quean did dye,*
> *this was her greatest gain."*

But it was not to be thought that Barnwell could escape scot-free. Justice, though belated, caught up with him. . . .

> *For murder in Polonia*
> *was Barnwell hang'd in chains.*
> *Lo, here's the End of wilful Youth,*
> *that after Harlots haunt,*
> *Who in the spoil of other Men*
> *about the streets do flaunt.*
>   *Finis.*

This sordid little tale did not revolt the men of the Restoration; the mating of Lust and Greed was a commonplace of high life and low, and no adage proved itself oftener than that thieves fall out.

The most mistaken word the song-inditer penned was the last one: "Finis." The saga of Barnwell was only beginning.

The Restoration had ended in bloodless revolution; Queen Anne had yielded the sceptre to the Elector of Hanover, and he to his son, when the crime of George Barnwell was again brought to popular attention. June 22nd, 1731, was the date, Drury Lane Theatre the place, *The London Merchant, or The History of George Barnwell*, by George Lillo, the vehicle.

Not for the good citizens of 1731 was the astringent realism of the Restoration. George Barnwell stepped forth before the candles of Drury Lane as a sentimental scoundrel, full of snivelling sensibility. Georgian London liked crime well sweetened with moral sentiments. Even those frivolous souls who had brought along copies of the street-ballad, intending to make odious comparisons, were constrained to drop the trashy things and feel for their handkerchiefs.

Freely flowed their tears as they beheld old Thorowgood, George's master, whose deepest faith was in twenty shillings in the pound and what he calls "merchandise"—that is, trade. "See how it is founded in reason and the nature of things," he instructs the worthy apprentice Truman (name of good omen!) —"how it has promoted humanity, as it has opened and yet keeps up an intercourse between nations far remote from one another in situation, customs, and religion; promoting arts, industry, peace, and plenty; by mutual benefits diffusing mutual love from pole to pole."

George Barnwell in 1731 was far from the callous young villain the Restoration understood; and Sarah Millwood's part in his crime is more than a casual "Why should you not? quoth she". In 1731 a conspiracy to murder entailed tearing a passion to tatters:

". . . her avarice, insatiate as the grave, demands this horrid sacrifice—Barnwell's near relation. . . . At the naming the murder of his uncle he started into rage, and breaking from her arms, where she till then had held him with well-dissembled love and false endearments, called her 'cruel monster', 'devil', and told her she was born for his destruction. She thought it not for her purpose to meet his rage with rage, but affected a most passionate fit of grief, railed at her fate, and cursed her wayward stars; that still her wants should press him to act such deeds as she must needs abhor, as well as he; but told him, necessity had no law and love no bounds; that therefore he never truly loved, but meant, in her necessity, to forsake her; then knelt, and swore that since, by his refusal, he had given her cause to doubt his love, she never would see him more— unless, to prove it true, he robbed his uncle to supply her wants, and murdered him to keep it from discovery. . . .

"Speechless he stood. But in his face you might have read

that various passions tore his very soul. Oft he, in anguish, threw his eyes towards Heaven, and then as often bent their beams on her; then wept and groaned and beat his breast. At length, with horror not to be expressed, he cried, 'Thou cursèd Fair! Have I not given dreadful proofs of love? . . . What caused me to rob my gentle master but cursed love? What makes me now a fugitive from his service, loathed by myself,

and scorned by all the world, but love? What fills my eyes with tears, my soul with torture never felt on this side death before? Why, love, love, love! And why, above all, do I resolve (for, tearing his hair, he cried, "I do resolve") to kill my uncle?' "

There couldn't have been a dry eye in the house as the dread deed was accomplished on a spate of frenzied eloquence:

"In vain does nature, reason, conscience, all oppose it; the impetuous passion bears down all before it, and drives me on to lust, to theft and murder—O conscience! feeble guide to virtue, who only shows us when we go astray, but wants the power to stop us in our course—Ha, in yonder shady walk I see my uncle. He's alone. Now for my disguise!"

Enter the good old man, deep in graveyard meditation:

"If I were superstitious, I should fear some danger lurked unseen, or death were nigh. A heavy melancholy clouds my spirits; my imagination is filled with ghastly forms of dreary graves, and bodies changed by death; when the pale, lengthened visage attracts each weeping eye, and fills the musing soul at once with grief and horror, pity and aversion—I will indulge the thought."

He does so at considerable length.

Barnwell, himself on the long-winded side, gives him considerable scope before finally dealing him his quietus. The old gentleman departs this life with a few closing words:

"O! I am slain! All-gracious Heaven, regard the prayer of thy dying servant. Bless, with thy choicest blessings, my dearest nephew; forgive my murderer, and take my fleeting soul to endless mercy."

Hearing himself twice nominated, and in very different characters, in this exordium, "Barnwell's Agonies were prodigious; he fainted away on the Body, and when he recovered was going to kill himself, only he remembered the Laws of Christianity forbid Self-Murder."

His copious remarks upon the occasion included references to Cain and Nero.

The ultimate fate of Barnwell must have squeezed the last tears even from the orange girls. The luckless Barnwell, manacled and in the condemned cell, had to dree the ministrations, in rapid order, of a worthy clergyman, his worthier master, his high-minded sweetheart Maria, and Truman, the voluble friend of his bosom.

Not content with that, Lillo in the last scene wheeled up the heaviest artillery of all, in the shape of the gallows itself, in whose shadow George got back a bit of his own by inflicting high-minded discourse on the resolutely intransigent Millwood. The ill-starred couple were presumably launched into eternity a split second after the curtains closed.

The epilogue, spoken by the so recently bereaved Maria, operated, one hopes, to restore gaiety; it certainly did not raise the standard of taste:

Since fate has robbed me of the hopeless youth
For whom my heart had hoarded up its truth,
By all the laws of love and honour, now,
I'm free again to chuse—and one of you.

But soft—with caution first I'll round me peep;
Maids, in my case, should look before they leap.
Here's choice enough, of various sorts and hue,
The cit, the wit, the rake cocked up in cue,
The fair, spruce mercer, and the tawney Jew.

Suppose I search the sober gallery?—No,
There's none but prentices, and cuckolds all a row;
And these, I doubt, are those that make 'em so.
                    (Pointing to the Boxes.)

'Tis very well, enjoy the jest! But you,
Fine, powdered sparks—nay, I'm told 'tis true—
Your happy spouses can make cuckolds, too.
'Twixt you, and them, the difference this perhaps,
The cit's ashamed whene'er his duck he traps;
But you, when Madam's tripping, let her fall,
Cock up your hats, and take no shame at all.

What, if some favoured poet I could meet,
Whose love would lay his lawrels at my feet?
No; painted passion real love abhors:
His flame would prove the suit of creditors.

Not to detain you, then, with longer pause,
In short, my heart to this conclusion draws;
I yield it to the hand that's loudest in applause.

The part of Maria was the right of every leading lady. It took Mrs. Siddons to discover the superior dramatic possibilities

of Millwood. But by the time Siddons was discovering Millwood, a number of strange things had happened to George
Barnwell.

He had, for one thing, become a millstone about the necks
of the 'prentices. *The London Merchant* was immediately perceived to be just the right dramatic entertainment for youths
in their indentures; it would elevate their morals and keep
them from murdering their uncles. Accordingly, it was played
in London with monotonous regularity every time these turbulent lads got a holiday—that is, on my Lord Mayor's Day.
They must have got heartily tired of it before their indentures
were up.

As far from monotony as possible was George Barnwell's
career in foreign parts. Everything happened to George.
My friend Professor Lawrence Price, of the University of Cali-
fornia, has collected in his unpublished *George Barnwell Album*
some amazing avatars of Barnwell-Barnevelt-Jenneval-Cleon
that in sum present a hilarious comedy of national humours.

The French seized upon Barnwell with avidity, and proceeded to make him over with zeal. They thought he needed
a lot of re-working:

"In very truth," cried Claude Dorat, "would one tolerate on
our stage such a revolting concatenation of crimes, such a series
of pictures, whose attraction has its origin in terror? Would we
tolerate such a monster as Millwood, who plotted naught but
villainies, who directed the dagger to the heart of a virtuous
man, and dragged with herself to the scaffold the unfortunate
youth whom she had led into guilt? Already I hear the outcry
of public indignation rejecting this fury and interrupting the
horrible spectacle. And yet that is the basis of the English play.
It is that which for forty successive presentations once held the
interest of a respectable nation. The reason is that the English
people are responsive to beauties, and take no account of
faults. . . .

"The English genius is like nature itself, sublime and unequal. The English reveal their own taste and their own
character when they delight to watch the grave-diggers tumble
corpses about and make jests at the grave, after the noble and
affecting scenes of *Hamlet, Julius Caesar*, and *Romeo and Juliet*.

They demand lively pictures at whatever cost. It requires strong methods to reach the sombre and melancholy soul of the nation. Thus predisposed, it is ready to excuse any means which produces the desired effect. Nothing appears to it absurd, as long as it can weep or shudder. Its sole form of criticism is indifference.

"The genius of the French is of a different nature. I venture

to declare it is weaker, more delicate, and more sensitive. The French demand to see nature upon the stage expurgated and hence altered." (Professor Price's translation.)

In conforming to "the genius of the French", George Barnwell ran through a bewildering series of metamorphoses. As Cleon, he embarked on the naughty project of pilfering from his uncle, but the finding of a will in his favour brought repentance and reformation. As Arces, Prince of Egypt, with a touch of Hamlet, he spared his soliloquizing uncle Sesostris. As

Barneval, he took part in a double suicide. As Jenneval, he repented in enough haste to save his uncle from an assassin hired by Millwood, and immediately profited by the action. The author of this last confection, M. Mercier, asked of his audience:

"Could they, without paling, have observed a madman led by thirst for gold and pleasure rush up to plunge a dagger into the veins of a virtuous man? No, they would have rejected the picture as not made for them, because they can scarce imagine that there might be a parricide among the sensitive souls who come to be moved and to shed tears at their theatre. One may be touched, alarmed, without the poet's wringing the heart in so deplorable a fashion. Must one wound in order to heal? Does it not suffice to surround the soul with the gentle feeling of pity, that victorious sentiment which forces us back upon ourselves in a fashion gentle and intimate at once?" (Professor Price's translation.)

Grimm thought not. He remarked sourly: "If one is afraid of scenes of punishment by death upon the stage, why create characters that deserve nothing less?"

In Germany they were not afraid of the execution scene; they improved upon it. At Altona in 1781 Seyfried announced *The Merchant of London* to be played *in English fashion*—that is, with a sixth act "in which I would let Barnwell be hanged and Millwood executed". The crowded theatre got an extra cold grue when, just as the curtain fell, the severed head of Millwood rolled over the stage. The innovation was popular; though, as Professor Price observes, its run must have been shortened by an eventual dearth of talent.

Another representation of the tragedy caused the death of the Duke of Hesse-Darmstadt. It moved him so deeply, in accord with his sensitive nature, that at the end of the performance he absolutely dropped dead of emotion. At still another performance an eager country bumpkin cried, appalled, to the masked Barnwell: "Stop, it's your uncle!" which earned him rather the plaudits than the jeers of the sentimental audience.

In Vienna the lovers of wine, women, and song were content to sit through the tragedy provided it was embellished with

Hanswurst-merriments. Hans Wurst, Columbina, Barnadon, and Scapon were customarily inserted somewhat arbitrarily into the plot that they might burst into song upon every possible occasion; even Truman, though in the condemned cell with Barnwell, did not blench from trolling out a stave in praise of patience. One doubts if it could have consoled George Barnwell much.

In short, George Barnwell was found to include within himself something for everybody, at least in eighteenth-century Europe.

> *Prepare, at Hookham's to endure the sneers*
> *Each Beauty lisps, when "Barnwell" strikes her ears.*
> *"Barnwell!" cries Emma, "pshaw, the name's enough*
> *To fright all fashion from such* hum drum *stuff!*
> *Stol'n, I imagine, from that vulgar play,*
> *That forms the pastime of my* Lord *Mayor's Day.*
> *How monstrous low-bred must the creature be,*
> *Who writes such trash—don't offer it to me!*
> *Give me some novel of a different kind,*
> *Where castles, ghosts, and dæmons are combin'd,*
> *To rouse one from the stupor of the spleen,*
> *With* sights *that never have, nor can be seen."*

Thus, in 1798, did Thomas Surr imagine the world of fashion condemning his three-decker novel *George Barnwell*. But Emma's strictures would have been ill-founded; Surr had taken care to furnish Barnwell with a full complement of the castles, ghosts, and dæmons so much in demand by Gothic taste. He encountered them wherever he turned. His father had in his modest garden "a small temple, built in the Gothic style, and dedicated to retirement", as well as a sufficiency of little monuments with classical quotations. George's wealthy uncle could naturally trump that. He had on his estate "the remains of one of those cemeteries for the living, called monasteries.— These mouldering and moss-covered relics afforded a more grand *coup d'œil*, from his park, than can be imagined by those whose contemplations have been confined to the *modern ruins*, with which it is fashionable to decorate the grounds of *modern villas* . . .''; and furthermore the ruins were haunted by "spectres of all sizes and shapes, of either sex".

It is no wonder that this romantic locale was selected by Mr. Mental, the melancholy atheist, as the properest setting for his nightly musical selections, ballads of a gloomy nature accompanied on the harp, which he was in the habit of rendering sitting on a tomb appropriately attired in a long black cloak and mask. Any residual surprise that might have been felt at his programme must surely have been dispelled upon learning that a prominent spectre among those haunting the place was none other than the late Mrs. Mental.

It was only with difficulty that the author finally tore himself —and George— away from such congenial company, and removed to the frivolous milieu of Mayfair. Here George listened with surprise to the gay round of amusements, described to him by one Mr. Rigby, in terms which would have done honour to Alfred Jingle:

"O yes—*excusez moi*— . . . I remember when I—I—I—was as great a quiz—*excusez moi*—as you, Sir—by going his round— I mean, looking in at the opera—squeezing a few *figurante*— lounging in the way of the scene-shifters, and getting hissed off the stage. Then whirl to Lady Strongbox—Splash away the Spanish—make an assignation for the morning—and off again to the House—take a lounge there for an hour—get a bow from the Treasury Bench—gape at Doctor Sceptic's doubts—and then to Brookes's—lose a trifle—get the headache—and dash home with two flambeaux by day light!"

Surr is so deucedly severe upon these water-flies that he barely contrives to bring in Millwood and get down to business before the first volume ends. "On a crimson damask sofa, placed under a brilliant mirror, illuminated by wax lights, reclined the Syren Millwood.—A most elegant white dress had superseded the sable weeds of the morning; with a Turkish turban, ornamented with gold cords and tassels"; to which armament she added the art of the physiognomist, giving guileless George a very flattering character—"I have studied Lavater," says she simply.

Adding a few disparaging remarks about the regulation of the passions by Reason, she then opened the musical part of her campaign, rendering, to harp accompaniment, a ditty so sad the youth dissolved into tears.

"In vain did the enamoured youth aim to repress the rising flame—in vain attempted to resist the maddening impulse of desire!—On the precipice of danger, he was ignorant of his situation. His cheeks flushed, his eyes looked wild, and he fell back on the sofa, overcome with the force of such new and powerful emotions."

From these symptoms the artful courtesan deduced that it was time for another musical number. She judged rightly: one more harp solo, and she was able to give gasping George the *coup de grâce*:

"She sighed—she gazed with looks of warmest love—she seemed to yield her soul to her desires—sunk by the side of Barnwell—reclined her head upon his cheek—pressed the warm lips to his, and conquered."

Such goings-on could lead to no good, and indeed led to nothing but ill. Barnwell murdered his uncle, late the happy possessor of a genuine mouldering ruin. Millwood dispatched Mr. Mental with his melancholy atheism on his unhoused soul. Barnwell died on the gallows, Millwood frantic in prison, Barnwell's mother of grief; and his Maria, for good measure, in the Ophelia tradition "fell, like a blighted blossom, to the earth, and with her last sigh mingled the name of Barnwell".

In conclusion, the author revealed his conviction, that the melancholy fate of Barnwell was "the consequences of CONCEALED ERRORS".

We might be still perusing such stuff were it not for the blessed human fact that cheerfulness, as Johnson's unsuccessful philosopher put it, is always breaking in. Even while Surr's curious Gothic confection was going into new editions, a more cheerful philosopher in the New World was making a plummy comedian's mincemeat of the ancient crime of George Barnwell.

George Barnwell stood at the shop door,

(sang cheerful Frederick Reynolds to the tune of *Bartlemy Fair O*)

A customer hoping to find, sir,
His apron was hanging before,
But the tail of his wig was behind, sir.
A lady all painted and smart,
Cried, Sir, I've exhausted my stock o' late,
I've got nothing left but a groat—
Will you give me sixpenn'orth of chocolate?

Her face was rouged up to the eyes,
Which made her grow prouder and prouder;
His hair stood on end with surprise,
And hers with pomatum and powder.

The business was soon understood—
The lady who wished to be more rich,
Said, sweet sir, my name is Millwood,
And I lodge at the gunsmith's at Shoreditch.

Now often he stole out, good lack,
And into her lodgings would pop, sir;
But as often forgot to come back,
Leaving master to shut up the shop, sir.
This woman his wits did bereave,
He determined to be quite the crack O,
So he lounged at the Adam and Eve
And he call'd for his gin and tobacco.

Then said Millwood, whose cruel heart's core,
'Twas so cruel that nothing could shock it,
If you mean to come home any more
You must put some more cash in your pocket,
Make Nunky surrender his dibbs,
Wipe his pate with a pair of lead towels
Or stick a knife into his ribs—
I warrant he'll then show more bowels.

A pistol he got from his love,
'Twas loaded with powder and bullet,
And he trudg'd up to Camberwell grove,
But he wanted the courage to pull it.
There's Nunky as fat as a hog,
While I am as lean as a lizard—
Now I'll come to the point, you old dog,
And he whipped a long knife in his gizzard.

Now, ye, who attend to my song,
A terrible end of this farce shall see,
If you'll join the inquisitive throng
That follow'd poor George to the Marshalsea.
If Millwood was here, dash my wigs,
Says he, I would pummel and lamb her well;
Had I stuck to my treacle and figs,
I ne'er had stuck Nunky at Camberwell.

The case to the jury was plain,
The news spread through every ale-house;
At the sessions in Horsemonger-lane
They were hung both in front of the jail-house.
With Millwood, George opened the ball;
Dear, dear! how we wept, Mrs. Crump and I,
To see them dance upon nothing at all,
And cut capers before all the company.

What next, George Barnwell? The Restoration George was
a niggling, mean young scoundrel. Lillo's George was a senti-
mental murderer, and Surr's high-flown and tedious in the
Gothic style. Barnwell in France was sissified, and in Germany
bloodied; while in the New World it was anything for a laugh.
Surely George Barnwell's possibilities have been exhausted.

Or have they? The case still remains to be "solved", in the
modern whodunit manner, by pinning the crime on somebody
else. Who *really* murdered Barnwell's uncle? Why, Truman,
of course! by eliminating Barnwell, at one stroke he got first
place behind his master's counter, and Maria to stand beside

him. The mere fact that he was never suspected by anyone, from the original ballader to the Gothic novelist, is in itself conclusive.

And surely, coming in the rearward with a further woe, will be the literary psychiatrist, ready to demonstrate that George Barnwell murdered his uncle in a schizoid state consequent upon an Œdipus complex. George Barnwell's career of crime may have scarcely begun.

It doesn't LOOK like Santa Claus

HEDUNIT

SAGITTARIUS

Crime marches on, but detection is faster,
    Nemesis silently pads behind;
Confident criminals come to disaster,
    The game's afoot and the clues unwind;
Hot on the scent we follow the master,
    Follow the master mind.

Holmes, at the head of the lynx-eyed procession,
    Holmes, with tight lips and countenance pale,
Holmes, in the van of the sleuthing profession,
    Holmes, stepping in where the Yard must fail.
Tecs and Inspectors in endless succession
    Follow the Sherlock trail.

Follow the snake down the rope, through the transom,
    Follow the Hound to the Devonshire tor,
Follow the rubies, an Emperor's ransom,
    Follow to India the Sign of the Four,
Follow the lead of the vanishing hansom
    Starting from Sherlock's door.

The speed of the chase was not then supersonic,
    The pace of the cab-horse a steady clip-clop,
The cult of detection was still embryonic,
    The joy of the man-hunt confined to the cop.
Did he guess that he'd started, that wizard sardonic,
    Something that would not stop?

Started a mania for singular cases,
    Started a craving few addicts restrain,
Started a saga of amateur aces,
    Whimsical, taciturn, dashing, urbane,
Started the public on hair-raising chases.
    Study the scarlet stain!

Brains against brains of the underworld pitted,
    Tingling excitement of fictional crime,
Mysteries solved, with loose ends neatly knitted,
    Solved with a nonchalance more than sublime.
Millions of Watsons, supremely dim-witted,
    Having a terrible time.

Bullet-hole, blow-pipe, mysterious injection,
    Time-table, alibi, manor-house plan,
Fanciful flights in deductive detection
    For highbrow and lowbrow and middlebrow fan;
But who does not turn with a pang of affection,
    Back where it all began?

Back from crime in the third dimension,
    Back to problems more concrete,
Back to the wellspring of invention,
    Back to the elementary feat,
Back to the cab, I need not mention,
    Standing in Baker Street?

All still follow with Sherlock leading!
    Over the edge of time's abyss
Wave a hand to those wheels receding,
    Settle down to an hour of bliss!
But for Holmes you would not be reading,
    Reading, dear reader, this.

INDEX OF AUTHORS